IN
COLD
PURSUIT

IN
COLD
PURSUIT

MEDICAL INTELLIGENCE INVESTIGATES
THE COMMON COLD

J. BARNARD GILMORE

Stoddart

Published in 1998 by Stoddart Publishing Co. Limited
34 Lesmill Road, Toronto, Canada M3B 2T6
180 Varick Street, 9th Floor, New York, New York 10014

Distributed in Canada by:
General Distribution Services Ltd.
325 Humber College Blvd., Toronto, Ontario M9W 7C3
Tel. (416) 213-1919   Fax (416) 213-1917
Email customer.service@ccmailgw.genpub.com

Distributed in the United States by:
General Distribution Services Inc.
85 River Rock Drive, Suite 202, Buffalo, New York 14207
Toll-free Tel. 1-800-805-1083   Toll-free Fax 1-800-481-6207
Email gdsinc@genpub.com

02 01 00 99 98 1 2 3 4 5

Canadian Cataloguing in Publication Data

Gilmore, Jon Barnard, 1937–
In cold pursuit: medical intelligence investigates the common cold

Includes index.
ISBN 0-7737-3119-9

1. Cold (Disease). I. Title

RF361.G535 1998   616.2'05   C98-931069-8

Cover Design: Bill Douglas @ The Bang
Text Design: Tannice Goddard
Page Composition: Mary Bowness

Printed and bound in Canada

*We gratefully acknowledge the Canada Council for the Arts and
the Ontario Arts Council for their support of our publishing program.*

To those whose colds were volunteered,
and all who volunteered for colds

Contents

Introduction

LEAVING HOME, 1900

"Of all the diseases common in man, [the common cold] has been surrounded by greater etiological and epidemiological obscurity than any other."[1]

— *Stitt, from* Practical Bacteriology, *1916*

We all have our own theories about how we "catch" the common cold. We say: "I caught a chill." "I sat next to a man with a nasty cold on the train." Or, "the weather changed suddenly." But the common cold does not work the way most of us think that it does, the way it first appears to work. This discovery has by turns surprised, confounded, entranced, and informed a long list of medical investigators, men and women who have devoted significant portions of their research careers to making sense of this familiar but puzzling illness. In their quest to understand how the common cold works, these medical sleuths have traveled to locales that are warm and cold, continental and oceanic, isolated and crowded. Moreover, they have won some teasing glimpses into how we really do catch our colds. In this book we will retrace medicine's historical journey of discovery, a journey that will take us twice around the world and in the process will allow us to explore a number of scientific curiosities and paradoxes.

Our journey proper begins in Spitzbergen, in the year 1930, surrounded by the polar ice above Norway. There we will encounter two simple and compelling observations that demanded and yet resisted an easy explanation, and which will inform much of our remaining journey.

In the end we will arrive at what I think is a simple and interesting resolution for some of the problems created by those early significant (and apparently contradictory) observations. We will also discover that the clear problems created by those original observations have evolved into intriguing new ones in light of the results from more recent medical intelligence work.

As we shall see, however, medicine's interest in the workings of the common cold actually began well before 1930, and it is only for narrative convenience that we start our journey where and when we do. A more appropriate, if arbitrary, starting date might be in the year 1900, when bacteriology truly began to flower, following the pioneering work of Pasteur and Koch. The scientific laboratory, the microscope, and the test tube then began to supplement the stethoscope, the thermometer, and careful patient record keeping as tools for better understanding the causes and cures of disease. Moreover, it happens that 1900 followed by just two years the discovery of the first virus, the tobacco mosaic virus, about which we shall learn more in chapter 10. And, as we shall also learn, 1900 came just fourteen years before the common cold was first attributed to a virus.

Today, it is "well known" that colds are caused by particular viruses. Moreover, these viruses can be made to stand still. Grainy gray pictures of them can be studied, looking stiffly up into the electron microscope. They are hard to read, these cold viruses, with their spiky haircuts. They are so Spartan. They are vanishingly tiny, and astonishingly tough. They do not shiver in the deep cold of a liquid nitrogen bath. And there they endure. They confess nothing to us about their own special psychology, even under the torture of ultracentrifuging. Nor do they seem to notice that the average person treats them as an enemy, despite the fact that there is little evidence that they intend anything like a complete subversion of our cells or ourselves. It is even possible that cold viruses are as helpful to our well-being as their excesses are discomfitting to us. (But of that, more later.)

Packing for the Journey

Before we leave home then, let us pack a few understandings. First, let us understand that it was not always clear (and may not yet be) that the symptoms of a common cold are directly caused by infecting viruses. For this reason, field studies of the conditions under which people do and do not develop colds have long had value. The ubiquitous natural experiments in cold transmission created by normal daily life could in 1900, and can to this day, teach us what are and what are not sensible questions to ask (and to answer) surrounding the mysteries of the common cold.

Thus, we will examine first the classic field studies of the common cold, with their tantalizing observations made in natural settings. Historically, field observations of this sort focused attention on a few particular questions, while postponing the pursuit of other questions. Later, we shall examine the classic laboratory studies that paralleled this work in the field, allowing us to frame certain answers to, and/or revisions of, the questions raised by the data from the field.

Before we start out, let us also agree on just what is meant by a "common cold." There never has been a completely objective medical definition that can reliably discriminate the common cold from, say, certain mild forms of influenza, or hay fever. And yet, even when colds are studied in today's sophisticated laboratories, most medical research personnel are quite comfortable with the tradition that allows the patient herself to have a say in whether or not a given illness qualifies as a true cold. (The reasons for the existence of this tradition will emerge as we go along.) Naturally, however, it would be more desirable simply to be able to say that a common cold is any illness "caused" by any virus that belongs to a previously defined set of common cold viruses. Any such definition of a common cold only returns us to our basic question, however, because which virus shall be called a common cold virus has never been very clear. And, more to the point, attributing the symptoms of a common cold to one particular resident virus turns out to be much more problematic than would be expected. Cause and effect are still shrouded in mystery where the common cold is concerned. For better or worse, a cold is defined by its symptoms.

Since 1900, the preferred medical term used for diagnoses of the common cold has been "acute coryza," a term that may be playfully (and correctly) translated as: "temporary, runny nose syndrome." Textbook definitions of the common cold rarely add very much to this succinct "definition," with perhaps the notable exception of William Osler's classic description of a prototypic cold. In his famous text from the turn of the century, *The Principles and Practice of Medicine*, Osler wrote the following about acute coryza.

> Acute catarrhal inflammation of the upper air-passages, popularly known as a "catarrh" or a "cold," is usually an independent affection, but may precede the development of another disease . . .
>
> Prevailing most extensively in the changeable weather of the spring and early winter, it may occur in epidemic form, many cases arising in a

community within a few weeks, outbreaks which are very like, though less intense than, the epidemic influenza.

The patient feels indisposed, perhaps chilly, has slight headache, and sneezes frequently. In severe cases there are pains in the back and limbs. There is usually slight fever, the temperature rising to 101°. The pulse is quick, the skin is dry, and there are all the features of a feverish attack. At first the mucous membrane of the nose is swollen, "stuffed up," and the patient has to breathe through the mouth. A thin, clear, irritating secretion flows, and makes the edges of the nostrils sore. The mucous membrane of the tear ducts is swollen, so the eyes weep and the conjunctivæ are injected. The sense of smell and, in part, the sense of taste are lost. With the nasal catarrh [i.e., discharge] there is slight soreness of the throat and stiffness of the neck; the pharynx looks red and swollen, and sometimes the act of swallowing is painful. The larynx may also be involved and the voice becomes husky or is even lost. If the inflammation extends to the eustachian tubes the hearing may be impaired. In more severe cases there are bronchial irritation and cough. Occasionally there is an outbreak of labial or nasal herpes. Usually within thirty-six hours the nasal secretion becomes turbid and more profuse, the swelling of the mucosa subsides, the patient gradually becomes able to breathe through the nostrils, and within four or five days the symptoms disappear, with the exception of the increased discharge from the nose and upper pharynx. There are rarely any bad effects from a simple coryza. When the attacks are frequently repeated, the disease may become chronic.[2]

Little has changed in the century since these words were written, and I am sure my readers could not fail to recognize at once this clearly drawn picture of some of their past ills. It is safe to say, however, that Osler wasn't quite confining himself only to colds in this description. The presence of fever, for instance, is no longer considered a characteristic normally associated with the common cold.

That said, there is little more we need to pack in preparation for this journey of ours. We will presently come to a point where we need certain information about the workings of the immune system and about the nature and formation of antibodies to cold viruses. This information, insofar as it exists, we can and will acquire later. Thus, it remains only to say a few words about your guide, and about certain of his biases.

Aren't Colds Just Simple Infections?

It happens that I was trained as a clinical psychologist. Consequently, I often used to take a certain degree of comfort in two rather inappropriate stereotypes: (1) that most M.D.s are blind to important psychological contributions to the symptoms of disease that they meet, and (2) at the same time, most psychologists are blind to important physical and bio-chemical causes of both human behavior and certain symptoms of psychological illness. Thus it was that one day, when quite unexpectedly I found myself arguing like the stereotypic M.D. in respect of common colds, rather than as the stereotypic psychologist, my interest in medical research on the common cold was ignited. It happened as follows.

Speaking about a mutual friend who was at the time suffering from a potent cold, a psychiatrist friend of mine attributed that cold to presumed unconscious conflicts and to certain symptomatic gains supposedly result-ing from our friend's illness. I replied, in effect, "Not so. The common cold reflects a simple infection caused by exposure to a certain kind of virus. It is not a neurotic symptom." Rashly, I then volunteered to check in the university medical library the next time I was there, to locate a study that would prove my assertion correct.

That was seventeen years ago, as I write this. I searched and searched through various libraries for proof of the simple cause–effect relationship that I assumed existed, and while today I still rather doubt that colds are any sort of symptom of a neurosis, it was only very recently that studies began to appear suggesting just when and how a few viruses might be ini-tiating cold symptoms.

Still, all that I did discover along the way was particularly interesting, suggestive, and significant. These discoveries led me to spend five years carrying out my own large-scale epidemiological research study of colds among student volunteers at the University of Toronto. Later, they led me to England, where I searched for further clues about colds in the archives generated from the many experimental trials held at Salisbury's well-known Common Cold Research Unit. This book is the result of my various dis-coveries, both in the library and out in the field.

My discoveries about the possible roles played by psychological factors in causing and curing the common cold are not featured largely in this book. Nor are discussions about various treatments that may speed the cure of colds or that might prevent them outright. These topics are certainly worthy, and research into them does contain its fair share of historical surprises. Yet these topics are secondary to the fundamental question about where colds come from, and today they remain less conclusive and more contentious than the facts about how we get our colds.

Finally then, before we arrive in Spitzbergen, what about you, the reader? If you are one of those thoughtful people who enjoy reading a good mystery, especially when it is non-fiction and when the victim has been us, I believe you will enjoy this read, this journey together. For reasons that will become clearer as we go along, I hope you will keep warm and comfortable for its duration.

PART I

CATCHING COLDS IN WORLDS SMALL AND LARGE

I

Cold Cargo: Longyear City, Spitzbergen, 1930

"This man claimed, as did all the other trappers questioned, that accidents such as falling through the ice, never give rise to 'colds' during the winter and spring; but only after the men have been to town in the fall or summer."

— *J. H. Paul and H. L. Freese, 1933*

One chilly September day in 1930, Dr. J. Harlan Paul arrived at Longyear City on the Arctic island of Spitzbergen to begin a major study of the common cold. There was in 1930, as there still is today, good reason to imagine that cold temperatures could play some important role in causing the common cold. At the time Dr. Paul arrived on Spitzbergen, temperatures at night were already reaching levels well below freezing. Soon they would be dropping much lower. Medicine had long been curious about the common cold, and Spitzbergen, lost in polar isolation and buried in winter snows, seemed just the right place to look for whatever clues to the nature and origin of colds might next await discovery.

The research project that Dr. Paul was about to undertake was actually the fourth in a series of studies looking at common colds. The three previous studies had all been less ambitious than the one now planned for Longyear City. One of these previous studies had been carried out in a small town in the backwoods of Alabama, another at a trading post in Labrador, and the third had recently been completed on the island of St. John in the Virgin Islands. These studies, like that arranged for Spitzbergen, had each been carried out under the general supervision of Dr. Wilson Smillie at Harvard's School of Public Health, with financial support from the International Health Division of the Rockefeller Foundation.

Dr. Paul, however, was new to the field of common cold research, and he had not participated in any of the earlier studies. Most recently he had spent one and a half years, serving partly as a scientific observer and partly as the ship's surgeon, aboard the large wooden sailing vessel *Carnegie* while it roamed the world's oceans measuring atmospheric magnetism and mapping the unexplored underseas. Then, tragically, on November 29, 1929, the *Carnegie* exploded and burned while loading gasoline at Apia, Western Samoa, causing the death of her captain and one other crew member. Dr. Paul happened to be ashore at the time and so survived uninjured to write an official history of the *Carnegie*'s last, abbreviated, voyage.

Now, one year later, J. Harlan Paul was ready for something new. He was thirty years old and single; already he had lived for a time in Shanghai, in Oxford, and in Heidelberg, and he had enjoyed each one of the three eventful years since his graduation from Harvard Medical School. At Harvard he had received both an M.D. degree and a certificate in Public Health under Dr. Smillie. A year of important medical research in a Norwegian factory town just seven hundred miles below the North Pole seemed to him exactly what was wanted for the coming year.

Dr. Paul arrived at Longyear City, Spitzbergen, accompanied by Mr. and Mrs. H. L. Freese and a young man named Charles Mullen. Mr. Mullen, age twenty, was to serve both as the animal caretaker and laboratory assistant for the work to be undertaken at Longyear City. Mr. Freese was an accomplished bacteriologist. He had spent the previous winter in the West Indies where he had cultivated the important bacterial cultures collected as part of the Virgin Islands study.[1]

The party arrived in Spitzbergen with plans for a lengthy stay, one that would last throughout the coming period of Arctic darkness, with its bitter winter temperatures, and on through the following summer. Dr. Paul and Mr. Freese were particularly interested in having a firsthand look at some of the effects that very cold temperatures might produce on the bacteria residing in the human nose and throat. In 1930 it had long been assumed, and for good reason, that some kind of bacterium might cause colds. A bacterium was known to cause tuberculosis, for instance. Another was known to cause diphtheria. Streptococci were already recognized as the cause of "strep throat." In their early states, each of these bacterial diseases will often masquerade as a common cold. Since bacteria can cause diseases very much like the common cold, clearly they might also be the cause of the common cold itself.

That is why Dr. Paul and Dr. Smillie were particularly interested in examining how temperature might affect the bacteria of the nose and throat. It was important to find out whether these bacteria change significantly, either during cold weather or prior to the onset of a common cold, or both. The scientific party arrived in Longyear City prepared to attempt the culture of any bacterium that might offer itself for study. And that is why, in their baggage, the members of the party carried with them so much rabbit blood, so much beef-heart infusion broth, so many special sera, and such bulky, fragile equipment.

Longyear City, Spitzbergen

In a report of the Longyear City study published in 1933, Dr. Paul and Mr. Freese described the setting for their study as follows.

> Spitzbergen is a mountainous arctic archipelago lying about midway between Norway and the North Pole, and about equidistant from Greenland on the west and Franz Josef Land on the east. The climate is rigorous but healthful. Winter temperatures seldom fall below minus 30 degrees Fahrenheit; while in summer the mercury may reach 60 degrees. Precipitation is scanty.
>
> There are no indigenous inhabitants; although many men have spent from 10 to 20 years on the islands. Aside from some forty trappers and mine watchmen who live in scattered huts along the coast, the population during the winter 1930–1931 was concentrated in the coal mining settlement of Longyear City, on Ice Fjord, and was made up almost exclusively of Norwegians. The people live in ordinary wooden houses which are reasonably comfortable, though overcrowded. The standard of living is relatively high. The food, which is all imported, is plentiful and wholesome. Nutritional disorders, such as scurvy and rickets, are no longer in evidence. Aside from the "common cold," communicable diseases are rare.
>
> The population of Longyear City at the time of our study totaled 507. This included fifty-one women, and forty children. During the summer the total rises to about 550, not including tourists. About 300 men work in the mine, while the remainder work outside. The trappers and watchmen in the outlying districts have almost no contact with the town proper except in summer.
>
> Longyear City is built on the sloping bank of a glacial stream, half a mile distant from the harbor, and about 50 feet above sea-level. At the waterfront are situated the power house, machine shops, and warehouses. The twenty workers employed there have their own barracks and mess

hall. Two miles down the beach, at Hotel Point, lives another group of men who operate the coal storing plant. These workers rarely come into town during the winter and constitute a self-contained community.

The shipping season is from 3 to 5 months in length, depending on ice conditions. There are no contacts with the outside world during the remainder of the year. Each summer four or five large tourist ships anchor off the town and send their passengers ashore for a few hours. In addition to these, there are always a few calls by fishing vessels and expeditions which come there to take on coal and other supplies. The regular traffic is almost entirely with northern Norwegian ports.[2]

During their long months of work in the Arctic, Paul and Freese were soon able to document that this ship traffic was dramatically linked to the presence of cold sufferers in Longyear City. However, they began their work by arranging to count, and whenever possible to take cultures from, every cold that occurred in this close-knit community and every cold to be found aboard each newly arrived ship. It was these count data that brought Paul and Freese their first surprise.

In Europe and North America, the typical working adult who does not live with school children will average approximately two colds per year. By 1930 this fact had already been well documented. In warmer climates, however, closer to the equator, the incidence of colds was known to be rather less than two colds per year.[3] Thus it was reasonable to expect that at Longyear City, closer to the North Pole, the frigid climate would be associated with an average of somewhat more than two colds per year. In fact, however, the incidence of colds seen by Paul and Freese at Longyear City actually averaged less than one cold per person per year, which is a value one might have expected to see only in the Tropics.

Moreover, the timing of the colds seen at Longyear City was not what might have been predicted given the imagined links between colder temperatures and the common cold. In the four weeks prior to the first winter cold snap in November 1930 there were consistently four to eight new colds recorded each week. But during the week of that first winter cold snap there were no new common colds at all. Then, during the following week, five new colds appeared. Yet in the next week there was only one cold. In the weeks that followed, the temperatures rose and fell while the weekly number of new colds steadily approached zero. The November cold snap had closed the harbor to ships; however, it might also be said to have begun closing down the local common cold industry.

The First Boat of Summer

All during the coldest winter period of darkness and isolation, the people of Longyear City were nearly free of common colds. In the thirteen weeks from March 1, 1931, through May 23, 1931, a total of only four new colds occurred. Then, at 9:00 p.m. on May 23, the first boat of the 1931 season arrived in Longyear City, bringing mail and fifty new Norwegian workmen. Paul and Freese described what happened next as follows:

> There were no obvious cases [of colds] among the arrivals of May 23; but one man was apparently in the "incubating stage," for within a few hours after landing he showed all the classical signs of a fresh "cold." At the time of examination on shipboard he had complained only of malaise and headache. Two men of the ship's crew were recovering from attacks which had begun in each instance about a week previously. One of these had a residual hoarseness, while the other had a slight purulent nasal discharge. These two men had no direct contact with the town proper, for the steamer moved to Hotel Point after discharging its passengers and mail.
>
> On the evening of May 25, about 48 hours after the arrival of the first boat, three cases of "common cold" developed in the town. One of the persons affected was the storekeeper, who had spent much of the previous 2 days in sorting dusty mail sacks, coming into close contact with hundreds of men — both winter residents and new arrivals. Another was an outdoor worker who had boarded the ship at the dock and had more than average contact with the new men. The third was a miner who could not trace any direct contact with the new arrivals, except that he was thrown [in] with them at meals, at the store, and at the post office. We were unable to trace any direct contact between the man with a "cold" who had arrived on the first boat and these three men.[4]

Forty-eight hours after the arrival of the first boat, these three people developed their colds. The next day, May 26, there were four more new colds. The following day, thirteen additional colds broke out. On successive days there were twenty-one new cases, then eighteen more, then twenty-five more, and on the last day of May in 1931, the epidemic peaked with twenty-seven new colds. By the time it was over, one week later, nearly half of the winter residents at Longyear City had developed their annual common cold.

More boats arrived in the harbor, and new colds appeared. Some people developed a second cold later in the summer. Others, who had escaped the first wave of colds, succumbed to a smaller epidemic that came in August. Only once that summer was there any week when fewer than ten new colds developed. These facts all seemed to point in one direction: people bring colds, and cold weather does not.

Paul and Freese had further reasons to conclude that people are more significant than weather in causing colds. Their resident colleague, Dr. Johan Friis, who was the physician to the mine at Longyear City, provided data on the colds that he had seen one year previous, during the spring of 1930. These were only those colds that had been troublesome enough to bring workers into the dispensary for some treatment. But in that year too there were no colds seen in the week prior to the arrival of the first ship. Within the first week after the arrival of this ship, however, forty cases of new common colds were seen. More than one hundred further cases were seen during the second week, and seventy more cases were seen in the third week after the arrival.

To physicians in ships that go long to sea, and to physicians in small remote communities, this pattern of infection was already unwritten medical lore. Colds seem to disappear during periods of isolation, and colds tend to run riot when the isolation is broken. But medical science needed the documentation provided by Paul and Freese in 1933 to fully appreciate the significance of human contact in the origin of colds. The question of the role played by the weather, however, was still open.

Whether Weather or Whether Not

Careful weather records were kept while Paul and Freese resided in Longyear City. Hourly variations in temperature and humidity were almost nonexistent during the winter period of total darkness and during the summer period of continuous daylight. Only migrating weather systems had any appreciable impact on changing the conditions outside. Inside the mines the temperature never changed — it was always eleven degrees Fahrenheit below freezing. Paul and Freese plotted changes in weather variables alongside changes in the incidence of common colds. The plot for the average weekly minimum temperature was typical of what they found. What had been true during that first cold snap in November 1930 was true in general. There simply was no correlation to be seen between colds and changes in temperature. The same conclusion applied for plots of relative humidity, precipitation amounts, atmospheric pressures, wind velocities, and the degree of cloud cover. Not one weather variable predicted changes in common cold case rates at Longyear City.

Ubiquitous Bacteria

The repeated bacterial cultures, which were grown from swabs made in the noses and throats of the people at Longyear City, soon documented an equally significant fact. The bacterial flora flourishing in local throats and noses proved to be much the same whether it was warm or cold outside, whether the person was suffering an active cold or was in good health, whether the person worked above ground or below ground, outdoors or indoors, or whether the person was a long-term resident on the island or a new visitor. The bacterial flora found were, in fact, strikingly similar to those already seen in those earlier studies done in the Virgin Islands, in Labrador, and in Alabama. If any bacterium did play a role in causing the common cold, Paul and Freese (and other scientists around the world) did not appear to be studying it. By the time Paul and Freese had finished their work at Longyear City, it seemed to medical scientists that bacteria rarely, if ever, play much of a role in initiating the common cold.

This conclusion was especially compelling because elsewhere the isolation of viruses had begun and soon it was demonstrated that something far smaller than any known bacterium seems to cause colds. By the end of 1931, then, many medical scientists, Paul and Freese among them, were referring to the agent that presumably causes colds as "the virus."

Making Sense of the Longyear City Observations

It would be easy to conclude from all these findings that common colds generally result when a person of low immunity is exposed to the right infective agent (let us too call it "the virus.") This would be a strong theory, yet a theory not without its problems. Many residents of Longyear City did not develop colds in the summer of 1931. Why not? Was their immunity high? Did they somehow escape exposure to the virus? Do we perhaps need another concept to explain their good health? To Paul and Freese something more seemed to be needed, and they asked whether *the* virus (for they believed there probably was only one primary virus involved) might be differentially infective over time. Something seemed to be changing either the power of the virus to infect, or the power of the population to resist infection, or both. Moreover, that "something" did not seem to be the weather. Here is what Paul and Freese wrote, discussing their work:

> The remarkable seasonal distribution of cases of acute respiratory disease in Spitzbergen brings up many interesting questions relating to the etiological agent responsible for the "common cold." A study of the records would justify the conclusion that the "virus" remained in the community throughout the year — that is, if we assume that "colds" are initiated by a specific "virus" and not by a variety of factors. Cases occurred in every month but March; yet, during the period of isolation, one patient did not seem able to transmit the infection to his neighbors. The explosive epidemic in May indicates that the community had by that time lost what immunity it had had. One would naturally suppose that persons who developed "colds" between February and May, let us say, would find a sufficient number of susceptible persons among their close contacts to carry on the infection, or to start up an epidemic in advance of the arrival of the first boat.
>
> Might it not be that this group of 500 persons was too small to permit the etiological agent [the virus] frequent enough transfers to retain its original potency? The steamers arriving in the summer bring to the town not only the infective agent, but also a considerable number of susceptible persons. Once these persons cease to arrive (usually in mid-October), there is a community in which practically everyone has had one recent attack or more. This may well be the critical period for the "virus," for only rarely will it find lodgment in a susceptible person. The following facts also suggest that some change occurs in the nature of the "virus" during the winter and spring months. Ten trappers and mine watchmen from outlying districts, who were under observation, made one visit or more to the settlement during the period of isolation and lived in close contact with the residents during their stay. None of these men contracted a "cold." However, all but two of them were infected upon their first visit to the town following the arrival of the first boat. In March, April, and May, several parties from the village made trips by dog-team to these outlying districts and lived for several days with the isolated men. No cases of "common cold" developed as a result of these visits; yet similar contacts in the summer often resulted in carrying the infection beyond the confines of Longyear City.
>
> The following case history is of interest because it indicates that a person may carry the "virus" with him for a considerable period after an attack and remain in good health.

August Stenersen, a lone trapper, living at a great distance from the settlement, came to town for mail and provisions just prior to the arrival of the first boat. He had been free from "colds" all winter and spring. On May 28, 5 days after the steamer arrived, he had a severe attack. Upon recovery, he returned to his hut where he lived in complete isolation for about 6 weeks, all this time in normal health. On August 7 he again set out for Longyear City, but fell into the icy water while launching his boat. Although thoroughly chilled, he continued on to a shelter in DeGeersdal, where he dried his clothes and slept. Late the following day he had attacks of sneezing and a watery discharge from his nose. The symptoms of a "cold" became progressively more severe as he approached town; and upon his arrival he had fever, chills, and a distressing cough with blood-tinged sputum.

This man claimed, as did all the other trappers questioned, that accidents such as falling through the ice, never give rise to "colds" during the winter and spring; but only after the men have been to town in the fall or summer. This suggests that a sudden chilling of the body may bring on an attack in a person who is apparently quite well, but who has had a recent infection or a recent contact.

Experiences of this sort were not uncommon on the non-magnetic research vessel *Carnegie*. Epidemics of the "common cold" would begin suddenly when the vessel was many days, or weeks, out of port. Three such occasions were noted, and in each instance the ship had just entered a cold current from warmer waters. We cannot conclude, however, that exposure to cold or marked changes in environment can in themselves initiate a "cold." The miners in Longyear City were constantly subjected to the most rigorous exposure during the winter, yet extremely few developed "colds."[5]

With this passage Paul and Freese have introduced much food for thought, and included with it is some local herring, red herring, which warrants prompt commentary. The "cold" that August Stenersen developed forty-eight hours after falling into the sea included fever, chills, and blood-tinged sputum. Usually, the common cold produces none of these symptoms, and the presence of such symptoms ordinarily would suggest either the presence of influenza or some serious bacterial infection. What is of significance in this account is the fact that severe chilling does not *normally* produce illness in these men. Is that because their lifestyle makes them somehow "hardy" and healthful? Or, is it because their isolation protects them from exposure to disease-producing agents? Or, is there a different explanation?

August Stenersen appeared to be as hardy and as healthful on that day when he fell into the water as he had been on similar previous occasions that did not lead to illness. Paul and Freese interpreted this observation to mean that sudden chilling might only lead to disease if the right kind of disease agent is present (but latent) in the body. Then it usually would lead to disease. And so temperature might, after all, be important, some of the time.

Moreover, there were also those small "epidemics of the common cold" that occurred on the last voyage of the *Carnegie* and that were said to be so clearly linked to changes in the local weather while at sea. But why then would the common colds seen in Longyear City show no such sensitivity to the arrival of sea storms and cold weather? Paul's book, *The Last Cruise of the Carnegie*, seems to mention only two of those "three occasions" referred to in the passage just quoted.[6] The first of these two occasions involved "a severe cold" that struck only the captain of the *Carnegie*, four days after the ship encountered a continuous cold fog and drizzle and eight days after leaving Iceland, traveling westbound in the North Atlantic during the month of August. Like the "cold" suffered by August Stenersen, this too was an unusually severe illness, causing the captain to be confined to bed for the first time ever in his long life at sea. Thus, here too, there is a suggestion that the captain may have had something more serious than a true common cold. It is significant that he alone among the crew of twelve was ill on this first occasion.

The only other occasion described in Dr. Paul's book on which "colds" visited the men of the *Carnegie* occurred during July, sometime between ten and fourteen days after leaving Japan, while the ship was eastbound in the North Pacific. Soon after encountering more cold fog and drizzle, "the whole party came down with heavy colds." Dr. Paul describes other times when the *Carnegie* found itself in cold weather, but he does not mention common colds at these times either among the crew or among the scientific party. In fact, while speaking earlier of the captain's illness, Paul had written of the common cold: "We were to be pestered with this common complaint in many ports, but on only a few occasions while at sea." Here then is an observation that would seem to corroborate the findings at Longyear City, to point to people as the reservoir for colds, and to call into question any role assigned to chilling as a cause of the common cold.

But for whatever reason, by 1932 when he drafted his published report of the Spitzbergen work, Dr. Paul was clearly unwilling to declare chilling irrelevant to the causes of the common cold. August Stenersen's non-cold and those colds seen in the North Pacific must have contributed to this unwillingness. Still, the data from Longyear City made it very clear that chilling could not be the major cause of colds that started when the boats returned each spring to Spitzbergen. What then was the major reason?

Harlan Paul was confident that the common cold was produced by a single disease agent, i.e., by a particular virus. All his interpretations of the observations at Longyear City grew out of that understanding. He did not speculate about the meaning of his observations should there be multiple varieties of colds, or multiple agents causing them. Instead, he assumed that the one cold virus changed and weakened as it circulated slowly among the confined and generally resistant populace of Longyear City. Then, with the arrival of the first boat of summer, Paul imagined that the virus rebounded into virility, due to the presence of new visitors with low resistance, and/or due to the awakening of some non-weakened versions of this same viral agent through contact with outsiders.

It is significant in evaluating these ideas that it was the townspeople, not the new visitors, who generally suffered the epidemic of colds. If it were an active and virile strain of the virus that arrived each spring (always, it seemed, arriving with the first boat), then why were so few people on that boat developing new colds while so many in town were developing them? The strong implication would be that the level of immunity was different between those in town and those arriving by sea. It was not the virus that was changing its strength, it was the townspeople who were changing their ability to resist the virus. During winter isolation, levels of immunity appeared to be dropping considerably. As Paul and Freese recognized, however, even this inference is puzzling because any such lowering of immunity levels should have been accompanied by increasing numbers of colds. Yet by March colds had all but ceased to occur on Spitzbergen, at the very time when immunity to colds presumably should have been at a minimum.

One solution to this dilemma might have been to postulate more than one agent as a cause of the common cold. In small isolated communities perhaps everyone could develop an immunity to any one such agent before those who had first achieved their immunity began to lose it again; for a time, then, no one in the population would be susceptible to infection and the disease would cease to circulate. Thus, colds would be seen to die out over the winter in the small population of Longyear City, but not in Oslo, where the presence of more people would allow multiple disease agents to remain in circulation for a length of time sufficient for the first group of cold sufferers to again have lost their temporary resistance to whatever agents caused their initial colds. The spring outbreak of colds at Longyear City might then be attributed to the introduction from Oslo of a fresh kind of cold agent, one that had not been seen locally for a while, and one for which general immunity had now died out in this small town.

Yet the notion of multiple agency in the causation of the common cold was contrary to the long present assumption, reinforced in language and convention, that *the* common cold was a single disease produced by a single causal agent. Faced in Longyear City with evidence suggesting that common colds might after all have multiple causes and might respond to multiple contributing factors, Paul and Freese could not in good conscience offer such an interpretation. And, even had they chosen thus to interpret their findings, it is doubtful in 1933, in their published report, that they could have been very persuasive.

Three Conclusions from Longyear City

However, Paul and Freese *could* be persuasive in three conclusions that they reached. First, they noted that the bacterial flora of the nose and throat do not seem to play any significant role in the initiation of common colds. The evidence for this conclusion was substantial. And that evidence was why, in the end, Paul and Freese could speak as comfortably as they did about the cause of the cold being a virus, an inference that was far from universally accepted at the time. It was always possible, of course, that some as yet undiscovered and uncultured bacterium might be found to cause colds. But Paul and Freese were confident that the science of the day had not missed any such bacterium.

The second conclusion was one that at least Dr. Paul found particularly surprising and counter to his own prior experience. Nonetheless, the data were very clear: the incidence of colds seen in this Arctic community was completely unrelated to, and unaffected by, weather variables. Of course, it was possible that on ships which roam at sea, and in other latitudes, things might be different. But if weather factors do affect the common cold, it would certainly seem they should do so in Longyear City as well. Yet there they clearly did not do so. Thus, the conclusion seemed unmistakable that weather factors do not, after all, play any major role in causing colds.

The third and most persuasive of Paul and Freese's conclusions was that the common cold "is spread by direct contact." It is contagious. People only get it from other people. And it was not simply the occurrence of the epidemic that annually and reliably followed the arrival of the first boat that supported this conclusion; so did the mathematics of that epidemic, with its exponential growth as new colds multiplied into new contacts and still further colds.

There was, however, one rather curious problem with each of these latter two conclusions. The problem was that a few years before, in studies carried out in the United States and in Holland, medical science had already satisfied itself that colds *do* in fact depend on weather changes, and they do *not* spread by direct contagion and contact. As we shall see, this problem, this new contradiction, marked the beginning of a particularly interesting and contentious debate about the causes of the common cold, a debate that continued for the next six decades, a debate that revealed much about the workings of science, about the mysteries of illness and health, and about the surprising world in which we live.

Colds Blanket America: Berkeley, Boston, Chicago, and New Orleans, 1924

"It seems strange that such a common and mild disease should not have been conquered by medical science, which has wrought such wonders in other fields. The failure is not due to lack of effort. The literature of the last hundred years shows evidence of much patient and careful work, especially on the etiology."[1]

— *A. Hilding, 1930*

The study that Paul and Freese carried out in Spitzbergen typifies much of the early work done in the field of epidemiology. Literally, of course, epidemiology means "the study of epidemics." Paul and Freese chose the word "epidemic" to describe the small explosion of cold cases they had observed in Longyear City, and indeed the word generally implies a sharp rise in the incidence of some disease, affecting many members of a particular community. But it is also possible to speak of an "epidemic" episode having but a single case, and epidemiologists are sometimes concerned with finding the cause of an illness affecting just one or two members of a single family. In the fuller sense then, epidemiology is the study of the particular conditions that trigger disease, as revealed by an exhaustive study of the various factors that have been present and absent whenever episodes of disease have been present and absent. Thus, the epidemiologist is a medical intelligence officer, a detective, one who tries to build the strongest case possible out of circumstantial evidence, often with impressive success leading to surprising conclusions.

It is ironic, then, that circumstantial evidence does not currently receive much respect in the courts of scientific opinion. Instead, the scientific community regards the data from laboratory experiments to be the more persuasive and prestigious forms of scientific evidence. Modern laboratory experiments are frequently held to be *the* correct means for determining the causes of things and for explaining the effects of those causes. And yet, circumstantial evidence can also be used to build an explanatory case that often is just as tight and convincing as the case afforded by the results from an elegant laboratory experiment. In astronomy, for instance, no laboratory can contain the stars. The great advances in astronomy have largely depended upon the timely observation of spontaneous experiments occurring far outside earthbound laboratory walls. The astronomer is given no choice but to play the role of a stellar epidemiologist, taking careful notes on the health of the universe. And still, astronomy flourishes.

In medical science, however, a good experiment is the preferred way to resolve most of the causal puzzles currently under study. This preference exists despite the fact that very often only circumstantial evidence can suggest the right experimental study, the study where at last the disease agent will seem to be caught in the act of causing disease. And if I say "*seem* to be caught," and not "*is* caught," that is because, although it is not widely appreciated, *experimental studies only bring us a different form of circumstantial evidence.* They do not provide the pure proof and undiluted truth that one might imagine.

Experimental evidence is often no less subject to influence by unsuspected contaminating factors, and generally no less ripe for alternative explanations, than is circumstantial evidence. The conclusions suggested either by experiments or by epidemiological studies could be misleading conclusions, and in each case they will mislead for the same reasons.

It is significant that both the scientist and the layman, while struggling to discount unwelcome implications deriving either from a laboratory experiment or from an epidemiological study, invoke precisely the same logical form of criticism in either case. The scientist will often declare that "proper controls have not been employed." In fact, most scientists today use the phrases "proper controls" and "experimental controls" interchangeably. In layman's language, this amounts to saying "the reason for those results is not the one you think; something else was really going on there, explaining your findings." Underneath these very different choices of words is the same criticism, and that criticism generally is as applicable to the conclusions of a given experiment as it is to any of those "natural experiments" recorded by working epidemiologists.

When Paul and Freese found strong circumstantial evidence that colds are introduced into a community by contagion, that is, first by contact with outsiders and later by personal contacts within the community, there did not appear to be any way that these particular observations, or the conclusions to which they led, could be mistaken. Paul and Freese had studied, over a long time span, a very large community that experienced many different changes, both in weather and in occasions providing exposure to outsiders. Although modern statistical techniques — for evaluating the likelihood of observing similar findings in similar samples if chance factors alone were to produce them — had yet to become well known, still, in this case it was safe to assume that the operation of chance factors did not undermine Paul and Freese's main conclusions.

Townsend's Grand Sample of U.S. Colds

And yet two studies already existed, seeming to prove that contagion is *not* after all an important cause of common colds. These two studies were known to Dr. Paul, who used one portion of them to highlight the surprisingly low yearly incidence of colds to be seen at Longyear City. But the more contradictory implications of these two earlier studies were neither acknowledged nor discussed by Paul and Freese in light of their own findings.

The first of these two earlier studies had its beginnings in the autumn of 1923, and it was carried out under the auspices of the United States Public Health Service (USPHS). At the time it was the most ambitious epidemiological project ever undertaken to study the common cold and it employed a number of Health Service personnel, including a number of surgeons and statisticians. The principal investigator for the project was Surgeon J. G. Townsend. On October 24, 1924, Townsend's preliminary report on his study was published.[2] In that first report he described the organization of the project and some interesting preliminary findings from it.

The organization of the project was indeed impressive. More than thirteen thousand university students were recruited as volunteer informants for one part of the study. They were to report on any and all respiratory illnesses they might be experiencing, over a one-year period. In addition, data on colds from the members of approximately 775 family households, totaling approximately 2,500 family members, were provided by the heads of those households. The students were located on campuses in eleven different U.S. cities, from Berkeley to Boston, and from Chicago to New

Orleans. The families were scattered throughout the mainland United States, many at Armed Forces bases, because the majority of the family group reporters were medical officers working for the Armed Forces or for the USPHS. Those heads of household who were not medical officers were generally university professors. Surgeon Townsend was quite proud of his samples because of their sizes, because of their geographical distribution, and because of their composition. He was convinced that the advanced education level of his volunteers guaranteed that "reliable and intelligent reports would be secured from persons of the class represented."

Student and professional informants in this study were mailed special report forms twice each month, soliciting data on all their respiratory illnesses. These report forms bore the imprint of the U.S. Treasury Department (parent body to the USPHS) and they carried the very suggestive title: "Epidemiological Study of Common Colds and other Minor Respiratory Affections." Because Townsend's volunteers were well educated, they would have known that the word "affections" was meant here in one of its original senses, as a synonym for "diseases." And yet the other meanings, which link with and enrich this interesting word, could not have gone wholly unnoticed by the respondents.

In the Townsend survey, six varieties of respiratory illness were defined on those bimonthly report forms sent to each volunteer. For the students, the illnesses were described as follows:

- Cold (includes "cold in the head" or "nose cold")
- Bronchitis (includes cold in the chest with cough)
- Influenza (includes "grippe" or "flu")
- Tonsillitis or pharyngitis (sore throat)
- Hay fever ("pollen fever" or "rose cold")
- Pneumonia (only if so diagnosed by a physician)

Informants were asked in each case when their attack began, and when it ended. They were asked whether the illness kept them from work and/or in bed, and whether it was seen by a physician. They were asked to check which symptoms from among a list of thirteen were present during their illness. And they were asked about possible triggering causes for the illness; for example, known exposure to the disease or to "drafts, chilling, wetting, overheating, or fatigue." Good, usable reports were received from 87 percent of the sample, generally within two weeks of the end of each report period.

In his 1924 report, Surgeon Townsend presented only some preliminary analyses of the semi-monthly incidence rates for a portion of the student illnesses from the period October 1, 1923, to June 30, 1924. There were no data given for September 1923, a month in which today we would expect a significant epidemic of colds to have occurred. In this first report, data from just eight of the eleven campuses were displayed in a chart showing the rate of illness per thousand persons for each half-month across the nine-month report period. Commenting on this chart, with its eight lines busily rising and falling in a complex pattern across the seasons, Townsend wrote:

> The most striking indication afforded by these graphs is the synchronous behavior of the incidence of respiratory affections in all of the localities plotted. While there are, of course, deviations from the general trend in individual localities, the major variations are common to all of the localities . . . . In the more detailed tabulation, which will be made later, the records will be presented for shorter intervals in order to reveal whether or not there is any significant lag in the various localities represented. But even upon the basis of half-month intervals the synchronous variation of the incidence of respiratory affections in localities as widely scattered as San Francisco,[3] New Orleans, Chicago, Boston, and Washington is unmistakably shown and is of extreme interest.[4]

The "extreme interest" to which Townsend alludes derives from two sources. Other analyses of the student replies showed that the common cold was responsible for almost all of the illness being reported. The lines on the graph reflected changes in this disease and no other. But the lines reflected a synchronous set of epidemics — all the lines seemed to rise and fall at much the same times. Epidemics of common colds did not seem to be starting in the north and sweeping south, nor were they starting in the west and sweeping east. They seemed to be starting and ending everywhere at about the same time. (We must keep in mind, of course, that this "same time" constituted a fifteen- or sixteen-day half-month.) The implication of this finding was that colds may not spread by contagious epidemics sweeping over the land. Instead they may be turned on and off by something that occurs in widely scattered places at nearly the same points in time. Although Townsend never speculated what that something might be, we can reasonably doubt that the weather is a likely candidate, given the distances from Berkeley to Boston, for instance, and given the very different weather patterns that would ordinarily influence Chicago and New Orleans.

The second report on the USPHS survey was published in 1927. It bore the subtitle: "Progress report II: based on records for families of medical officers of the Army, Navy, and Public Health Service and of members of several university faculties." With this article, Townsend was joined by co-author Edgar Sydenstricker, principal statistician for the project. The earlier report had focused on the preliminary analysis of data from eight of the eleven student campuses. This second report focused on the preliminary analysis of the data from the 775 families (2,498 persons). The families, unlike the students, constituted something like a representative sample of the population as a whole. In fact, one of the first things that Townsend and Sydenstricker reported in their article was how their sample compared to the population of the whole United States at the time of the 1920 census. The family sample was not unlike the population. However, because families had been selected as such, it did have somewhat more people between twenty-five and forty-four years of age, and between birth and four years of age, than were to be found in the population as a whole. The family sample was also somewhat under-represented by five- to nine-year-olds (an age range where colds are especially frequent) and by those over fifty-five years of age (in whom colds are relatively infrequent).

It was in this second report that Townsend addressed the issues of how a cold ought best to be defined and diagnosed. His efforts were aided by the fact that the same six-variety classification scheme was used by the students and by the physicians and professors reporting for the family study. Moreover, all the report forms included a symptom checklist that allowed Townsend to determine which symptoms were associated with the six different diagnoses.

While the classification of respiratory diseases into those particular six classes may have been convenient for the use of the laymen and the clinicians alike, this convenience came at a cost. Townsend and Sydenstricker noted:

> Obviously, however, the classification is unsatisfactory from a statistical viewpoint. In the first place, the classes are not defined on any single consistent principle, and some are less clearly defined than others. Thus, the class "hay fever, pollen fever, or rose cold" is defined on an etiological basis, as including those cases attributed by the reporter to the effects of irritating pollens; whereas at least three of the other classes . . . have a *definitely specified symptomatic* basis [e.g., "sore throat"] and the other two, "influenza" and "pneumonia," are likewise symptomatic but refer to

symptoms which are not definitely specified. These criticisms, that the classifications are partly etiological and partly symptomatic and that the various
class limits are not equally clearly defined, apply, however, to all the nosolog-
ical classifications that have as yet been devised, and in the present state of
knowledge seem unavoidable.[5]

Symptoms and Problems in the Diagnosis of Colds

Townsend and Sydenstricker then went on to discuss a more serious difficulty. Their six diagnostic classes are not mutually exclusive. Faced with an
illness involving a runny and/or congested nose, a sore throat, a cough, and
inflammation behind the eyes, one reporter may record a "head cold,"
another may record "bronchitis," another "sore throat/pharyngitis," while
others may record some two of these three, or even all three. And just as the
six classes might be confused, so some of them, such as those just listed, may
not in fact represent different or distinct diseases. It may be, perhaps, that
almost all sore throats are just "colds," even though not all colds produce
sore throats. If, however, sore throats are rarely reported during the same illness as those bringing with them a notable cough, or if illnesses with cough
are rarely seen complicated with runny nose, then there is good reason to
suppose these to be independent and distinct diseases. Thus, Townsend and
Sydenstricker looked closely at the linkage between the reported symptoms
and the diagnoses used by their experienced, clinician reporters.

Leaving aside pneumonia, each of the five remaining diagnostic categories, including "influenza" and "hay fever," when used by itself, had
associated with it, at least some of the time, every one of the thirteen
symptoms being reported. The most frequently reported symptoms for a
"cold in the head" were (a) "running nose," 81 percent of cases, (b) "obstruction of nostrils," 44 percent of cases, and (c) "sudden onset," in 37 percent
of cases. But "running nose" was even more frequently reported with cases
of hay fever (82 percent of those cases). "Obstruction of nostrils" also
occurred more frequently with cases of hay fever (46 percent), than it did
with the common cold.

Other symptoms showed a similar lack of specificity. "Cough" was
reported in 91 percent (but not 100 percent) of cases diagnosed "bronchitis with cough." Cough was also reported to be present in 47 percent of
influenza cases, however, and in approximately one out of every three
head colds.

"Sore throat" was reported in 83 percent (but not 100 percent) of cases diagnosed "sore throat, tonsillitis, or pharyngitis." Sore throat was also reported in 29 percent of influenza cases, however, and in one out of every seven head colds.

"Fever" was a symptom reported in 79 percent of influenza cases, but also in 42 percent of sore throat cases, 30 percent of bronchitis cases, and in one out of every eight colds.

"Aching in body or limbs" was reported in 67 percent of influenza cases, but also in 29 percent of sore throat cases, 15 percent of bronchitis cases, and in one out of every seven colds.

"Headache" was cited in one out of every five colds, but it was also seen in 16 percent of bronchitis cases, 31 percent of sore throat cases, and 58 percent of influenza cases.

Thus, whatever the symptom, every respiratory disease seemed capable of causing it. Moreover, the common cold was clearly capable of producing any one of the symptoms being reported. This meant that the common cold could not even be ruled *out* by the presence of some subset of those symptoms.

How is it possible to study a disease that is so easily confused with other, different, diseases? What does it tell us when hundreds of doctors in the USPHS study have given similar-looking illnesses different diagnoses, and have given somewhat different clusters of symptoms the same diagnosis? One thing it might signify is that "the" common cold is, as the choice of language suggests, just one disease, one that has many unimportant variations. This would mean that it is easy to study the common cold because it is so common, and because sophistication in diagnosis is not necessary. But another inference might be that only "pure" cases of common cold should be studied. Thus, the rule might be that cough, sore throat, and fever should not be allowed to complicate these pure cases.

Townsend and Sydenstricker noted that while it would be safest to follows this latter rule, their results were largely unaffected by adopting their more liberal set of cold-defining criteria. They were persuaded that almost all of the respiratory disease they saw that was not pneumonia or influenza or hay fever was some variant of the common cold. Consequently they classed as a common cold any illness where that diagnosis had been given, even if sore throat or bronchitis were also diagnosed for the same illness.

This definitional decision by Townsend and Sydenstricker set a precedent that has rarely been superseded in research dealing with the common cold. A "cold" is still a cold, is just a cold. We are all considered competent diagnosticians of our own colds by most epidemiologists and by most experimental scientists studying the common cold. Influenza is something separate, yes. And hay fever. But colds, at least in their beginnings, are wonderfully various even as they are somehow recognizably the same. The modern etiological definition of a cold that would say "a cold is any illness resulting only from infection with a cold virus" is always an implicit definition. But no reliable laboratory test existed, even as late as 1995, to show that a particular cold virus had been the only infective agent behind a given illness.

Age, Gender, and Other "Risk" Factors for Colds

Thus fortified with generous numbers of "colds" for use in their statistical study, Townsend and Sydenstricker turned to examine the 1924 incidence rates for colds, and to explore how these rates varied according to age, gender, and time of year. Adjusting for the special age distribution of their sample, and correcting it statistically to represent the age mix of the entire U.S. population in 1920, this USPHS survey suggested that the average number of colds in America for 1924 was 1.46 colds per person. Overall, males had 3.5 percent more colds than average, and females had 3.5 percent fewer colds than average. As a group, children under five years of age had 50 percent more colds than average, while people older than fifty-four years had nearly 50 percent fewer colds than average. The decline of colds with age was found to be steady except between the ages of twenty-five and thirty-four, when the incidence seemed to rise slightly.

The possible reasons for this rise in the rate of colds among young adults were not considered by Townsend and Sydenstricker. The traditional explanation for the increase has been that between the ages of twenty-five and thirty-four many adults have young children who are under five years of age and/or at school, and these groups of children catch many colds. Because those colds elicit caretaking and frequent close contacts, there are many opportunities for the child to infect caretakers, and consequently the parents of young children catch more colds. This is a very satisfying explanation provided that colds do, in fact, spread by contagion, and provided that caretakers frequently catch colds a short time after their charges do. Unfortunately, however, the USPHS study of 1924 cannot really tell us whether these two conditions truly obtain.

Another relevant clue to understanding the role played by contagion from their children in the rise in average cold incidence among young adults, can be found in the rates of colds seen in the two sexes. In the

Townsend and Sydenstricker report for 1924, most of the rise in cold incidence between the ages twenty-five and thirty-four came not from the females, but from the males. Males accounted for more than 80 percent of the total rise. They doubled their rate of colds in contrast to that for the group ten years younger. Females showed a corresponding increase of only about 10 percent over the cold incidence for females ten years younger. If caretaking really did produce contagion of colds during 1924, we might have expected it to show up more prominently in the women, not the men. And if kisses between spouses were to produce contagion of colds, we might have expected the wives to more nearly approach the husbands in their increased rate of colds, at this time in their lives. (But of this too, more later.) Perhaps then contagion does not produce colds after all. But if contagion does not produce colds, then what does? And why would the young adult men have experienced more of it, whatever "it" is?

Townsend and his colleagues never did examine weather as a factor relating to cold incidences in various parts of America. But they reported seasonal variations confirming the general impression that colds are least likely in mid-summer and most prevalent in the fall and winter. They reported data for both the families, and for twelve thousand of their college students, over the entire 1924 calendar year. The incidence curves for the students and families, across the twenty-four half-months, were remarkably parallel, though the students consistently showed a rate that averaged almost twice that of the typical family member. It happens that both curves began at their maximum in January, then dropped each month thereafter to a minimum in July, rose to a sharp near-maximum in late September, and dropped off until another epidemic produced a maximum in late November.

In 1924 epidemiologists had long been aware that deaths from respiratory diseases tend to be most frequent in mid-winter, and that such deaths increase rapidly in incidence beyond the age of fifty-five. Thus, Townsend and Sydenstricker were surprised to find that the prototypic respiratory disease, the common cold, is actually *least* prevalent among people over age fifty-five. Moreover, colds are not particularly prevalent in mid-winter when the corresponding death rate from respiratory disease is highest. Common colds seem to be quite prevalent in the early fall, however, at a time when the corresponding death rate is still quite low. Thus, common colds and life-threatening respiratory diseases would seem to derive from conditions that are generally quite independent of each other.

The 1927 publication by Townsend and Sydenstricker was also the first to document the fact that, for north temperate latitudes, September is the month for predictable cold epidemics, not February, as previously had been assumed. In the Americas and in Europe, colds really are predictable in the early fall, and at no other time of the year can one be as sure to find them easily. We will have to ask why that is. But for now, there are few if any clues from the early USPHS study as to what the answer may be.

What we do see in the studies that Townsend directed are two strong suggestions that person-to-person contacts may not be important in spreading, or in causing, colds (an implication that is quite at variance with the conclusions from the Longyear City research). Still, they remain only suggestions, and there would yet be room for contagion to play a major role in causing colds if contagion were to occur quickly and efficiently (that is, well within fifteen days), perhaps even by mail, from Boston to Chicago to Berkeley to New Orleans.

Townsend and Sydenstricker might have gone much further. They might, for instance, have analyzed the timing of colds within families to get much stronger evidence for or against the thesis that contagion is a major cause of colds. They might also have published the results of the promised examination of cold incidences over periods of time shorter than half a month, but they never did do so. From the beginning, their purpose had been far more general than to search out answers to one specific question about the role played by people in causing colds. Nor did they ever intend to examine how weather might trigger epidemics of colds. Issues such as these were for others to examine. It was not long, however, before these issues were examined very thoroughly, this time in Holland.

3

Contagious Doubts: Amsterdam, Holland, 1925

"Now it may be all the more easily imagined how at times of very variable temperature or sudden falls of temperature of the air, the chance increases that the decrease of the body temperature may exceed the physiological limit and the body be rendered susceptible to commensal infection."[1]

— *J. J. van Loghem, 1928*

At the University of Amsterdam in 1925, the Chair of Hygiene was occupied by the eminent bacteriologist J. J. van Loghem, M.D. Van Loghem had already enjoyed a long career as a bacteriologist. But now, intrigued by some of the implications of Townsend's American research on the common cold, van Loghem was thinking of becoming an epidemiologist as well.

What particularly interested van Loghem was the strong suggestion in the recent American data that something other than direct personal contact is necessary to trigger most cold epidemics. This suggestion fit very nicely with some less traditional ideas that had been occupying more and more of van Loghem's own thinking. And so, inspired by the first reports out of America, van Loghem at last reactivated a plan that he had been considering for some time, a plan to carry out a large-scale epidemiological study of his own. That study was completed in 1926, and its rich yield of data was tabulated over much of the following year.

Van Loghem usually published his work in Dutch or German journals. Perhaps because of the related American work, however, van Loghem chose to publish the findings from his ambitious new epidemiological study in an English-language journal. His article appeared in print in 1928, and for many years to follow it was one of the most frequently cited studies in all the literature dealing with the common cold.[2]

Trained in the study of parasites, van Loghem was practiced at making certain distinctions that medical science can, normally, happily ignore. Some of these distinctions seemed to van Loghem to be crucial for the proper understanding of the common cold. Consequently, in his 1928 research report, van Loghem chose to begin by reintroducing some important conceptual distinctions with these words:

> Among the causes of such diseases as [the common cold] . . . we clearly distinguish two important ones. In the first place we recognize their infectious character, even if the specific causal organisms cannot be identified. In the second place we recognize the influence of the cold season. Opinions differ a good deal as to the relative importance of these factors: microbe and temperature. For one person the microbe is the main thing, the cooling influence of the season of secondary importance; for another the converse may be true.
>
> . . . For many people the idea of *infection* — in the sense of morbid change as a result of invasion by and growth of micro-organisms — is inseparably connected with the idea of *contagion.* And yet a distinction should be made here. The time is past, when exclusively the obligatory parasitic organisms, transferred from one victim to another, could be considered the sole cause of disease. There is a growing interest in usually harmless bacteria and viruses that live as *commensals,* generally with healthy hosts, on the surface of the skin and the mucous membranes, and only cause disease under special circumstances.[3]

This concept of the commensal organism, one that lives for a period of time in harmony with its host, without the damages of infection, but one that can become parasitic and infectious under certain conditions, held the key to understanding the common cold in van Loghem's view. The word "commensal" literally means "table companion." The *commensal* bacteria and viruses feed with us companionably. But a *parasite* ceases to eat *with* us and begins, not so companionably, to feed *on* us.

The traditional view had long assumed that the agent causing the common cold is just another parasite. It was presumed to jump from person to person, infecting them on arrival, and causing disease unless or until it was driven out by the work of the immune system. But by 1925, in research on those bacteria that are typically resident in our bodies, van Loghem and others had found considerable evidence to suggest that even healthy and uninfected people often carry with them the agents of such diseases as diphtheria, meningitis, and pneumonia. Such diseases only seem to break out as infections under special circumstances. The nature of those special circumstances was in 1925, as it was in 1995, something of a mystery.

Why Does the Commensal Change Its Spots?

Whatever combination of circumstances it is that changes a commensal organism into an infectious one, it must have its effects either in or on that organism, or, in ourselves. Either the disease *agent* suddenly changes into something nasty and stronger, or *we* suddenly become inviting and weaker, or perhaps a little cycle of both occurs. But what would cause the commensal to change its spots, and what might make us more inviting for attack?

Van Loghem proposed that *chilling* was the major factor responsible for starting the common cold. And, in van Loghem's view, the effects of chilling probably acted on our body's defenses, and not on whatever bacterium or virus was responsible for causing colds. There were experimental data supporting van Loghem in this view, and in the introduction to his 1928 article he reviewed some of those data, in his stilted prose, as follows:

> It is easy to understand that several pathologists have tried to ascertain experimentally the significance of refrigeration for the effecting of infection. Everyone remembers Pasteur's experiment, how he succeeded in breaking the natural resistance of a fowl against *B. anthracis* by artificial lowering of its temperature. Neither this classical experiment nor the numerous experiments made on animals by others throw much light upon the ætiology of respiratory diseases of man.
>
> Experiments on human beings are of more importance. It is certainly worth noting when one reads of persons who, under the conditions of certain physiological experiments at low temperature, regularly caught a cold. But we have also to give attention to Chodounsky with his protocols, which, according to him, prove that cooling down is of no significance as a cause of illness. Chodounsky was able to take very hot or very cold baths, and then expose himself to an icy draught without getting ill. But he was spared no criticism. Notwithstanding his advanced years — he made these experiments at the age of 57 and 63 — Chodounsky was strong and hardened by a daily application of cold water. Indeed we know

from his protocols that his thermoregulating system functioned excellently. As a matter of fact these cold stimuli, with which he did not succeed in catching cold, did not lower his temperature but, as in the classical experiments, made it rise.[4]

If the wording above is awkward, still, it has a kind of arrogant charm about it. Apparently, van Loghem did not feel any duty to provide his readers with references to the interesting set of studies mentioned here, and it is doubtful whether these studies were much better known in 1925 than they are today. Since van Loghem writes already convinced that chilling predisposes people to infection, it is notable that he does not tell us more about those physiological studies where low temperatures were thought to have caused such "regular" colds.

I infer from this that perhaps he has misplaced his references to these studies, and has decided that these references do not matter anyway since they pale in importance when put alongside the data he is about to share with us from his own more recent work. The references do matter, however, for as we shall see, the evidence van Loghem alludes to here could be rather helpful in choosing among theories that try to resolve the contradictory conclusions implied by later research into the role of chilling in causing common colds.

It is distinctly possible that the physiological studies mentioned by van Loghem were those of Stuart Mudd, Samuel B. Grant, and their coworkers at the Washington University Medical School in St. Louis, Missouri.[5] Mudd and Grant were bacteriologists who believed that bacteria cause the common cold, perhaps in response to cooling in the nose and throat. They performed experimental studies, chilling volunteer subjects while measuring any changes produced in the nose and throat. Using a special wire probe, Mudd and Grant measured the temperature of the mucous membranes of the nose, throat, and tonsils. They took bacterial cultures and sampled mucous. They did not find quite what they expected. They expected to see mucous congestion as a consequence of chilling. Instead they found vasoconstriction and ischemia, which is to say, they found that the blood supply to the surfaces of the nose and throat initially drops off, although later it will frequently rebound to higher (and warmer) levels. This does not lead to nasal congestion, nor to much change in the local temperature. But Mudd and Grant reported one other significant observation in 1919, as follows: "In four instances, exposure [to chilling] was followed by a 'cold' or sore throat."

Four instances do not constitute "regularly catching a cold," and so perhaps this is not the experimental study that ten years later van Loghem had in mind when he wrote the passage quoted above. Mudd and Grant themselves acknowledged that the procedures employed in their study caused a certain amount of trauma in the throat, and could easily have left the throat sore, without any infection being the cause. The Mudd and Grant experiments do not suggest that chilling has any effect in increasing the likelihood of catching a cold. In fact their experiments left Mudd and Grant believing, as van Loghem also clearly believed, that regular exposures to cold stimuli will "harden" one, presumably because such exposures somehow tone the vascular response system, leaving the body more effective in combating the stresses produced by subsequent exposures to chills and frosts.

Whatever the truth may be concerning van Loghem's memory about "certain physiological experiments at low temperatures," he was certainly correct when he noted that the "classical studies" had predicted the effect of cold treatments on Chodounsky resulting not in lowering his body temperature but in raising it. By 1925 it was indeed well known that when stressed by chilling, the body's immediate response is to increase body heat, in a fashion that initially results in a rise rather than a fall in local body temperature. However, van Loghem was untroubled by this fact, even though it is only a drop of body temperature that presumably causes the conversion of commensal friends into infectious enemies.

The reason van Loghem was untroubled by this apparent contradiction between the theory and the physiological reality was that he saw it as only apparent. In fact, van Loghem assumed that most chills do not produce infections precisely because most chills do result in a slight rise of body temperature. But when the body cannot meet the challenge of a cold environment, sooner or later the body temperature will fall, and it is then, presumably, that the commensals will rise in revolution.

Thus, in introducing his new epidemiological study, van Loghem wrote:

> We have to acknowledge that parasitical microbiology has failed ætiologically in this field. So let us accept another working hypothesis and try to test the notions of "colds" and "catching cold" by ascertaining . . . how far *disturbance of the regulation of the heat of the body* may be considered the primary cause of commensal infections.[6]

Van Loghem's italics here also acknowledge the potentially contradictory effects of exposure to cold because literally all he says is that *thermoregulation* is disturbed. A rise in temperature too may, after all, increase susceptibility to commensal infection. Whatever his personal convictions on this matter, van Loghem's theory had him covered either way: when temperatures fall, and when they rise.

The Design of van Loghem's Epidemiological Study

Of course, if common colds are infections caused by commensal organisms, then human contact might ordinarily play little or no role in the outbreak of colds. This was precisely the implication of the American data that so intrigued van Loghem. Colds seemed to begin simultaneously in different parts of America, as if contagion from person to person were not involved. The trouble was that the American data were summarized in two-week blocks, and within that time travelers from city to city might just conceivably export colds from place to place. America might be a global village, and airships might be its vehicles of contagion. Thus, van Loghem felt the need to do his own Dutch study, and he wrote:

> For the sake of accuracy I made a not unimportant change in the American technics on two points. In the first place I obtained as informants not students but almost exclusively heads of families (doctors, dental surgeons, masters, chemists, officials, and other intellectuals); secondly I did not send the questionnaires twice a month, but once a week.[7]

Van Loghem began collecting data on September 20, 1925, and he continued sending out questionnaires for thirty-seven weeks, until June 5, 1926. Prior to starting this study, by mid-September, van Loghem had enrolled almost 7,500 volunteers, divided among seven geographical regions in Holland. By the end of the study that number had dropped slightly to 6,900. The fewest number of participants (581) were in the north of Holland. The largest number (1,667) were in the area around The Hague and Rotterdam. At home in Amsterdam, van Loghem had 1,159 volunteers. With samples so large, very small differences in cold incidences can acquire true significance.

The logistics of such a study, obtaining volunteers and keeping the data sheets flowing, required a very special set of skills and a very special social organization. Van Loghem certainly did not lack what was required. He continues:

The head of the family had promised his willingness to co-operate by signing a slip, on which he gave the family name, address, initials, sex and age of the members of his family. These data were hectographed on 35 (later on increased to 37) lists of questions, 35 envelopes too were hectographed with the family name and address. The lists and envelopes meant for one family were numbered 1–35 and then all were sorted according to the weeks. So by September 25th we had in readiness 35 parcels, each of about 1,600 envelopes (with the lists of questions and reply envelopes enclosed) of which parcels one was sent every week. They were always dispatched on Friday afternoon, so that the collaborators always had the list of questions for the past week in their possession on Saturday. In my opinion this administrative regularity has been highly favourable to the regular filling up and returning of the lists.

The weekly list of questions was composed very simply. For each member of the family a blank space was left to be filled in with *no* (no new cold) or *yes* (caught cold). In case of [a] cold there was also stated: nose cold (coryza), sore throat (angina), hoarseness (laryngitis), cold with cough (bronchitis) or slight influenza. . . . No inquiry was made about serious illness.[8]

Van Loghem's Discoveries

The enviable health of the Dutch postal service in 1925 was not matched by the health of the Dutch people. In the very first week of his study (September 20–26, 1925) van Loghem found 27 percent of his subjects had colds, presumably *new* colds. Although this figure dropped to nine percent by mid-November, the incidences of colds reported to van Loghem during his study have rarely been equaled in studies anywhere else in the world. As the weeks went by, the incidences of new colds rose and fell. Over the entire thirty-seven weeks of this study a total of 29,653 colds were recorded. That is an average of four and one-quarter colds per person in thirty-seven weeks, or six colds per person per year if summer cold rates were to continue at the spring average.

In each of the seven separate geographical districts studied by van Loghem, the results were similar. When the incidence of colds was plotted week by week and the seven lines placed together on a single graph, the correspondences appeared very striking. With a few shallow exceptions, all the lines appeared to rise and fall in concert. Generally they all peaked and all troughed during the same or adjacent weeks, and the levels of peak and trough all seemed to correspond, i.e., the highest peaks and the lowest troughs seemed to occur at the same points in the season. To van Loghem, and to his many readers in the years that followed, these data confirmed "the synchronous character" of cold epidemics. Epidemics do not seem to start at one place and then by contagion spread outward across the land. Instead, cold epidemics seem to start together, synchronously, all over the land, and they wax and wane in concert.

If a new infection, spreading by contagion, is not the source of each winter cold epidemic, what then does give rise to each wave of colds? As we have seen, van Loghem already suspected that the answer was the weather. In his 1928 report, he went on to say about the data in his graph of the seven districts:

> The joint oscillations of the "colds" lines raises the question, whether similar oscillations are to be found in the weather conditions of the same period.
>
> As our objective is the cooling power of the outdoor air we have not only to think of the temperature but also the motion of the air and its state of moisture. With an eye to the habits of our informants, however, we have to take special account of the temperature indoors. Now, with the airy Dutch way of building, it is true that the latter is not independent of the motion of the outdoor air, but as part of the cooling factor indoors we can hardly consider that motion. So when examining weather conditions during the period of inquiry I provisionally restricted myself to the temperature of the [outdoor] air. The clear results that were at once put into my hand when I drew a diagram of the easily obtainable decade [i.e., the ten-day average] temperatures is one of the causes of this provisional restriction.[9]

Since cold temperatures were what interested van Loghem, he plotted his temperature data upside-down, putting zero at the top of his graph, and putting high temperatures at the bottom of his graph. Thus, on this graph, peaks represented waves of cold weather, while troughs represented times of warmer weather. And on the same graph he plotted the incidence of common colds that developed during the parallel periods of analysis. Here, peaks represented times of epidemic colds, in other words, high frequency colds.

The resulting graph has an interesting, if slightly confused, tale to tell. It begins, of course, with the last ten days of September. The *average* temperature at this time was rather warm for Holland. It was about

12 degrees Celsius (53 degrees Fahrenheit), a typical average for warm fall days, and an average not to be seen again in Holland until the warm days of late May, 1926. But as we already have seen, the incidence of new common colds that van Loghem found in the first week of his study was remarkably high. Colds presumably affected something more than 25 percent of his sample. It seems very likely that part of this high incidence figure is due to some confusion on the part of some informants, and perhaps as well to an understandable desire by volunteers to send in immediate eventful reports. Only *new* colds in the previous seven days were to have been reported each week, but in that very first week, all previously existing colds were new to the study and the older colds must have been a temptation to report.

Van Loghem made no comments about the validity of the high initial incidence of colds reported to him, probably because the opening week was not of overriding interest in a study designed to focus on change and development. But the opening week also happened to be the week when van Loghem found more colds than during any other week of his study. It is then significant that no autumn wave of cold weather had yet hit Holland. Because the pattern van Loghem saw in the remainder of the graph of weather and colds seemed to show such convincing parallelism, with peaks of cold and peaks of disease occurring at about the same times, the "clear result" previously mentioned seemed obvious, whatever might be the apparent exception during that first week of the study. Visually, at least, and overall, there appeared to be a close association between waves of cold temperature and waves of new common colds.

In the 1920s there was no well-known statistical measure for quantifying the amount of association or parallelism existing in two sets of data, which is to say, no such statistic was widely used or generally expected by readers of the scientific literature. Visual impression was quite satisfactory as a proof of association. It is true that to look at van Loghem's composite graph, the same number of peaks and valleys appear laid out in much the same places on each of the lines for temperature and cold incidence. However, a closer look reveals that the occasions of most severe frost sometimes were associated with very small peaks of cold incidence, while marked peaks of disease sometimes had very small waves of cold temperature attached to them. True association should show that the stronger waves of cold temperature are associated with the stronger disease epidemics, and both should be found occurring together in the same ten-day blocks of time. On even closer inspection, however, it becomes apparent that van Loghem's peaks and troughs for weather and disease factors often occur in different, even if adjacent, "decades." Perhaps the "clear results" van Loghem reported are not as simple and straightforward as he had claimed.

Today, an appropriate statistical measure of association, the correlation coefficient, would be used to supplement the testimony of the visual impression given by van Loghem's graph. To employ the correlation coefficient most effectively, van Loghem's precise figures for weather and for cold incidences would be required, and it would be best to have these data sorted by days. Unfortunately, van Loghem does not provide such data. Still, from the graph he has published, it is possible to estimate to within about three percent what each ten-day figure should be, and to calculate a correlation coefficient which should be quite accurate, at least to the first decimal place. This I have done for the twenty-six "decades" of the Dutch study.

A central theme in van Loghem's argument is that colds will occur simultaneously in different cities and towns. Since his graph presents separately the incidence of colds in Amsterdam and in the rest of Holland, these two incidence rates can also be correlated. That correlation indeed proves to be high. I calculated it to be about 0.83, which, when translated out of the statistical realm, is almost exactly two-thirds of the metaphoric distance between no association whatsoever and full or perfect association.[10] However, the correlation between the waves of cold weather and the waves of common colds is considerably lower. I calculated that the correlation coefficient for the inverted temperature levels with the incidence rates for Amsterdam common colds was about 0.42. (The corresponding figure for the rest of Holland was about 0.47.) These figures represent rather modest levels of association, somewhere between 20 percent and 25 percent of the distance from no association at all to full association. What was "very clear" to van Loghem is certainly part of what may be there, but it is not at all the strong factor that he implies.

Van Loghem had continuous, daily temperature data at his disposal, so it is not immediately clear why he chose to group his weather data into "decades" of ten days. One might have expected that he would group these data by weeks, as he had already done for his reports on the incidence of the common cold, or by days, which might have revealed that colds were actually starting shortly before cold weather came, or, say, four days after it came. It is certainly convenient to compute the average of ten data, because dividing by ten is so very easy. But colds may run through rather more than two generations over a ten-day period, and their spread across Holland in such a time period would be easily possible should contagion be an important factor. Van Loghem recognized the problems created by the American reporting period of two weeks, but curiously he still declined to analyze his own data by days, or by pairs of days, or even consistently by weeks.

Van Loghem's Second Test for the Contagiousness of Colds

All this notwithstanding, van Loghem's data remain very powerful arguments against the view that colds are merely parasitic and that they occur by simple contagion. For van Loghem added a new and very significant kind of analysis to his epidemiological study, giving an important independent check on the contagiousness of colds. The *reasoning* behind this new type of analysis can be illustrated as follows. Imagine a population of two hundred animals scattered about the countryside that happen to live evenly divided into two kinds of groups. One kind of group has few members: let us suppose it contains four individuals per group, and there are twenty-five groups. The other kind of group has many more members: let's say twenty individuals per group, each living in one of five different groups. Now suppose that a contagious disease is introduced at random to ten animals in the entire population. What will be the effect on the disease incidence seen in the general population and in each of the groups?

Looking first just at the groups, large groups stand more chance of having at least one initially infected member than do small groups, merely because each large group has more members in it than the small groups do. In the lottery of this new disease, each large group holds more tickets, and so the larger groups stand a greater chance of having the dubious honor of at least one "winning" member. If the ten originally infected animals are representatively distributed in the population, then half of them will be scattered among members of the five large groups, which means that about three large groups will have one or two initially infected members. The other five initial cases of disease will be scattered among the twenty-five small groups, which generally means that four or five of those groups will have one infected member while the other twenty or twenty-one small groups will have no infected member at all. Thus, only a small proportion of the few large groups will escape initial infection but a large proportion of many small groups will escape initial infection, even though only 5 percent of the members of each subpopulation has been infected.

Moreover, the same logic holds true for between-group contagion once the disease has started. Transmission from any infected animal to animals *outside* that animal's own group will, on average, reach a higher proportion of the larger groups than the smaller groups because the number of large groups is small and there are more members in each large group. But at the same time, *within* both kinds of groups, any infected member is likely to infect the others in his group at a rate higher than the between-group rate of contagion simply because there will be many more opportunities for contacts inside the groups than outside them. More time is spent with members inside one's own group than with individuals outside of it.

Two conclusions follow from this reasoning. The first conclusion we have already seen: when a disease is contagious, a higher proportion of the few large groups will have one or more infected members than is true among the many small groups. But second, because contagion *within* every group should be more efficient than contagion between groups, a larger number of individuals living in large groups will end up suffering the disease each time it appears than the corresponding number of those individuals who live in smaller groups. This means that over a long time period, with any reoccurring disease (such as the common cold), if that disease is contagious, then the individuals who live in larger groups will average more cases of the disease per unit of time than will the individuals who live in smaller groups. Moreover, the difference in the sizes of the two kinds of groups need not be nearly as large as in this example to have a profound effect. Even a 20 percent difference in group size would make itself felt in higher observed incidences of the contagious disease, seen over time, in the larger groups.

But what if a disease does *not* spread by contagion? Still, the first conclusion above does not much change. Since infection is now always random with respect to group membership, large groups continue to be initially (and always) more likely to win the lottery of infection. However, since cross-infection between groups does not occur, it no longer reinforces this favoritism for large groups. Far more significant is what happens *within* any infected group. If the disease is not contagious, then it does not matter whether the others in a group are infected or uninfected. Everyone has the same probability of becoming infected over time no matter what the size or the health of the group they live in. Thus, the second conclusion above does change. *If the disease is* not *contagious, then over a period of time there will be no average difference in the amount of disease visited upon members living in large groups compared to members living in small groups.*

It was this second conclusion that van Loghem recognized and used as his second test for whether or not colds might be spreading by contagion. For if colds are contagious, then those who live in large families should average more colds per year than do those who live in small families. But if colds are not contagious, there should be no difference in the incidence rates of colds for individuals who live in large versus small families.

Accordingly, in his study, van Loghem divided the households into two types: those with five or more members, and those with four or fewer members. This resulted in 670 "large" families, averaging 5.7 persons per household, and 853 "small" families, averaging 3.2 persons per household. (Thus, van Loghem's "larger" families were 75 percent larger in size, on average, than were his "smaller" families, and in every case they were absolutely larger.) During the thirty-seven weeks of the study, the common cold incidence rates for these two types of family groups differed from each other by less than three percent overall. Within the larger families the average seen was 4.3 colds per person. Within the smaller families the average was 4.2 colds per person.

A difference much greater than this would be expected if contagion were a significant factor in the spread of common colds, even allowing for regular intermixing of the different groups at offices and schools and other public places. Moreover, large families are generally large because they have more and younger children. Children average considerably more colds per year than do adults. Consequently, a *slightly* higher incidence rate for larger households is to be expected even if contagion plays no role whatsoever in producing cold epidemics.

Thus, van Loghem's data, showing (1) no elevated infection rate in larger families, and (2) various epidemics of colds occurring nearly simultaneously in widely scattered cities across Holland throughout the winter, combined to convince him, and many of his readers, that the common cold is *not* a contagious disease. For van Loghem, the most reasonable alternative conclusion seemed to be that the common cold represents a commensal infection, one that is initiated by some factor that is associated in turn with a drop in outdoor temperature.

A Night Chill Brings on the Next Cold?

But of course there remained one clear problem for van Loghem's conclusion about the role of chilling in starting colds. Why were there such dramatic numbers of colds seen in the very first week of his study when no corresponding decline was to be seen in the average daily temperature during either the second or third decades of September? This indeed presents a puzzle. Van Loghem was ready with a solution, however. Thus, he wrote:

> The solution is, as I suspect, in the *cold nights* that characterized the week of September 11th–16th and which cannot be detected in the average [overall temperatures] of decade II because of the high day temperatures. Then arose the great number of colds, of which we noted many in the first week of our inquiry. Many who took part in the research remember this. In Table I is given the maxima and minima of those September days. One sees how the temperature mounted to 18 and 19 degrees [Celsius] in the daytime and cooled down to 2.3 degrees C. at night.[11]

Van Loghem then reprints the daily maxima and minima for September 1925, recorded at De Bilt, just outside Utrecht in the center of the country. On September 11, and again on September 14 and 15, are to be found the very cool nights with warm daytime temperatures referred to above. All other nights are seen to be generally warm, right through to the middle of the second week of the study, on September 29. Then, on this one date is seen another much colder night, followed by days warmer even than some days earlier in the month. It is not until October, and the third week of reporting common colds, that the average daily temperature begins any noticeable regular decline. And by that time, van Loghem was recording less than half as many new colds as were reported in the first week.

Thus, the only three particularly cold nights that are available to explain the most significant cold epidemic of van Loghem's study occurred respectively, nine, six, and five days prior to the first *day* of the first week of that study. If only new colds were being reported to van Loghem, and if cold nights triggered the mechanism that allowed so many fresh fall colds to begin, then the delay in the working out of that mechanism must be at least six to eight days long (the shortest period before the study began), and more likely much longer. (I assume that not all the colds reported for the first week, September 20–26, occurred on September 20.) An alternative might be to argue that those early cold nights started a few colds, which by contagion later led to all the rest. But of course, van Loghem's own data suggest that contagion played little detectable role in causing colds later in his study.

Van Loghem published his findings secure in the conviction that indeed cold temperatures, and the ensuing "disturbance in thermoregulation," are responsible for colds. He believed strongly that colds do not depend on the health of those around us; instead they depend upon our own hardiness and our own thermoregulatory health.

Perhaps, then, colds are caused by commensal organisms that are always with us. They are not caught in forbidden puddles, or from muddy creeks or melting snows. Nor are they caught from the runny-nosed kids next door. But if colds result from a faulty reaction to the stresses of cold weather, we must recognize that this reaction does not seem to be immediate. It seems from the Dutch data that it may be two, or four, or six, or even many more days later that we develop a cold. Such a lag would be curious, if real, and the question of its existence will need to be examined further.

How Can Colds Not be Contagious?

And now, what are we to make of the Spitzbergen data? How could the arrival of the first ship following the winter period of isolation cause so many colds if colds are not contagious? Why do the miners and trappers of Spitzbergen say that falling into the icy sea never produces colds, except after contact with outsiders? Why was there no correlation between the temperature and the incidence of colds seen in Longyear City in 1930–31 when a noticeable (if modest) correlation had been seen in Amsterdam in 1925? The existence of more than one kind of cold would provide one possible answer to such questions. Still, one might then be left trying to explain why only one particular kind of cold circulates in Amsterdam, while another kind circulates in Longyear City. Perhaps knowing something more about viruses would help to provide an answer.

Hundreds of different common cold viruses have now been identified. Yet there are some basic questions we are still left asking of these viruses. We have now met two of these questions: (1) Are colds really contagious, as the Spitzbergen data strongly imply, or are they not, as the Dutch data strongly imply? How could colds be transmitted by people, and yet not appear to be contagious? And then (2) do changing temperatures, or bodily chilling, affect outbreaks of colds? This seems like a straightforward yes-or-no question. Why then is there so much room for uncertainty?

These two main questions are not as distinct and separate as they may at first appear. To answer each of them it will help to look deeper into the epidemiological record. Van Loghem's findings cannot be dismissed. Still, further studies of populations living in remote isolation have appeared to confirm many of the conclusions of Paul and Freese, that colds are not temperature dependent and that they do seem to be very much dependent on contagion from others. What then are we to make of these inconsistent findings?

4

Isolation Lost and Regained: Tristan da Cunha, the South Atlantic, 1961–68

". . . In April 1967 B. L. was returning from Cape Town and developed a cold 2 days before coming ashore. When he got home he passed it on to his family, whence it spread to the community. On the other hand, in October 1967 D. R., a young woman who was not known to visit the ship and who worked in the hospital, was apparently the first case after the arrival of the ship 3 days before. No further case was detected until several days later, when another young woman who probably had no close or direct contact with her developed a cold. Another gap occurred and then an epidemic developed quite rapidly."[1]

— M. Shibli et al., 1971

A few hundred miles south of a point approximately halfway between Cape Town and Rio de Janeiro lies the subtropical island of Tristan da Cunha. The island is the largest of a chain of local rocks and islets that perch atop the mid-Atlantic ridge in the South Atlantic Ocean. No shipping lanes pass close by, and the nearest major port is on the island of St. Helena, 1,500 miles to the north. Cape Town is 1,700 miles to the east, and Montevideo is more than 2,300 miles to the west. The island, like all the others along this ridge, is volcanic in origin. In shape it resembles Mt. Fuji. It is nearly circular, and is about twenty-four miles in circumference.

The volcanic crater at the top of Tristan da Cunha is 6,500 feet above sea level. In this crater is a lake, and around that lake every winter lies snow. At the warmer foot of the mountain there is a plateau, densely covered with tree ferns, encircling the island. Steep cliffs drop from this plateau into the sea, except to the northwest, where a second, lower plateau is to be found before smaller cliffs start down again to the sea. On this lower bench sits the small settlement of Edinburgh, and nearby are the places called Little Beach and Big Beach where, depending on the winds and swells, small boats can sometimes land. Early in October of 1961, slightly fewer than three hundred people were resident in Edinburgh. It was springtime. A few of the local residents were suffering from asthma as a result, but apparently none of them had a common cold.

It was never easy to earn a good living on the island of Tristan da Cunha. The island was first settled by an American, Jonathan Lambert, in 1810. He attempted to create a refit station for ships working the South Atlantic or bound around the Cape of Good Hope. Within a year or two of his arrival, Lambert apparently had drowned. The island was not occupied again until the first permanent settlers arrived in 1816. At this time the British sent a garrison to the island to prevent it from being used as a base for any attempted rescue of Napoleon, imprisoned on St. Helena far to the north. That garrison was withdrawn one year later, but a few of its number elected to stay behind, hoping to market local sea-elephant oil and seal skins. At that time, fur seals were abundant on the island, but by 1961 they had long since disappeared from overhunting.

Because the climate on the island is benign, it has generally been possible to farm and fish there. In the settlement of Edinburgh the temperature averages about 50 degrees Fahrenheit in mid-winter (July) and about 65 degrees Fahrenheit in mid-summer (January). On the plain beside the town, vegetables may be grown, and cattle and sheep often have been pastured there. Early overgrazing resulted in the loss of most of the original vegetation, however, and most of the trees on the island were soon lost as firewood. No indigenous animals were found on the island, but rats and mice from ships soon became such pests that periodically a "Ratting Day" was declared. Prizes were offered for the most rodents killed, and for the longest tail produced. Potatoes and fish have always been the main food staples on Tristan. Yet fishing was always risky. Often long periods would go by when the weather prevented the islanders' canvas boats from being launched, and then no fishing could be done. Birds on the island were soon all but eliminated by indiscriminate killing. Consequently, the diet on Tristan da Cunha was not particularly varied. What variation there was came from imports and from visiting ships. Despite this limited diet however, the people of Tristan da Cunha generally seemed to enjoy good health.

Three of those first settlers who stayed behind when the original garrison was dissolved in 1817 were William Glass, his wife Mary, and their young son. One hundred and fifty years later, Glass was one of only seven surnames comprising the permanent island population. Inbreeding on the island has been very marked, but it too has not seemed to have much impact upon the health of the islanders. A medical team that examined the permanent residents of Edinburgh late in 1961 was impressed by the striking physical resemblances among them all.[2] However, almost none of the few medical problems that were seen could be traced to inbreeding per se. The one possible exception was that many of the islanders were unusually susceptible to asthma, and especially so after an attack of the common cold. There seemed to be a constitutional predisposition to asthma that was shared by almost everyone.

Significantly, common colds were reported to be normally uncommon on Tristan da Cunha. The dramatic exceptions to this rule seemed to be on the infrequent occasions when ships would call in at the island directly from Cape Town.[3] At such times severe cold epidemics would sometimes sweep through the village. According to the islanders, ships calling from more distant ports rarely seemed to trigger common colds.

The weather on the island, while generally mild, is not unlike weather that traditionally has been said to lead to frequent colds. Humidity is high, and a layer of cloud usually hangs under the mountain peak, stretching miles out to sea. Rainfall is plentiful, and winds are often strong and unpredictable. Still, when asked about illness, the people of Edinburgh invariably said that unless a ship had recently called at the island, itself only recently out of some large port, the islanders were completely free from common colds. Neither poor diet nor wet chilly weather appeared to cause those few colds that were reported by the residents of Tristan da Cunha.

Then, on October 10, 1961, without any preliminaries, and for the first time since the island had been inhabited, the volcano at Tristan suddenly began erupting. Within twenty minutes an orderly evacuation of the island had begun. Eventually everyone on the island was safely transferred by canvas long boat to a small fishing ship, and thence to one of the rocky isles some miles away. Not long afterward they were moved again, by a larger ship, to Cape Town. Then, a few weeks after the eruptions began, they were taken by plane to an empty army camp in England. Here they came under special medical scrutiny as part of a project that had been quickly arranged by the Medical Research Council of England. Significantly, by the time the islanders arrived in their new English homes, under close medical supervision, almost all of them had raging colds. Even so, they were of surprisingly good cheer.

Acclimatizing to English Colds

The winter of 1961–62 was remembered later as a particularly severe one in England. Soon after they arrived, many of the islanders' colds turned into something more serious. Eventually three of the 259 refugees in England died from what was described as an "overwhelming respiratory infection."[4] When the islanders were exposed to the outside world, and when cold viruses apparently then infected them, those viruses seemed to have more serious effects than was typical for the indigenous Europeans. It was hard to deny the implication that the visitors from Tristan had very little immune strength with which to fight English common colds, in contrast to the resistance shown by local residents who had not spent their lives isolated from such colds.

After residing in England for a time, the party of islanders appeared to gain that immunity to common colds enjoyed by other local residents there. The colds suffered by the group from Tristan appeared to become less frequent and, when they did occur, less severe. As if in sympathy with this decline in the eruptions of respiratory disease among the refugee islanders, the violent coughs and sneezes from the volcano back on Tristan da Cunha also began to wane, becoming less and less frequent and less and less severe. Consequently, as early as January 1962 it seemed to the Royal Society an opportune time to send a scientific expedition to study the volcano at Tristan. The expedition team included twelve of the islanders who had been forced to leave. On their return, they found that the buildings of Edinburgh were not in fact badly damaged. By May of 1963 some repairs had been made, and it was considered safe for all those who wished to return to the island to do so.

Returning to the Isolation on Tristan

The return of the islanders to Tristan da Cunha presented an opportunity for research on the common cold that, to their great credit, British scientists recognized was much too good to be missed.[5] Would the islanders take back with them their newfound strengths in dealing with common colds? Or would they, once back on Tristan, revert to their former pattern showing no colds during the long isolation periods, then an epidemic of severe colds when certain ships came to call? And could those earlier accounts be true, saying that only ships coming quickly from Cape Town trigger colds? To answer these questions, the medical officer posted to Edinburgh with the returning islanders solicited their help in keeping track of all colds occurring on Tristan between January 1964 and June 1968.

The first party of fifty-two islanders returned to reside again on Tristan da Cunha in May of 1963. They were followed in November by 198 more. Twelve islanders remained in Britain and did not return. For three years 250 of the original island people lived at Edinburgh in the company of the new medical officer and his family and six other administrators and their families. Then in April 1966, thirty-seven islanders elected to return to life in Britain. Of this group nine changed their minds and went back to Tristan in October 1967, and six more decided to go back in August 1968. Thus, the native population of Edinburgh was 250 for three years, and then for two years it ranged from about 212 to 227.

During this four-and-a-half-year period it was possible to keep track of the first arrival of all ships and to keep track of all but a few of the colds that occurred in Edinburgh. It was much harder, however, to monitor the health of those who were on the arriving ships, and to monitor when certain of the islanders joined and left the two fishing vessels that regularly came from Cape Town to work in Tristan waters. These ships would sometimes return briefly to Tristan to take on water or to drop off local residents who had been working temporarily on board. Despite the uncertainties caused by these gaps in the records, the findings from this classic epidemiological study of the common cold proved to be very interesting indeed.

Eight cold epidemics occurred during the years of this study on Tristan da Cunha. With but three possible exceptions (discussed below) every individual cold that occurred during the four years of this study was clearly associated with one of the eight cold epidemics. Each one of these epidemics affected between 20 and 50 percent of the residents of Tristan. Still, on average, the overall incidence of common colds among the islanders proved to be less than one cold per person per year. This incidence was far less than had been seen while the islanders were in Britain, even during the latter part of their stay there. Thus, the isolation experienced on Tristan immediately seemed to reinstate a general freedom from colds.

During the period of this study, five of the eight cold epidemics seen on Tristan da Cunha began within four days following the arrival of a ship from Cape Town. We will examine the other three epidemics shortly, but these five are of some immediate interest. There were twenty-eight occasions over the four and a half years of research when ships did arrive directly from Cape Town. Thus, the overall probability that a ship from Cape Town would soon trigger an epidemic was 5/28 during the period of study. And in general, the percentage of shipping arrivals that led to epidemics was between 15 and 20 percent.

Significantly, on each of the nine occasions when a ship arrived from some port of origin other than Cape Town (which would mean that the ship had been rather longer at sea) no colds at all followed. One particular ship, that every autumn brought supplies and passengers from Cape Town, often appeared to be the source of a subsequent cold epidemic on the island. In the autumn of April 1965, however, no such epidemic followed the arrival of this ship. Notably, that April 1965 voyage was the only one during which this ship went first to Gough Island, 230 miles to the south, where a South African weather station is maintained. This intermediate stop resulted in a long delay, so that it was more than three weeks after leaving Cape Town before the ship finally landed at Tristan.

The British scientists studying colds on Tristan suggested that during three weeks of isolation at sea, colds will generally die out in small communities of sailors. The absence of an epidemic in April 1965, following the arrival of the Cape Town ship from Gough Island, was to them an especially striking confirmation of this idea. In the next two years, when that same ship came directly to Tristan from Cape Town (a journey of about six days), distinct epidemics of colds did follow almost immediately. However, one must not lose sight of the fact that at other times of the year, other ships coming directly to the island arrived from Cape Town and no epidemic of colds followed. Moreover, although this was not stressed in the published report by the British medical scientists working on Tristan, it is also significant that in late April of 1964, one year before the longer voyage cited above, the arrival of that same ship was also associated with no common colds at all, despite the fact that in 1964 the ship did come directly from Cape Town.

Taken overall, these events suggest that after two or three weeks of isolation in a small community there may be a cessation of all colds. But isolation also seems to lead to a corresponding increase in people's general susceptibility to new colds when they are exposed to others from outside the isolated community. We have seen this now in three different settings: on ships to Tristan da Cunha carrying fewer than one hundred people, on Tristan itself with fewer than three hundred people, and at Longyear City, Spitzbergen, with fewer than six hundred people. A question that naturally arises is, how large can an isolated community be and still show such a pattern? If the people in a city of, say, ten thousand, or perhaps half a million, were isolated, would colds ever disappear there? It is too early yet to try to answer these questions because it is still not clear why colds "die out" in isolated groups, if that metaphor is even appropriate to describe what is really happening.

Van Loghem suggested that colds don't "die"; rather, he suggested that they may just become symbiotic again. Colds cease to be infectious and become commensal. But if this is correct, we are then faced with two further puzzling questions. First, just how and why does isolation stop colds from being infectious, returning them to the commensal state? And second, why then would the arrival of new visitors seem to be so necessary for causing infections to begin again?

A major modification of van Loghem's hypothesis offers an appealing answer to these two questions. It could be that (1) there are many different viruses that cause colds, and (2) that a community builds up some form of immunity to those viruses that are in current circulation, and then (3) "new" viruses, to which little or no immunity exists, cause colds when they are introduced from outside sources. A theory in this form does not really recognize any commensal role for viruses, however, and so it faces the problem of explaining again why so many colds in Holland in 1928 started up in widely scattered locations at almost the same time. Moreover, with this modified theory it is difficult to explain why the same new virus should produce such a severe reaction upon being introduced into a previously isolated group while producing only mild reactions in the members of some larger and non-isolated population.

Epidemics that May Not Have Been Triggered from Abroad

Meanwhile, we have yet to look at those three epidemics of colds on Tristan da Cunha that did *not* seem to follow immediately upon the arrival of a ship from Cape Town. The first such epidemic occurred in December 1965 (mid-summer) and its cause was clear. Twenty islanders had been at sea aboard the MV *Gillian Gaggins*, a fishing vessel on her maiden voyage out of Cape Town. The islanders had gone aboard the ship to work with the Cape Town crew. After only a week fishing in Tristan waters the ship's main refrigerator broke down, necessitating repairs back in port. Nearly half the islanders who thus returned early to Edinburgh were by then suffering from colds developed on the ship, and these colds were soon observed in others in the community. Employment on such ships was often taken, but usually did not result in cold epidemics ashore. Typically, the island laborers would have their colds in the first two weeks of work, while still at sea. They would only return to Tristan da Cunha after three or more weeks, by which time they were symptom free and apparently non-infectious.

The second epidemic that occurred in the absence of a recently arrived ship from Cape Town began about January 26, 1966, almost exactly one month after the last cold in the epidemic just discussed. It happens that two ships from Cape Town had called at the harbor two weeks prior to this epidemic, at the start of the summer fishing season. Because four days is the longest time typically observed between the arrival of any ship and the start of an epidemic of colds, it seems clear that the arrivals of these two ships were unlikely to have triggered this epidemic two full weeks later. What might explain this epidemic, however, would be an unnoticed visit ashore by an islander who had gone to work on one of these ships. Another possible explanation could be a contact made during an unrecorded brief call by one of these ships to take on fresh water. Such calls were not uncommon on Tristan da Cunha. This explanation is also reasonable because islanders (though not the Cape Town crew members) who were working on these ships would still have been subject to colds at the time when this second epidemic began. The timing is correct.

The last of the three epidemics that did not correspond to the known arrival of any ship began in February, 1968. The epidemic itself began about February 24, but it was preceded by those three individual colds mentioned previously, the only colds in all four years that were not clearly part of a concurrent community epidemic. One of these three colds began around the first of February, and two more began about February 15. Prior to February 1, 1968, there had been no colds recorded for at least seventy-five days, since the end of the previous epidemic in October/ November 1967. The initial cold early in February might well be attributed to the arrival of a ship from an unspecified port (not Cape Town) that had been noted about three days before. Also, a ship from Cape Town had arrived to begin the summer fishing season about twenty days before this cold. That fishing vessel might have come back to take on water at Tristan, as noted above, bringing a late infection with it.

The next two colds in this final series, occurring two weeks later, would not ordinarily be thought to have derived from the first one because they came so long after it. It is possible that unreported colds occurred, bridging this time span, but if such colds did exist then they were an unusual phenomenon. In all the previous epidemics recorded on the island, only occasionally were there gaps to be seen in the timing of sequential colds. Moreover, those previous gaps were never more than about six to ten days in length. Consequently, the epidemic that began another ten days after these second two colds, late in February 1968, may represent the only one of the eight recorded epidemics that should not be attributed to the arrival of a visiting ship. And of course even this last epidemic might in fact have begun very soon after the arrival of the ships late in January if it took some weeks to reach a strength that came to the attention of the medical officer on Tristan who was, at that time, busily occupied arranging the end of this study of four and a half years' duration.

What Might It All Mean?

Thus, should one already be persuaded by the view that colds always die out in small isolated populations, and, moreover, that colds will only later reappear in such populations if reintroduced from outside, then these data from Tristan can be construed to lend clear support. Maintaining this view requires only a few small steps of faith to explain away the three epidemics just considered. And we have seen how such explaining might easily be accomplished. The questions that then become uppermost are (1) how and why do colds "die" when they die out, and (2) why do the new colds introduced from outside seem to be so severe and so widespread in isolated populations? Experiments with cold viruses found in various isolated environments might help answer the first question. And recent discoveries about the workings of the immune system might help answer the second question. We shall have occasion to consider both in due course.

The data for the Tristan epidemics do not, however, require the conclusion that in general colds die out and are reintroduced from outside. Other conclusions too would fit the Tristan experience. Still, one conclusion seems inescapable from that research carried out with the help of the islanders on Tristan da Cunha: something very like contagion does seem to trigger colds after all, at least in isolated small communities. Perhaps things are different on large continents, but perhaps they are not. The American and Dutch data still constitute good reasons to doubt that simple contagion — the passage of parasitic and infective virus from person to person — accounts for epidemics of the common cold. Yet on Tristan, and on Spitzbergen, these small isolated communities rarely if ever saw any common colds until after the arrival of outsiders. And sometimes the pattern of transmission, from contact to contact, seemed too obvious to be doubted. If colds are passed from person to person, then how is this transmission effected? Is it through the air? Is it by direct physical contact? Is it by indirect contact, for example, from the spoons and glasses, the coins and doorknobs that we all use and share? Does cold weather play a role, moderating the way colds may be passed? These too are all issues for which helpful evidence now exists, and in due course we will consider that evidence as well.

Still, before we look again at weather studies, there is more to learn about isolated populations and how colds affect them. For instance, it could be very helpful to look at isolated populations of a size much larger than the six hundred people at Longyear City, Spitzbergen. However, until the advent of space colonies, the global village that our world has become practically forbids such a study, at least over any time periods of much more than a week. But there are other isolated populations we *can* successfully study. Let us next turn to consider the sealed environments of nuclear submarines and the frigid environments of Antarctic life, with just a glance at the open air of one more remote tropical island along the way.

20,000 Leagues Under the Sea: Scotland, Spain, and Guam, 1961–73

"The advent of nuclear submarines and of space vehicles has introduced mankind to an environment with which humankind has had no prior experience. In these vehicles man has taken the first steps towards sealing himself for indefinitely prolonged periods in closed, recycled, artificially replenished atmospheres. In all his previous history man has been exposed to such environments for a few hours or days at most; now he is subjected to a biological impact of unknown consequence on a round-the-clock basis for many weeks; tomorrow, as space and deep submergence exploration carry man even further from his customary habitat, he may live under such conditions for years."[1]

— *H. M. S. Watkins, 1970*

In one sense the medical research carried out at Longyear City and on Tristan da Cunha was neither unique nor rare, for the general health of small isolated populations had long been a subject of special interest to medical intelligence. Even so, opportunities for the careful study of such populations had been few in number. Much of what was known about the general health of isolated people came from the incidental reports of travelers, and from surgeons and masters on vessels ranging far afield. Special attention paid to the common cold in such accounts was rare, however, if only because someone else's common cold is usually quite unremarkable. Even the distressing epidemics of deadly measles and syphilis, provoked by the early European intrusions into remote oceanic realms, generally led neither to careful studies nor to frequent accounts in the popular and scientific literature of Europe.

Typical among the accounts of coldlike illnesses that we do have from travelers is the following oft-referenced passage by Thor Heyerdahl, from his 1958 book *Aku-aku*. The book is an account of Heyerdahl's experiences on Easter Island, which lies in an isolated region of the open South Pacific Ocean. The permanent population of Easter Island is only a few hundred people, and visitors were, until recently, quite uncommon. The passage quoted below is particularly significant, in part because it is usually said to confirm that colds are particularly severe when a lengthy isolation is broken. Heyerdahl begins, writing about the time when the ship that had brought his return expedition to Easter Island sailed away, leaving his party behind:

> When the *Pinto* had gone, life on the island quickly fell back into [its nor-mal routines]. The *cocongo* had not yet begun to spread in earnest. *Cocongo* was the natives' great terror — the annual influenza epidemic which always accompanied contact [from] the mainland. It came and went with the reg-ularity of clockwork. After the ship's visit it always raged in the village for a month or two. It got into chests, heads, and stomachs; everyone was ill, and there was always a toll of human lives before the *cocongo* passed and left the people in peace for the rest of the year. But this year the epidemic was unusually mild so far. The natives found their explanation at once: the expedition ship had brought the island "good luck." That of course was the reason no one had fallen ill when we ourselves had come to the island.[2]

The "cocongo" that Heyerdahl describes generally began much as would a common cold, but often became more complicated. Four things are impor-tant to note in this passage. First, Heyerdahl himself does not mention the common cold here. Yet this passage has more than once been cited as if it applied to colds, showing that they are introduced to isolated populations only from outside sources. Moreover, the presence of stomach symptoms, the implied constitutional involvements, and yes, the deaths, are not typi-cal of simple colds.

Second, unlike the more precise reports from Tristan da Cunha, the "colds" described by Heyerdahl were said to occur without exception, every time the ship paid its yearly visit to Easter Island from Chile, sparing no one. But third, like the colds suffered by the islanders on Tristan, the "colds" described by Heyerdahl were generally much more severe than those among the sailors and visitors who seemed to be the ones bringing them to the island. Fourth, the "colds" on Easter Island seemed to take longer to die out than those seen at Tristan da Cunha. And because Easter Island is so far from Chile, these "colds" seemed to be able to survive a much longer passage at sea prior to arrival, compared with the colds booking passage from Cape Town, bound for Tristan.

What is consistent then in this anecdotal report by Heyerdahl is the suggestion that isolation leads both to the absence of colds and to a loss of immunity to new respiratory infections. Such infections must then be reintroduced from outside that isolated realm. And when disease is reintroduced, it is greatly increased in its severity. The inconsistencies with prior research in Heyerdahl's report center upon the symptoms described and upon the timing of the illness. We are told that an illness that seems like influenza comes regularly to Easter Island with the arrival of visiting ships. Elsewhere it is generally just colds that are seen, and these do not follow every such arrival. Only one of the eight epidemics seen on Tristan da Cunha lasted more than five weeks, not counting a few straggling cases and cases with residual chest symptoms that might hang on for a time longer. As was also the case on Spitzbergen, the peak of the cold epidemics seen on Tristan invariably came between ten and twenty days after the start of the epidemic. Since the population of Easter Island was no larger than on these other islands, much the same timing might have been expected for the *cocongo* if it were a variation on the common cold. Heyerdahl's timing is not precise, however, and perhaps his "month or two" is approximately consistent with the course of cold epidemics seen elsewhere.

I believe the *cocongo* that Heyerdahl describes was a true influenza the first year he was on Easter Island. But even that year, in some people, common colds probably came before influenza. In other years the *cocongo* was almost certainly nothing more than the severe common cold that is so widely documented and so typical of isolated populations whenever their isolation is broken. To believe otherwise leads to some difficult questions and to some complicated theorizing. For this very reason, however, it would be worth the expense of the research to discover whether Heyerdahl was correct after all. If influenza did indeed come "like clockwork" to the people of Easter Island, did they have a special immune status that rendered them unusually susceptible to influenza? If not, we might also then have from Easter Island the first datum suggesting that psychological factors (cultural expectancies, local beliefs, and so on) could play some role in determining the symptomatic expression taken by respiratory diseases.

However, given our considerations so far, there is as yet little need to suppose that psychological factors should be invoked when attempting an understanding of the workings of the common cold.

Weather too is an unlikely source for any apparent differences between the colds seen on Easter Island and those elsewhere. Easter Island is subtropical, but not equatorial. While it is generally warmer than Tristan da Cunha, there are still daily variations in temperature, variations in the strength of the trade winds, and seasonal variations in many weather-related variables.

Where the Weather Never Varies

But now, let us imagine an island that experiences none of these variations, an island where temperature, humidity, sunlight, and air movement do not vary for sixty days at a time. In the decades after the Second World War, for the very first time, a number of such islands were created artificially and populated by volunteers. These islands are better known as nuclear-powered submarines. And they have proven to be quite interesting places for studying the common cold.

In 1970, a report was published describing common cold research aboard a group of United States Polaris-class submarines. The senior author of this report, Dr. H. M. S. Watkins, described the Polaris environment in these words:

> In a Polaris submarine on patrol, a population of 130 to 140 highly motivated, physically select, healthy young men are confined in a closed congested space for approximately two months during which the submarine ordinarily never surfaces. The air environment is completely recycled and regenerated. Devices to remove atmospheric chemical and organic contaminants include inert filters to remove dust particles, activated charcoal filters, electrostatic precipitators, carbon monoxide burners, and carbon dioxide scrubbers. All of these to some extent also removed airborne microbial contaminants, but their overall efficiency in this respect had not been extensively examined prior to these studies.[3]

The studies to which Dr. Watkins refers took place between 1962 and 1967. During each two-month patrol, medical officers aboard selected Polaris submarines attempted to keep track of all respiratory disease, however minor, by regular examinations of, and interviews with, officers and crew. Complex arrangements were often in place to store air samples, blood samples, and gargle wash samples, taken at set intervals, for study back home in the laboratory at the conclusion of the patrols. The researchers hoped that the viral and bacterial causes of any observed diseases might thereby be isolated and traced. There were, it happens, many common colds seen during these studies. But almost none of those colds could be traced to its particular viral cause or human source. Instead, what was particularly significant about these studies was the epidemiological patterns seen in the timing of the colds.

Before considering these patterns it is helpful to know something about the routine of the early Polaris submarine patrols. Two complete crews existed to operate each Polaris submarine. These two crews alternated patrols. At the end of each two-month patrol, the submarine arrived at its base where it underwent any needed repairs and modifications. A total "refit" was done, cleaning out all used materials from the completed patrol, and carefully loading all the supplies needed for the next patrol. This refit could take from twenty to thirty days, and sometimes it could be a time of hard work and little sleep for the new crew preparing for the next patrol. Each new crew was flown to the refit base at the end of its leave, a few days before the submarine was due to arrive. Members of the old and new crews worked closely together for the first few days after the arrival of the submarine, and they lived together aboard the same submarine tender at the base. This tender was the supply ship for the submarine and it housed the permanent repair crew as well. Following these few days of overlap and debriefing, the old crew flew home on leave.

At the refit bases, which were usually overseas, members of both submarine crews, as well as members of the crew from the tender on which they all lived, had easy access to local towns and townspeople. Thus, not only was there no isolation once the submarine was in harbor, but returning submarine crews were immediately exposed to any circulating cold viruses that were both "local" (from the region around that base) and "foreign" (recently imported from back home by members of the new crew). Unfortunately, the research done on this unique population of isolated men never did include a look at this most significant point in their tour of duty — the first ten days following the loss of isolation. This time period was not included in the studies because the men finishing their patrol were so very busy, and because they scattered on leave soon after breaking isolation.

What is true for the returning crew, however, is equally true for the new crew. The new crew is exposed to a number of potentially fresh colds during the refit period because these men have only recently assembled from scattered locations back home. Thus, both "local" and "foreign" viruses may be available for seeding colds in the new crew as well. Moreover, if fatigue or change of diet or change of climate or even certain psychological factors associated with ending a period of leave should have any role to play in changing one's susceptibility to a cold, then the members of the new crew stand a good chance of suffering the consequences, despite being young, strong, and a select group of physically fit men.

The first three patrols reported on by Watkins and his colleagues sailed out of Holy Loch, Scotland, after three weeks of refit. During the first patrol, research procedures were being perfected and so only a general summary of the findings was reported. There were a number of colds seen in the first two weeks of this patrol, and few if any after that time. At no time, however, on any patrols, were severe colds seen.

The second patrol left Scotland in September 1961. At the start of isolation, approximately 25 percent of this crew had colds in various stages of development. The number of colds rose over the next ten days until approximately two-thirds of the crew had colds. From then on the number of colds declined. At the end of three weeks of isolation approximately 30 percent of the crew still showed some cold symptoms. At the end of six weeks only 10 percent still reported symptoms. Only two brief new colds were reported by the crew after two weeks at sea. One of these seemed to begin on the thirty-fifth day of the patrol, and the other on the thirty-eighth day. Most colds were relatively long-lasting in this environment. The typical (median) length of all the colds was three weeks. Had these been the sailors who regularly called in at Tristan da Cunha after three weeks at sea, colds might well have resulted in the islanders.

The third patrol in the study left Scotland in March of 1962. When this patrol began its isolation, approximately one-third of the crew had colds. One week later, half the entire crew was affected, but thereafter the incidence dropped again until it reached 10 percent of the crew in the fourth week. At this point a need for repairs caused an unscheduled call at a refit station, where for two days the crew had limited contact with the men aboard one of the tenders. On returning to sea new colds broke out, and five days later approximately 30 percent of the crew had cold symptoms. At the end of six weeks, when the last data were collected, the cold incidence was back down to about 10 percent of the crew. Again, then, the evidence here seemed to point to isolation as the cause of colds dying out (if only in a small population) and to contacts with new people as the trigger for new colds. The two apparent exceptions in Patrol II, when fresh colds broke out three weeks after the last previous cold, could become significant however, and they must neither be forgotten nor too quickly dismissed.

Watkins and his group made further studies in 1964 and 1965 during five successive patrols sailing out of Rota, Spain, on a submarine of newer design. By this time the refit periods had been extended to a full four weeks, to allow for all the work necessary before a patrol could begin. This meant that many of the colds experienced by the new crews began before the patrol left port and before careful monitoring of symptoms became feasible. Watkins explained why no complete records had been kept of colds occurring during the refit period (other than cases seen at sick bay, which were always recorded) as follows:

> At that time the significance of the refit — a time of great strain for a crew introduced precipitately to a different environment overseas, often immediately after a last night "on the town," living at first on the tender under objectionably crowded and climatically uncomfortable conditions, stressed by a tremendous volume of work preparing the boat for sea — was not fully appreciated, and no detailed records of [the] prevalence of mild respiratory infections were prepared. It must be appreciated that men under these conditions commonly do not report to Sick Bay for treatment, so these mild or chronic infections as a rule appear in the medical records of a patrol only in terms of comments by the medical officer. However, conversations with such medical officers clearly indicate that this refit period, in which a crew is seeded with the microbial flora of the tender crew and local population ashore at the overseas harbor, in addition to that introduced from home communities in the United States, governs the pattern of upper respiratory infections customarily seen on patrol.[4]

Patrol VII was typical of those monitored out of Rota, Spain. At the beginning of this patrol, in March 1965, 56 percent of the 146 crew members had colds. The incidence of colds declined continuously over all eight weeks of this patrol, at the end of which 12 percent of the crew were still experiencing some cold symptoms. Among these very late colds, one had been continuous for all eight weeks while three others had been continuous for the final five weeks. "Colds" lasting this long are normally quite unusual and very probably they have been complicated by secondary infections or by allergic reactions.

Because a total of 105 crew members on Patrol VII had at least one cold during the period of isolation, and because thirty-five of this number had more than one cold, the total incidence of colds over just the eight weeks from March to May was quite high. The average incidence worked out to just under one cold per person per patrol.[5] Only forty-one members of the crew (28 percent) had no colds at all. Not only were there a large number of colds, but they tended to last somewhat longer than colds often do. Considerably more than half of all the colds recorded on this patrol lasted longer than seven days, with a typical (median) length of approximately ten days. Three weeks into the patrol, 18 percent of the crew had colds, which was a drop of 67 percent from the original number. And yet thirty-one new colds (21 percent of all the colds seen) began *after* three weeks of isolation had already passed. It is safe to say that here again, had this been a boat calling at Tristan da Cunha after three weeks at sea, many sailors would probably still have appeared to be infectious.

The other patrols out of Rota, Spain, showed a pattern similar to that seen on Patrol VII. More than once some of these other patrols needed to make unscheduled two-day visits to harbor, following which a modest increase in colds was observed exactly as was reported above for Patrol III.

Who Catches Colds, and Why?

On each of the patrols in this series out of Rota, a certain proportion of each crew developed no colds at all, while another proportion of each crew developed multiple colds. Watkins and his colleagues asked what crew characteristics might be related to an unusually high susceptibility to the common cold. What variables predict multiple colds? As it happens, a crew member's region of origin, residence area, marital state, and previous medical history (other than previous common colds) showed no relationship at all to the number of colds caught while on patrol. But there was another set of variables that did appear to have a certain degree of predictive value, suggesting an increased risk for developing cold symptoms while on patrol. These variables are very interesting, even mysterious, and they afford certain clues to deciphering the answers to questions that will arise later.

Perhaps the least surprising predictor of more colds than usual is a recent history of colds. Watkins found that those reporting they averaged more colds than other members of their family, more severe colds than their fellows, and more colds last year than in the year before that, tended to have more colds on patrol than those not so reporting. Also, those with a history of sinus trouble (but not allergies) and those who had a cold during the recent leave period, were more apt to be among the group having more colds while on patrol. Age also predicted the number of colds that would occur. Just as Townsend and Sydenstricker observed in their large USPHS survey, younger members of the crew (under twenty years of age) tended to have more colds than did the older crew members. Watkins also found a new reversal of the age trend at the top of his age scale. Crew members who were older than age thirty-five, like those below age twenty, were also more likely to have more colds.

The fact that senior age predicted more colds probably had to do with something *associated* with such age rather than with the variable of age itself, because the decline in numbers of colds with age has been consistently reported in most other studies of colds in males. In this special navy population, higher age was associated with many other things, however, including (a) long service in submarines, (b) the likelihood of holding the rank of Chief Petty Officer, and (c) the number of children the sailor had at home. Each of these three variables, examined individually, was found to have significant association with the number of colds seen on patrol.

The number of children at home correlates to some extent with the number of colds that parents will have in a year, supposedly because children bring home more colds from school, and children are "better" at spreading these colds around the house than adults generally are. Thus, it is possible that only the number of children at home is a true predictive factor in the submariners, and that age and rank and service history show up as predictors only because they link with this family factor. If this were correct, then repeating Watkins's predictive analysis, while holding constant the number of children at home, would show us that all other variables no longer had any predictive power of their own.

It happens that there are statistical tools for accomplishing such a test, without undue effort and without looking only at some special subset of sailors, all of whom happen to have the same number of children at home. These statistical procedures will determine the degree to which variables overlap with each other in their predictive powers; that is, how much they may each uniquely contribute to the prediction of some criterion, such as the number of colds people will catch. Watkins did not report any such analyses, however, nor did he publish the data that would permit others to do these for themselves. We must keep in mind then that while it somehow seems unlikely and surprising, long service on submarines, and the particular duties of Chief Petty Officers, might increase the risk of contracting colds while on patrols.

Perhaps the most surprising and interesting predictor of colds discovered by Watkins was a sailor's sleeping location aboard this type of submarine. Across five different patrols, men who slept in one certain tier of bunks (not specified by Watkins) showed significantly more colds than did the men who slept in other tiers. This finding certainly suggests some very interesting possible discoveries about the causes of certain colds. Was the air movement over these bunks unusual? Did the men in these bunks have special high-risk duties on board? Were they always senior crewmen with many children at home? Was it especially difficult to sleep in these bunks? Alas, we are not to know any answers to these questions, for Watkins was silent on the subject. He observed only that this finding suggests that "close contact" is a cause of contagion with colds.

With one notable exception, none of the patrols ever showed a full new epidemic of respiratory disease once isolation had begun. This one exception occurred on Patrol IV at the start of the fourth week of isolation when a moderately severe coldlike illness, accompanied by headache, severe sore throat, unusual fatigue, and body pain, began circulating among the crew. The illness was seen in thirty-four men, lasted for about a week, and was approximately equally prevalent among men who had recently had colds and men who had not. It was never determined exactly what this disease was, but it was notably different from the common colds seen prior to that time on this patrol. Tests of blood and nasal washings from affected and unaffected men on Patrol IV ruled out known influenzas and parainfluenzas as well as a number of other agents that can cause such symptoms. But it was never clear what had touched off this epidemic, nor who had been the first person affected by the disease.

Because this outbreak began after twenty days of isolation, which is very much longer than the known incubation periods of similar diseases, it seems unlikely that it started by direct contagion from a crew member infected prior to sailing. Because the disease appeared to be so very contagious once the epidemic had started, it also seems unlikely that there was an infected crew member who had been carrying an active variant of the disease from the beginning of isolation until the outbreak of the epidemic. The implication is that colds may sometimes start in the absence of similar colds to start them. Rare though this kind of report may be, "new" colds seem to be able to start by themselves, even in isolation, without contagion being involved at all. Van Loghem may be correct: colds may very well begin from commensal agents always living with us. Or it may be that the agents causing common colds can lie dormant, suspended in the air or upon the surfaces of objects, until we come into contact with these agents and give them a chance to infect anew.

When Are Colds Common, and When Rare?

Watkins and his colleagues carried out one final set of analyses of the common cold incidence in Polaris submarines. These analyses were based upon the medical records of sick bay visits over more than one hundred different patrols occurring during a one-year period in 1967–68. Because many colds are mild and do not result in a visit to sick bay, the analyses done in this phase of the research underreported the true number of colds that occurred. Moreover, all respiratory diseases were lumped together for these analyses, so not all the illnesses counted would be simple common colds, even if most would be. Finally, the medical records, kept by the many different medical officers, may not have been entirely reliable. Consequently, only general comparisons of large subsamples from this database offered the promise of useful information.

Watkins and his coworkers found that 60 percent of all sick bay visits during refit, and 77 percent of such visits during patrols, were for respiratory diseases, mostly all for common colds. Four principal harbors used for submarine refit were then analyzed as groups. These were: Holy Loch, Scotland; Guam; Rota, Spain; and Charleston, U.S.A. No differences among these four harbors were seen in the number of sick bay visits occurring for reasons other than colds or stomach ailments. In patrols based at each of these four harbors, the average number of sick bay visits per week ranged from 4.1 to 4.5 for general medical problems. But for colds, and for stomach ailments, there was a significant difference among patrols leaving from the four different harbors. Combining data for respiratory diseases and gastrointestinal diseases, Watkins found the respective average number of visits to sick bay to be 6.5, 4.9, 4.0, and 3.5 for Holy Loch, Guam, Rota, and Charleston.[6] He concluded that going overseas, and particularly going to a different climate, increases the likelihood of disease, particularly respiratory disease.

Here then we encounter another clue suggesting that chill or colder weather could be a trigger for colds. Since all patrols experience the same climatic conditions once they are under way, the geographical effects seen here, even after leaving the refit harbor, appear to reflect events begun while at that harbor. Still, if temperature levels are so important, why is

Guam second highest, rather than lowest? The importance of *changing* temperatures might well provide one answer, but the data from Spitzbergen, showing no association between cold incidences and temperature changes, is still a puzzle under such a theory.

It would be interesting to learn whether the harbor effects were seen at all seasons of the year, or primarily during the times of greatest climatic contrast. There were not sufficient data to analyze for seasonal effects at each of the four harbors, but combining all patrols from all harbors suggested that the incidence of colds does change a great deal from month to month. In 1967–68 colds were more than twice as frequent on patrols leaving in certain months compared with those leaving in others. But the particular months of high and low overall incidence occurred during both the summer and the winter, with no discernible seasonal pattern to be seen.

Also in 1967–68, good medical records were gathered for twenty-one patrols, detailing just the incidence of respiratory disease seen in sick bay all during the refit period and then throughout the following patrol. These data were summarized by week, for each of the four weeks of refit leading up to the patrols, and for the subsequent eight to ten weeks of isolation while on patrol. Over the course of the whole fourteen weeks, the average number of sick bay visits due to respiratory disease declined steadily from an average of about sixteen in the first and second week of refit, to 10.1 in the first week of patrol, and finally to 1.1 in the ninth week of patrol.[7]

This pattern is not quite what one would expect if refit alone seeded new colds and then the isolation of patrol caused them to die out. If exposure at the time of refit were the source of new colds, then the peak incidence of colds for the new crew should probably have come later than the very first week of refit. The timing of the crest of an epidemic is often assumed to depend in part on (1) the efficiency with which infections supposedly "pass" from person to person, (2) on the incubation period of the disease, and (3) on just when during its course the disease is most infective to others. The fact that the respiratory disease seen at sick bay crested at about the time of transition from week 1 to week 2 would suggest either that colds had been occurring among the new crew members even before they assembled for the start of refit, or colds during refit had very short incubation periods and they quickly became only briefly contagious. The former seems more likely, since although it seems probable that the sailors coming out of the isolation of a long patrol would be (like the citizens of Longyear City and Tristan da Cunha) highly susceptible to new colds, the old crew did not show the expected epidemic. Colds must have been spreading among members of the new crew well before refit began, and particularly so during the early part of the preceding leave period.

The Tristan research led many to conclude that three weeks is the amount of time needed for the members of small isolated populations to stop infecting others with the colds that might have been in general circulation among them when isolation began. But the research with Polaris crews suggests that three weeks may not be enough time for colds to die out since on board the submarines it was common to see new colds even in the sixth week of patrol. Of the twenty-one patrols studied closely between 1967 and 1968, six of them (28 percent) still had at least 5 percent of the crew reporting to sick bay for respiratory complaints after the end of six weeks in isolation.

For all but five of these twenty-one patrols there came some point in time after which colds were much reduced in frequency, and the epidemic of colds had clearly passed. On three patrols this point was reached during the refit operations, before sailing. On other patrols it occurred later, well into the time of isolation. Isolation then is not necessary to end an epidemic of colds. Even so, the typical (median) point in time when epidemics clearly finished was not during refit, it was following two and one-half weeks of isolation, during the patrol itself.

Individual patrols often had multiple waves of colds, showing more than one epidemic peak. (Generally, the second or third peaks were smaller than those coming in the weeks before.) During each of the four weeks of refit, and during each of the first three weeks of isolation, at least one such epidemic "peak" (mode) of colds was seen in approximately 24 percent of all patrols. But beginning with the fourth week of isolation, such a peak was seen only about 10 percent of the time across the various patrols — less than half the previously consistent rate. Thus there is after all something notable about three weeks of isolation in these data. But here three weeks of isolation is not a marker for the end of colds and the end of infectivity. Rather, it is a marker for a shift to much reduced levels of occurrence.

Here we meet a surprisingly deep question, not only for understanding the common cold, but for understanding all epidemic diseases. Why do epidemics end? Two quite different forms of answer to this question are popular, and they are not mutually exclusive. Both answers assume that contagion occurs, but the first suggests that epidemics end when the disease runs out of new susceptible victims; the other answer suggests that the disease agent itself weakens in some way, becoming less and less effective at continuing the epidemic.

Given the assumption, the first of these two explanations appears on the surface to be necessarily, mathematically, true. Thus it has long been assumed to be literally true. If a "new" disease starts circulating among a population, it readily "finds" susceptible individuals to infect because such people are so plentiful. But the longer it circulates, the longer it must take to "find" the fewer and fewer uninfected susceptibles remaining in the population. And when finally it takes "too long" to find that next victim, then the epidemic "dies out." If this is what really happens with the common cold, then the time that it takes to die out will vary with the size of the population, and with the efficiency of transmission from person to person.

If the ships that call at Tristan da Cunha have crews of about fifty, and if this first theory were correct as an explanation for why epidemics end, then perhaps three weeks would be well past the point when most cold epidemics would have ended on those ships. Polaris submarines, having much larger crews, seem to require longer than three weeks to become cold free, though something significant still seems to occur at about the three-week time point in most Polaris patrols.

One may account for this "something" in more than one way. It may be, for instance, that there are two types of common colds, one type that falters after three weeks of confinement in a single population, and one that does not. The Polaris data would suggest that if this were correct, then the former type is more than twice as common as the latter. Or, it may be that three weeks does mark the average end of the average cold epidemic, but that prior to the time of isolation new varieties of colds are being introduced to replace the older varieties that are by then three weeks old and dying. This is an interesting theory, but it would mean that dozens of "different" varieties of colds would need to be in circulation at a time. We will have occasion to return to this theory because many different species of colds often do in fact seem to circulate simultaneously.

Then there is the second theory for why colds die out, the one that says the disease itself weakens as it passes from generation to generation through successive waves of susceptibles in the population. It is not at all uncommon to see this phenomenon in the laboratory. Virus particles grown in one test tube are inoculated into another, and later the process is repeated. The later and more cultivated virus often does not show the virulence and the damaging effects of the original wild virus. But why this happens is not clear because the virus particles themselves do not appear to change at all as these passages occur.

Of course, neither of the two main explanations for why cold epidemics come to an end may yet prove to be completely satisfactory. It is possible, for instance, that host factors also play an important role in stopping epidemics. It may be that there are cycles of susceptibility among the members of a population so that cold epidemics end when any such cycle ends and people reenter a more normal period of increased resistance and immunity. Improbable though it sounds, the data considered so far are also perfectly compatible with a theory arguing that individuals somehow share information useful to their respective immune systems. If a person were able to broadcast information useful for resisting a circulating virus at the same time that he or she (or someone else) was broadcasting infective virus particles, then epidemics of the more familiar sorts of virus might often be controlled well before everyone in the population became infected.

It is unfortunate that in the rich Polaris submarine data examining common colds under conditions of isolation, the most interesting time in the duty cycle, the time when isolation ends, was never included for close study. In earlier research undertaken on the bacteria to be found in the air of Polaris submarines, as these might be associated with the corresponding respiratory infections seen in sick bay, the same limitation occurred.[8] In that study too, colds peaked in the third week of isolation and were very common during the two-week refit period prior to sailing. And the same limitation on recording colds at the end of isolation applied to a subsequent study of Polaris submarine crews carried out between 1970 and 1973.[9]

But We Don't Live in a Yellow Submarine

These studies confirm that the "colds" seen in isolated nuclear submarines often take from three to six weeks to die out, and that sometimes new epidemics of colds will begin even after one or two weeks of isolation. Colds among submariners appear to be more frequent than among the general population at the same ages. But why that may be is puzzling. There is a strong suggestion in all these data that mixing people who have come from scattered locales will significantly increase the incidence of colds seen during the first few weeks following their assembly. Less obvious, and equally important, these studies show that even in an environment where weather variables no longer vary, where sunlight never penetrates, where the temperature hardly changes and the winds never blow, where the humidity is a constant ideal value, still, colds do not cease. Among fit young men selected in part for their health, colds in submariners are not even less common than they are in the general population. Instead, mild colds in submarines are common, and when they do occur they often hang on for longer than might normally be expected.

So far, we still lack data on colds that occur in submarine crews coming out of isolation after time periods of differing lengths; furthermore, all the submarine data deal with the same population sizes — the 140 who staff modern nuclear submarines. Thus, it is still very hard to estimate the effects of the time spent in isolation, and the size of the isolated population, on the decay rate of colds and on the later susceptibility to colds seen when isolation ends. There would be great epidemiological value to having such data.

Fortunately, there is one other source of epidemiological data that sheds some light on such matters. It has long been a tradition during Antarctic exploration and research to keep careful medical logs. Legend quickly grew from this anecdotal literature that in Antarctica the air is so very cold and so very clean that no cold germs live there. And, according to the legends, isolated polar explorers never get colds. Medical intelligence has known for some time, however, that these legends are false. Let us look next at what the evidence really shows.

6

Presents from Home: Antarctica, 1908–78

"During the afternoon and evening of 26 January four men, including J. E. H., were engaged in hosing down the station area with seawater pumped from beneath the harbour ice. While maneuvering the canvas hose their hands and patches of clothing not covered by rubber over-garments became damp and cold, but subjectively they did not feel any greater cold discomfort than they had experienced during the previous year. Thirty-six hours later, three (including J. E. H.) of these four men noted the onset of sore throat, mild rhinorhea [i.e., watery nose] and muscle aches."[1]

— A. S. Cameron and B. W. Moore, 1968

The 1907–9 Shackleton expedition to the Antarctic was not the first of its kind, but it was the first to reach the south magnetic pole and, more to the point here, it was the first to mention direct observations of the common cold in its official reports.[2] A key member of Shackleton's group was its physician, Dr. Eric Marshall. In the appendix he wrote for Shackleton's book about the expedition, Dr. Marshall described a number of significant medical events, including those classic ingredients of high adventure: severe frostbite and the amputation of gangrenous toes. But Dr. Marshall also chose to comment upon common colds, and when he did, here is what he reported:

It is an interesting fact that the members of the expedition did not suffer from colds during their stay in the Antarctic save in August 1908, when a bale of new clothing was opened in the hut, and all the men were at once seized with acute nasal catarrh. The symptoms were quickly dispelled when we took exercise in the open, and those who remained in the hut recovered after two or three days.[3]

By implication, Marshall refers to these symptoms of August 1908 as if they were colds, but what he describes here are not in fact common colds. Rather, they are something much closer to hay fever. Marshall uses the term "acute nasal catarrh" to characterize the actual symptoms observed, beginning moments after opening that bale of clothing. (A "catarrh" is a copious stream of mucous, from an irritated mucous membrane.) The nasal catarrh that Marshall documented was of strikingly sudden onset and limited duration. Moreover, relief from the symptoms was almost immediate upon leaving the hut where the bale had been opened. But common colds do not behave this way. They appear to take a full day and more to incubate. As later chapters will show, when different people are experimentally infected with colds, all at the same time, they will begin showing symptoms with somewhat different latencies, not all at once as Marshall describes. Nor will cold symptoms be quickly relieved by step-ping out into sub-zero night air. On the other hand, reactions to allergens present in the bale of clothing *would* behave exactly as Marshall describes.

With the passage of time, this famous paragraph by Dr. Marshall was imperfectly remembered, and it became distorted into a myth saying that colds do not occur in Antarctica unless they are introduced by germs that hitchhike on supplies (or people) brought in from temperate climates to the north.[4] Moreover, it was thought that such supplies had to have been packaged during a time when cold germs were in the air and spreading. As we shall see, however, sometimes new colds do seem to occur in Antarctica, just as they do in Amsterdam, Berkeley, or Cairo, and they appear to do so without new people or freshly opened packages to explain them.

Until very recently there had been only Marshall's account of a cold epidemic occurring in an isolated population following the opening of a package from abroad. Most other accounts, like those from Spitzbergen and those from Tristan da Cunha, suggested very persuasively that only new people bring new cold germs to isolated populations, not the mail, not old clothing, nor, it seemed, commensal virus living in the respiratory tracts of those who are joined in isolation.

Marshall's account of the "colds" seen during Shackleton's Antarctic expedition did not end with the paragraph quoted above, however, although that paragraph is the only one that was well known. In fact,

Marshall continued his report with the following very interesting additional observation:

> On the return of the expedition to New Zealand the *Nimrod* laid up for one day at the mouth of Lord's [R]iver, Stewart's Island, and a number of the staff went ashore to bathe and fish, &c. All who went ashore suffered considerably from the inflammation caused by the bites of sand flies, yet it was only those members, who, on arrival at Lyttelton and Christchurch, New Zealand, who [*sic*] were not immediately seized with colds.

Stewart Island is a small island just below New Zealand's long South Island. It has a good harbor with a small town attached, but that harbor town is not at the mouth of Lord's River. Thus, it is doubtful that the returning members of Shackleton's expedition made any direct human contacts (other than with the crew of the relief vessel) until they arrived at Lyttelton harbor, outside Christchurch. If a number of the group were then "seized with colds" and a number were not, and if these two subgroups did exactly match those who had not earlier suffered from the bites of sand flies and those who had, then a strange and suggestive implication would be that an immune response to sand fly allergens might have provided some special form of protection against the common cold.

New Zealand truly is as beautiful as the travel pictures suggest, but the fierce sand flies in the south are much too tiny to show up in the inviting travel posters. For anyone who has ever suffered the multiple bites of these insects, how satisfying it would be to think that at least this experience may have brought one good (if temporary) immunological fortune. While it is not easy to see how any such protection might operate, this does not mean that the phenomenon cannot be real. In fact, it would be relatively simple to test for any prophylactic effect of sand fly bites, but apparently Dr. Marshall's observation has never been followed up, either by an experimental test or by an observational study.

Since the time of Marshall's report, research in the Arctic and the Antarctic has nicely filled out our picture of where and when colds may occur, at least for the case of small isolated populations living in polar climates. Moreover, the findings from these polar studies have particular relevance to answering the following three questions: (1) Are cold epidemics only started after the loss of isolation, that is, following the arrival of new people recently departed out of a larger population? (2) Are the colds that occur after a long cold-free time of isolation both more severe and more numerous than they would be otherwise? And (3) does the size or the location of the isolated group have any modifying role to play? The data from the Polaris submarines do not tell us how to answer these questions, although they do hint that new colds may occasionally be seen five and six weeks after isolation has begun. But for decades all the evidence had pointed the other way; in particular, it pointed to the conclusion that those who live in the splendid isolation of polar snows might also live in fortunate insulation from all common colds.

Are Colds Always Introduced from Outside an Isolated Population?

Almost a century before the Shackleton expedition to the Antarctic, the members of an expedition by Captain William Parry spent more than two years among the Eskimo population on the west coast of Baffin Island, in Canada's Arctic reaches. Parry's surgeon reported on an interesting (and rare) outbreak of disease among this isolated group, suggesting that the only respiratory diseases to be seen among the Eskimos come from contacts with the outside world, and that the Eskimos (like the natives on Tristan da Cunha) have much more severe reactions to such diseases than do those Westerners who are used to them. The outbreak described here sounds more like an influenza than a form of common cold, but in the three members of Parry's party who themselves contracted the disease, the symptoms were those of a modest common cold. Here is Parry's report:

A description of an epidemic resembling influenza which we witnessed among [these Eskimos] is given to show that the degree of immunity developed to certain pathogenic organisms is still slight. Owing to the loss of a Hudson Bay Company boat it was necessary to send four Eskimos and a trader three hundred miles for supplies from the outside world. On their departure all were well. A day was consumed getting the supplies loaded. At the end of the second day of the return journey the Eskimos all developed symptoms of a respiratory infection with general malaise, cough and expectoration. Before returning, the trader also was slightly ill with the same symptoms. Three days after the arrival of the sick Eskimos in camp the other Eskimos began to show the same symptoms. The illness spread with great rapidity and soon everyone was affected. Five days after the onset of the general epidemic the victims began to show gastrointestinal symptoms, generalized abdominal pain, diarrhea, . . . and in some cases vomiting. The infection spread from tent to tent and from our settlement to an island settlement seven miles distant. Later, when all the Eskimos who were resident on the west coast of Baffin Island came to the camp, everyone fell a victim to the epidemic. The average duration of the symptoms was three weeks and there were no fatal cases. Three of us from the outside world living in the camp developed a very mild form of the disease but without the gastrointestinal symptoms.[5]

Without the gastrointestinal symptoms this influenza looked for all the world like a common cold. Perhaps this epidemic was caused by one of the parainfluenza viruses and was complicated by a bacterial infection resulting from the poor hygiene in the camps. Or perhaps it truly was an influenza virus that was circulating so freely in the Eskimo villages. Whatever it was, like the colds presumed to be viral seen one century later at Longyear City in Spitzbergen, it seemed undeniable that a disease introduced into a long-isolated population is likely to be more severe and more widespread than the same disease among people who are regularly exposed to strangers from afar. It is quite unusual, and consequently quite dramatic, to hear of such a very high rate of infection among the members of an exposed group.

But how typical would this observation be? And would common colds cause similar reactions in similarly isolated populations? One century later, in 1928, another account of disease among the Eskimos was reported as follows:

In the summer of 1926, as members of the Greenland Expedition of the American Museum of Natural History made their way up the west coast of Greenland, it was noted that in certain of the settlements every native was the victim of an acute respiratory tract infection, while in others no evidence of such infection was present. Investigation revealed that in the former [villages] some contact had invariably been made with the outside world prior to [our] coming; while in the latter [villages], within forty-eight to seventy-two hours of [our] arrival, all the natives developed acute respiratory infections with sneezing, coughing and spitting. It was thus possible to know with certainty whether or not such contact had been made by the presence or absence of coughing among the natives who always lined up on the shore to greet the expedition as it approached.

Farther north, among the Polar Eskimos, where it was certain that no outside contact had been made that year, there was never the slightest evidence of acute respiratory tract infections at the time of the arrival of the expedition, but within seventy-two hours nearly every Eskimo of the settlement developed such an infection. It was not necessary for any member of the expedition to have an acute respiratory infection for the malady to appear among the natives. Some of [these] settlements were revisited after an interval of three to four weeks, when it was found that though the infection had subsided in some subjects, in others it was still present, but abating.

Dr. Knud Rasmussen, the Arctic explorer, who was a member of the expedition, gave us considerable information about the course of such epidemics. In the fall of the year the infection subsides and does not reappear until another contact has been made with the outside world, no matter how long delayed. This indicates that persistent carriers do not occur among these people as they do elsewhere; nor do Eskimos appear to develop any immunity against such infection from year to year.[6]

It is particularly interesting that in each of these Arctic villages the phenomenon of nearly total contagion is reported. Moreover, even though no member of the expedition had any overt symptoms of a cold, someone or something accompanying the expedition proved easily infective to many of the Eskimos in those villages that had yet to meet any outside visitors. Why this should be is something of a mystery, a mystery that will deepen somewhat later on when we learn that attempting the deliberate transmission of colds from person to person, or from things to persons, is not nearly as easy to achieve as might ordinarily be expected.

Thus, faced with the accounts above, the tempting conclusion is that isolation had radically lowered the Eskimo's resistance to common colds. Perhaps it had, but studies in Antarctica suggest that by itself, isolation may not after all lower one's resistance to the common cold.

Operation Snuffles, and Beyond

Research on respiratory disease in isolated Antarctic parties began in earnest in the early 1950s, leading up to the much expanded presence of active research stations during 1956, the International Geophysical Year, and in the years immediately following. The United States' effort, part of its "Operation Deep Freeze," included a ship-based virology laboratory and a research program dubbed "Operation Snuffles."[7] One of the goals of this program was to identify possible viral causes of colds observed both at certain isolated Antarctic stations and on the icebreaker USS *Staten*

Island that supplied these stations. Viral identification was attempted by looking for the arrival in the blood of "antibodies," substances that are produced when the immune system recognizes an infection and mobilizes to fight it. Antibodies are generally specific to a single disease agent, and their presence means the organism (or, in this case, the isolated station personnel or ship worker) has been previously infected by that agent.

Thus, the American researchers took blood samples at regular intervals, trying to spot any new viral antibodies that might have followed the colds that occurred during this study. And whenever colds did occur, they were carefully documented, with samples of nasal wash taken for viral culture, isolation, and identification. Unhappily, no viruses were identifiable from this early work, but some interesting epidemiological data were gathered.[8] Very few colds were recorded during the period of this research, suggesting again that isolation in small groups leads to the disappearance of colds.

In 1957, however, a very dramatic and much discussed outbreak of respiratory disease occurred in the Antarctic, at the new Scott-Amundsen station created by the U.S. Navy right at the South Pole. Scott-Amundsen lies at an altitude of more than 9,000 feet (2,800 meters) above sea level, and winter temperatures of minus 60 degrees Fahrenheit (minus 50 degrees Celsius) are common there. Eighteen men had been living in complete isolation at this pole station for over eight months, and there had been no colds among them since early in isolation. On October 17, as the full midnight sun began its slow rise in the polar sky, a mail drop occurred.[9] No colds or other illness followed the opening of either this mail or the supplies that were dropped at the same time, even though the mail arrived still warm from packing, and some letters were as recent as one week from their mailing in the U.S. (where fall colds were then prevalent). Soon, on October 26, the first plane of summer landed at the pole but it was unable to take off again due to engine trouble. Suddenly there were sixteen extra people at the station, many of whom had colds at the time. Almost all the rest of the *new* arrivals developed colds within forty-eight hours of their landing. But the eighteen regular occupants of the station remained healthy.

Four days after the arrival of these drop-ins, the wintering party, with the exception of one man, received Asian flu shots from vaccine brought in on the plane. (The new arrivals had had their shots before flying in.) These shots produced a low-grade malaise over the next few days among the men who received them. As for the sixteen new airmen, one week after they arrived most of them were recovering from their illnesses, which had been severe in many cases, some with high fever. However, none of the wintering party of men had yet experienced any symptoms of a true cold. Then, over the next few days, every man who had taken a flu shot developed what seemed to be a worsening chest cold. In many cases these colds complicated, and became severe. Many of the affected men experienced a lengthy laryngitis. The one man who had avoided having the flu shot developed only a slight cold, for one day, some time after all the others began their colds.

The sources of these illnesses, those suffered by the sixteen airmen, and those suffered by seventeen of the eighteen men stationed at Scott-Amundsen, were not identified at the time. Some writers have asserted that all these illnesses were influenza A2, but it is not clear that this is true.[10] If the vaccine given the men included A2 influenza, then an A2 antibody rise (i.e., a rise in the concentration — or "titre" — of that antibody) in the subject's blood serum would be expected from the vaccine itself, even without any illness, and this would not rule out the possibility of a different source for the illnesses described above. But no such rise was reported.

Of particular interest in this account is the fact that even though many of the arriving airmen had respiratory diseases, and almost all of them had some such disease soon after arriving, the men at the station who had been isolated for eight months and more, who supposedly would then have had much lowered resistance to respiratory illness, did not show any signs of contagion of this illness for the first full week of exposure. It wasn't until a time *four days after* taking the flu shot and two days after the period of malaise caused by those flu shots that they became ill. Ordinarily, as for instance was the case in Longyear City, Spitzbergen, new arrivals bring colds (or influenza) within three days of their arrival.

This account then is the first to suggest that the new arrivals in an isolated polar environment may be more susceptible to respiratory disease than are those who have already become acclimatized to that isolated environment. While this suggestion seems to conflict with the Eskimo accounts just considered, and with the memorable facts concerning those colds at Longyear City, Spitzbergen, and at Edinburgh, Tristan da Cunha, the conflict is not total, and it may signal that our earlier hypotheses about loss of immunity during isolation have been too simplistic.

Antarctic research has now provided further evidence that initially, when people first become isolated in small groups, their susceptibility to common colds does not after all increase. Another hint of this came in 1961 with the publication of a paper giving statistics on the colds seen during Operation Deep Freeze.[11] That paper showed that in October

1959, during the annual spring changeover of personnel at McMurdo Sound, "the rate of acute upper respiratory infection of any and all types among the dwindling wintering over group was less than one-fourth that of the in-coming reliefs and summer 'tourists' who brought infection with them or developed it on the ice."[12] To be precise, among 132 men in the previously isolated wintering over party, the incidence of infection in the few weeks while they were still on the ice with the newcomers was about 2.3 colds per person per year. Among the 290 relief personnel and summer staff the incidence of infection over the same period was about 9.7 colds per person per year.

All but a few of the personnel selected to take part in Antarctic work were chosen in part for their superior physical fitness, so these figures also suggest that fitness alone does not protect against the common cold. Even a yearly incidence rate of 2.3 colds is more than adults of this age might normally experience during just that month that follows the end of winter. It is, however, also true that the overall rate of respiratory disease between 1956 and 1960 for all the men participating in Operation Deep Freeze (including those on ships) was less than half the rate for the U.S. Navy as a whole.[13] Whether this reflects the special selection of men for Antarctic duty, or the fact that these men spent their North American winters down south in the polar "summer," or some other factor, is difficult to determine. Men serving on ships in Antarctica had a rate of respiratory infection that was, in turn, less than half that of the men serving on the ice. Thus it would seem unlikely that special selection or general fitness accounts for the small number of colds seen.

When Big Boys Play in Very Cold Puddles

In 1965 A. S. Cameron and B. W. Moore began to study the health of twenty-seven men wintering over at the Australian research station at Mawson (68 degrees south latitude).[14] The isolation of this Australian party began in early February of 1965. Almost at once, the few colds its members were experiencing disappeared. Complete isolation continued for eleven months, until the following January when there was a brief visit from a small party of Russian airmen who had themselves been in isolation for over one month. One of the Australians ("J. E. H.") then spent one week working with a Russian field party. On his return to Mawson station, J. E. H. suffered some gastrointestinal distress for three days. Some ten days later many of the others in the party experienced similar gastric symptoms, which they attributed to the eating of some mutton that had been repeatedly frozen and thawed.

Then, a few days later, a significant event occurred that Cameron and Moore described as follows:

> During the afternoon and evening of 26 January four men, including J. E. H., were engaged in hosing down the station area with seawater pumped from beneath the harbour ice. While maneuvering the canvas hose their hands and patches of clothing not covered by rubber over-garments became damp and cold, but subjectively they did not feel any greater cold discomfort than they had experienced during the previous year. Thirty-six hours later, three (including J. E. H.) of these four men noted the onset of sore throat, mild rhinorhea [i.e., watery nose] and muscle aches. The sore throats persisted for 1 week.
>
> The relief ship arrived on 3 February and during the changeover and on the return voyage six other men had similar respiratory symptoms, but all cases were mild. . . . Seventeen [of the twenty-seven] men, including five who had infections during the relief and on the return voyage, developed upper respiratory tract infection of moderate severity on returning to Australia. Twelve of them developed symptoms within a fortnight of dis-embarkation, and symptoms lasted from 7 to 14 days.[15]

It is not clear what to make of the sore throats that followed the wet cold work of hosing down the station at Mawson. No bacterial cultures or viral cultures were reported for these illnesses. No rises in levels of antibody concentration (the so-called antibody "titres") were detected, rises that might indicate what infective agents had been at work. Cameron and Moore commented on those first colds of late January 1966 as follows:

> It can be postulated that a virus was seeded into the Mawson population directly by the [Russian] visitors or indirectly by J. E. H. and that the later apparent infections were examples of virus activation . . . in men who were engaged in a cold job for some hours. There was no evidence for cross-infection from these men to the other personnel. Another factor which may have played a part was a general climatic change with a significant temperature drop . . . which occurred at this time. This would suggest that if virus activation is a reality, it is dependent on a number of environmental factors, and may explain the difficulty experienced in inducing activation in volunteer experiments.[16]

The idea behind "virus activation" is the idea we met first in the writings of van Loghem in Amsterdam. It suggests that cold viruses may either lay latent in our bodies, or they may be commensal, replicating within us in a slow undestructive fashion before being triggered into some infective and symptomatic state. Cameron and Moore here imply that whatever agent caused the sore throats and running noses one and a half days after J. E. H. and his coworkers worked while wet and cold (and, after the temperature took a sharp dive) probably had not been present at Mawson until the recent contact with the Russians.

Does Isolation Make the Next Cold More Probable?

This Australian research again suggested that colds do not always completely cease in an isolated population, yet they may not reappear until contact with an outside world has been reestablished. The "colds" observed during the research at Mawson, on the voyage home, and soon after arrival at home, were not notably severe nor notably widespread. Thus, in this group of men, there was no clear evidence that some heightened susceptibility to colds follows an isolation of one year's duration. But there was some evidence here suggesting that "fresh" cold germs might remain latent for one month (the time that the Russian airmen had been isolated), that they might well pass to others without signs of infection, and that they might remain latent until triggered into activity by events such as a severe chill.

One further finding from the Australian research is of interest. Newly developed assay techniques for the purpose of revealing certain common cold antibody levels were employed on these men. (See later chapters for a more detailed discussion of antibody levels and their relationship with common cold contagion.) These assays revealed moderately low levels of those antibodies at the start of isolation, implying low levels of immunity to reinfection by corresponding viruses. However, there was no significant further *reduction* in the concentrations of these same antibodies one year later, despite the cold fatiguing work and crowded living conditions these men endured. Nor was there any apparent change in the levels and types of bacteria resident in the noses and throats of these same men during the time of this research. So if isolation does "weaken" one's defenses against the common cold then it is not yet clear where and how it does so.

Indirect evidence was reported at about this same time that was also hard to reconcile with the hypothesis that isolation leaves one more susceptible to new colds. In a review of medical work in Antarctica, Ove Wilson, a Swedish medical officer who had been with the Norwegian-British-Swedish Antarctic Expedition of 1949–52, reported information he learned from the British researcher R. Goldsmith concerning colds among members of two British stations during the International Geophysical Year. After a year of isolation at Halley Bay in the Weddell Sea, a group of men boarded their relief ship and many of them soon caught "severe colds." This ship carried on to Shackleton Base where a second party had wintered the year in isolation, and there this second party joined the first on the relief ship. But none of the men from Shackleton Base caught colds, despite the presence of fresh colds on board the ship.[17]

A very similar report was attributed to D. Edwards with respect to the party that wintered over at Macquarie Island in 1965. On mixing with the members of the incoming 1966 expedition, some of whom had colds, none of the previously isolated party caught any of their colds.[18] Again then, there was some suggestion that isolation does not automatically lower whatever resistance one may have to infection with the common cold.

In 1968, Antarctica was the site of another experiment with common cold virus.[19] As part of this study, recently discovered antibody levels to four different cold viruses, and to influenza A2 and C, were regularly monitored in thirteen men throughout a period of winter isolation. In general, levels of antibody against colds of the types monitored did not fall during the year of isolation. Since antibody levels appear to offer one index of resistance to infection, these data too suggest that isolation may not lead to lowered resistance.

The actual experiment performed on a subsample of seven volunteers in this party began two months after the start of isolation. The experiment involved giving these volunteers nose drops that contained either (1) an active virus, known from previous research (discussed later, in chapter 11) to produce colds in some volunteers, or (2) an inert liquid. Four men received the "cold" virus while three received the inert placebo. Each of those four who received virus came down with colds between thirty-six and sixty hours later. One of the three placebo recipients came down with a cold thirty-six hours after the first treated volunteer did. The delay in onset of this cold was consistent with the assumption that it had been transmitted onward from one of those men receiving the original virus. None of these five colds was particularly severe, however, and none appeared to be even as severe as the average cold caused by this same viral preparation when it was used in experiments on "control" volunteers in England.

Thus, the authors of this study concluded that, contrary to earlier appearances, isolation probably does not lower resistance to colds. What these authors did not mention is that in the similar experimental trials being held in England it was very rare for all four of the members of a volunteer group given active cold virus to develop colds the way the four volunteers in this Antarctic experiment did. In England only about 40 to 60 percent of those given active cold virus actually developed colds from this virus. Contrasted with those English results, the 100 percent rate of infection seen in the Antarctic, and the rare instance of a case of apparent secondary contagion from a cold in an infected volunteer to another volunteer originally receiving placebo, would actually suggest *increased* susceptibility to colds after going into polar isolation. Even so, the crowded and informal conditions existing at the Antarctic research station could easily account for the one case of contagion. And similar factors, even chance factors, might be invoked to explain the slightly higher incidence of experimental colds produced in this Antarctic study.

But then, starting in 1975, rather different data on changing susceptibility during isolation were gathered at McMurdo Station, the U.S. Antarctic base of operations. For each of three years, in the early spring, approximately 140 newcomers arrived to join approximately fifty to eighty-five personnel who had lived at McMurdo in isolation all winter. This combined mix of about two hundred people was then itself largely isolated for the next five weeks, until the arrival of the summer research season with its influx of summer scientists. During this five-week readying period the only active cold viruses at work were presumably those that had arrived with the newcomers.[20]

Colds were monitored daily in all personnel, by interviews conducted in the communal mess lines and by supplemental visits to those working in outlying buildings. Overall, the rates of colds seen in the previously isolated men and in the newcomers were quite similar. In the first year the average incidence of colds, during thirty-seven days of joint work, was 6.8 colds per person per year among the newcomers, and 5.9 colds per person per year among the wintering-over group. In the second year, the average incidence of colds, during thirty-eight days of joint work, was 3.0 colds per person per year among the newcomers, and 4.6 colds per person per year among the wintering-over group. Combining both years, the averages were 5.0 colds per person per year in the newcomers and 5.2 colds per person per year in the winter-over group, which is essentially the same (high) rate in both groups.[21] Moreover, the duration and severity of the colds seen in both groups, whether early or late in the joint work period, also were essentially the same. While the absolute levels of cold incidence here are high if sustained for an entire year, they are not much more than the rates generally seen during the peak fall cold periods during the same month up in the northern hemisphere.

This work carried out at McMurdo Station was later successful in identifying four different "cold viruses" circulating among the base personnel. Of particular interest was the fact that it could be shown that most people at the base were "susceptible" to these viruses, insofar as they had low or nonexistent antibodies against them. Yet among just this large group of susceptible people, fewer than 25 percent of them became infected by any of these viruses, and on average only about 15 percent of susceptibles caught the colds being studied. Despite the crowded and informal conditions at the station, and the large amount of social mixing and environmental stress placed on the personnel, colds were not very contagious, even among people working closely together and sleeping in adjacent bunks.[22]

Were Any of the Antarctic Colds Commensal Colds?

Because the evidence for increasing susceptibility to colds during isolation seemed conflicting and confused, in 1968 T. R. Allen of the British Antarctic Survey undertook a three-year study of colds among the members of the British Antarctic research group.[23] During this period, the British occupied six different bases in the vicinity of the Weddell Sea and the Antarctic Peninsula. Approximately one hundred men were involved in the study. Each man used a special symptom card to record the details of any and all respiratory illness that occurred while he was in Antarctica, but also, in many cases, to record any colds occurring in the six months after returning to England, at the end of each tour of duty. The severity of each cold symptom and each cold could then be measured, if only approximately, using these cards.

Perhaps the most significant and unexpected finding of this research was the documented outbreak of colds that occurred at one of the Antarctic bases after seventeen weeks of continuous and total isolation.[24] Fourteen men began isolation at Adelaide Island Base, situated on the west coast of the Antarctic Peninsula (and approximately on the Antarctic Circle) on March 18, 1969. These men were all in good health, and ranged in ages from twenty-one to thirty-five years. At the end of June, soon after a large mid-winter celebration and party, two men left the base by dog team and were gone for six months. These two men did not experience any symptoms of respiratory disease before or after leaving the base.

On July 14, 1969, one of the twelve remaining men at Adelaide Island Base came down with a headache, and on the next day, July 15, he had a clear cold, with pronounced sneezing, nasal discharge, and nasal stuffiness. Also on July 15, a second man developed headache, followed on the next day by the symptoms of a cold, with notable sneezing present. A third man also developed all the nasal symptoms of a clear cold on July 16 at the same time the second man did. Additional colds broke out in five more of the men during the next five days until eight of the twelve had developed clear cases of this illness. Among the four men who did not have cold symptoms, two experienced a single (different) day each of pronounced sneezing, but they showed no other signs of possible infection. Two of those four men who escaped colds worked in a different hut from the others during the daytime, and slept separately in the same small cubicle of bunks. One of the four men without cold symptoms generally slept during the daytime and worked at nights so that he had rather less contact with the others than did most of the group.

Blood samples and nasal wash samples taken from all these men were subsequently analyzed to try to determine which virus may have been responsible for these colds, but no virus could be identified.[25] Many considerations seemed to rule out the possibility of an allergic cause of these symptoms. Moreover, a bacterial cause seemed unlikely for other reasons, although it was not entirely ruled out. The prevalent influenzas were tested and ruled out. However, in their report, the researchers mentioned two factors that may have unleashed these colds.[26] First, severe winter weather and darkness during the entire two weeks prior to the first signs of infection had kept the men indoors and together in the central hut much more than usual. And then four days prior to the first signs of symptoms there had been a precipitous drop in outdoor temperature amounting to a full 24 degrees Celsius over thirty-six hours. Two days before the first colds, at the presumed time when infection and incubation began, the temperature was still well below "normal" for that locale.

Thus, unusually cold temperatures and bad weather combined to constitute the first possible contributing factors mentioned in connection with this surprising epidemic of colds among these isolated men. The second possible factor was the now familiar and traditional one for isolated men who will get colds in the Antarctic, namely the opening of new boxes that had been in storage since the beginning of isolation. At mid-winter (June 21) a celebration had been held involving the opening of presents. Moreover, Allen reported that:

> . . . suits were worn which contained soiled but usable handkerchiefs. . . . [Yet] the interval of 3 weeks between midwinter [i.e., the party] and the start of the outbreak makes it unlikely that infection occurred at midwinter, especially as the two men who left the Base soon after the celebrations had finished showed no evidence of respiratory disease.[27]

We are left then with the inference that these colds may have had a commensal origin, and thus may have lain dormant among the pool of men until finally triggered by some unidentified factor, perhaps the sudden and pronounced cold snap. But if this is correct, it is also true that commensal infections of this type, and their resulting cold epidemics, appear to be quite rare. There are currently just three reports of any "colds" ever having been observed after long polar isolation has begun, without the introduction from outside of any new personnel and with them, "fresh" colds. The first of these three reports is Marshall's, concerning the opening of a bale of new clothing, with which we began this chapter. But this report describes allergic reactions, not colds. The second of these accounts concerned the outbreak, described above, at Adelaide Island soon after that mid-winter party (with new clothing worn) and a severe cold snap. The third report of colds after long polar isolation comes from the British station at Halley Bay in 1970, and it has not yet been examined.[28]

Twenty-six men were isolated at Halley Bay during 1970 and for the fifteen weeks prior to mid-winter none of these men exhibited any signs of any colds. At mid-winter, the traditional party was again held, previously stored presents from home were opened, and at some point games were held outdoors at very low temperatures. Three days later two among the twenty-six men reported severe nasal symptoms, accompanied in one case by sore throat, and in the other case by severe headache. These colds lasted four and three days respectively, and no other men at the station reported any similar symptoms.

These two Antarctic reports of colds coming after many weeks of good health and total isolation, together with that single suggestive and unexplained outbreak of colds reported at Tristan da Cunha some weeks after the last ship was known to have called, together with the reports in the Polaris submarine studies that even many weeks into a patrol new colds occasionally are seen, and sometimes these colds are followed by a minor epidemic on board, all now suggest that long latent infections, or infections arising from otherwise commensal organisms, constitute possible (but apparently very infrequent) sources for the common cold.

Small Isolated Populations Differ, One from Another

So let us now review. We began this chapter with three questions in mind. These were: (1) Are cold epidemics only started after the loss of isolation, that is, following the arrival of new people recently departed out of a larger population? (2) Are the colds that occur after a long cold-free time of isolation both more severe and more numerous than they would be otherwise? And (3) does the size or the location of the isolated group have any modifying role to play?

Nothing we have seen out of Antarctica suggests that the size or location of the isolated group makes much difference, at least up to sizes near 180 personnel, at locations north and south, and high and low on the Antarctic continent. There is that one intriguing report noted earlier, that U.S. Navy personnel serving on ships in the Antarctic had half the number of respiratory infections seen in men on the ice. The traditional explanation for this has been that personnel on ships serve in what is generally a warmer and more hygienic environment. But the heat on ships in this region is neither dependable nor uniform. And the local hygiene may yet prove largely irrelevant: the hygiene on navy ships in Antarctic seas is not likely to be much different from the hygiene on navy ships in temperate waters, yet one study showed a higher incidence of colds was noticeably higher on navy ships working outside the Antarctic ocean.

The first two questions posed above seem to have clearer answers. It is not simply when isolation ends that a new outbreak of colds may occur, and yet, if there is no exposure to new people then the likelihood of new colds starting up in a population that is free of colds is indeed small. Both the Longyear City and Tristan da Cunha data strongly support this conclusion. We may safely conclude that prolonged isolation probably does not stop all colds, but complete isolation might stop all epidemics after a number of weeks have passed.

The large epidemics following the arrival of the first ship at Longyear City, or Tristan da Cunha, or the epidemics following the arrival of Shackleton's party returning to New Zealand or the arrival of Parry's suppliers returning to Baffin Island, all suggest that during isolation susceptibility to the common cold somehow does increase. And yet the

Antarctic data have uniformly suggested the opposite, that colds are neither more numerous nor more severe upon breaking a period of long isolation than they are upon entering one. True, on breaking isolation colds often do occur, but it is this loss of continuing good health that is curious, not the supposed "severity" of those ordinary colds that resume following the re-establishment of outside contacts.

But what then are we to make of the severe respiratory illnesses affecting the residents of Tristan da Cunha, of Easter Island, and those affecting the Eskimo populations visited by Parry in 1821 and by the 1926 Greenland Expedition from the American Museum of Natural History? The epidemics of "colds" described there all sound more widespread and severe than normally would be expected. Perhaps colds are more severe in these particular populations because of some important difference(s) between them and the members of those rather smaller populations that have been studied in Antarctica and in Polaris submarines. The difference could be partly in the degree of inbreeding peculiar to island populations and to small Eskimo populations. The difference could be partly in differing childhood experiences with disease. Or it could be partly in the time they have spent isolated from the world's general disease pool.

Further Data from the Arctic

Before we draw any final conclusions on the topic of colds in polar environments, we should note a few further accounts drawn from the explorer's literature. The first of these was reported retrospectively by G. Meldorf, looking back over earlier records of respiratory disease among Greenland Eskimos for 1867–68, and later for 1897–1903.[29] Meldorf was one of the first to report to the world that severe epidemics of colds regularly followed the arrival of ships to previously isolated villages. Significantly, however, he reported that these epidemics were seasonal, being most visible in the spring and in the fall. Moreover, he linked these epidemics to occasions of high humidity followed by colder, drier weather. Meldorf proposed that ships will introduce an infection, and that damp, then cold weather will subsequently "activate" it, starting it on its contagious rounds.

Thus, Meldorf was among the first to document an apparent link between weather patterns and common colds. Paul and Freese later reported no such links of colds to the weather at Longyear City in 1930, while van Loghem of course did believe he had seen such links in Holland in 1925. But Meldorf's hypothesis is puzzling, because in Arctic villages such as those on Greenland and Spitzbergen, the first ship in spring almost always provoked an epidemic of colds, regardless of the preceding weather. And since the first ship cannot arrive until a continuing spell of warm weather melts the harbor ice, rarely would there be a marked episode of colder, drier weather just when the ship arrives.

The isolated Eskimo village of Angmagssalik on the east coast of Greenland, with a population of about eight hundred, was studied in 1935–36 by Arne Høygaard, an Oslo physiologist.[30] He also noted an historic link between the arrival of the first ship of spring and outbreaks of infectious disease. And yet Høygaard reported that "before the ship arrives, when people from isolated settlements meet in the spring, colds are common but not so widespread and of such a long duration as the annual epidemics of colds after the ship's arrival." Here then we have the first suggestion that a contact with the outside world is *not* strictly necessary to produce new spring colds after a period of cold-free winter isolation in the Arctic.

A second such suggestion comes from another Norwegian investigator, Otto Abs, who studied the population on Spitzbergen just a few years before Paul and Freese began their study.[31] He contradicts the general conclusion of Paul and Freese, reporting that in the spring, prior to the arrival of the first ship, when people from one place on Spitzbergen visit people from another place, small epidemics of colds sometimes followed. However, he also confirmed the existence of the epidemic that regularly follows the arrival of the first ship later in the spring. Studying the summer arrivals of ships, Abs concluded that epidemics of colds are more likely when a ship brings new workers than when it does not. Moreover, he felt that workers who had been longest in residence on Spitzbergen seemed to get the most severe colds in the epidemic that occurred each spring. The epidemics of colds he reported did not appear to have a clear peak nor a clear end, but they tended to run on until the last ship had left on the arrival of harbor ice. Over the winter period of isolation, the small epidemics of colds that occurred seemed to Abs to correspond to times of high humidity (which implies times of *warmer* weather).

In Antarctica we have seen at least one case where colds seemed to start following the visit of another cold-free and long-isolated group of people. Colds such as these may be rare events, but they really do happen from time to time. We need a theory about common cold transmission that explains why it is rare (but not impossible) for colds to arise among long-isolated, cold-free populations, why it is rare (but not impossible) for colds in such populations to occur following contact with cold-free visitors from outside, and why it is so very common that colds will regularly follow the arrival of outsiders into large Arctic (and tropical) communities after a time of isolation and general freedom from colds.

Now if these phenomena were the only ones that a good theory of the common cold needed to explain, there would be many theories from which to choose, and we might next look at the strengths and weaknesses of each such theory. But a number of further facts about colds have been uncovered by medical intelligence, facts that also must be made to fit whatever theories we create. We must not forget, for instance, van Loghem's insistence that cold weather is a potent factor in starting colds, despite Paul and Freese's contradictory findings about that disputed fact. And now we see that Meldorf and Abs each believed that humidity had an important role to play in starting colds. We have been looking at colds in small and large communities, across divers geographic settings. Now it is time to look more closely at colds in divers climates and weathers. Does cold weather truly trigger colds?

PART II

CATCHING COLDS IN WORLDS COLD AND WARM

Behind the Passing Cold Fronts: London, 1768, to Cirencester, England, 1956

The situation of St. Kilda renders a North-East Wind indispensably necessary before a stranger can land. The wind, not the stranger, occasions an epidemick cold.

— *From Boswell's* The Life of Dr. Johnson, *1786*

The pair of Chinese ideograms that read "common cold" when translated into English might more literally be rendered as "hurtful wind" or possibly "naughty wind" or "mischievous wind." This idea, that changes in the winds and weather will cause common colds, particularly when these changes result in chilling, is found not only worldwide, but across the centuries as well. In almost every language with Indo–European roots, one of the words denoting the common cold, or the phrase that translates "to catch a cold," also puns on the word for low temperature, exactly as does the English word *cold.* We say "I've caught a chill" and generally we mean "I'm coming down with a cold."

Similarly, in German, *erkalten* means to become cooled or chilled, *krankheit* refers to illness, and the common cold is *erkaltungskrankheit.* In Swedish, *kold* means cold temperature, *kyla* means frigid weather, and the common cold is *forkyld.* In Dutch, *koud* means cold temperature, *verkoud* means to be made cold, *heid* refers to the head, and the common cold is *verkoudheid.* Some exceptions include Danish, where *kold*, or *fryser*, refer to cold temperatures but the common cold is *snue. Snue* means wily, cunning, or sly in Danish. And *snue* can also mean a nap, a snooze. The French word for cold temperature is *froid*, while the common cold is generally *rhume.*

Still, in French one may say "*J'ai pris un refroidissement*" to mean "I have caught a chill [or a cold]." Similarly, the corresponding phrase in Latin is "*frigus accepi*," and *frigus* comes from the same root that gives us *frigid.*

Whatever may be the folk perspective preserved in language, however, scientific studies of the possible effects of cold weather upon the incidence of common colds have not been nearly so unanimous in attributing colds to bodily chilling or to weather effects. Paul and Freese provided but one early example of a cautionary study suggesting that weather and chilling are not after all important causes of colds. Many other studies too have suggested no role at all for weather variables. Yet a number of epidemiologists, like van Loghem before them, have gathered data strongly implicating falling temperatures among the causes of some colds. And as we shall see, even rising temperatures have, on occasion, been linked to certain increases in the incidence of the common cold.

The existence of some form of link between common colds and temperature changes would hardly be surprising, especially given our names for the disease. Even so, the nature of any such link is anything but uniform and obvious. I don't suppose I was the only child in the world who got soaked in the puddles of a cold spring day only to discover that after all I did *not* catch the cold I was told to expect the next day. In the populated regions of the northern hemisphere, as in Antarctica, the law saying that enduring a sharp chill will lead one to catch a strong cold makes a regular habit of breaking itself. One might wonder then if perhaps our beliefs about chilling are simply a mistake, a mistake made because shivers and chills are often (incorrectly) thought to be the first noticeable symptoms of a cold. Thus, these symptoms of chill may be taken for the cause of the "cold" that soon follows, rather than being more correctly seen as the first expression, the first symptom, of this illness.

The trouble with this last hypothesis is that it is much more likely that chills will *not* be the first symptom of some cold than that they will be. Moreover, as the work of Townsend and Sydenstricker showed so long ago, pronounced chills often accompany the beginning of rather different diseases, particularly influenza and pneumonia, and we do not name these diseases "colds" even if we do tend to attribute them (probably correctly, in part) to the effects of cold weather.

In temperate latitudes, colds seem to be much more noticeable during colder seasons than during warmer seasons, that is, during the winter rather than the summer. Perhaps this is why our language suggests the equation of the temperature and the disease. Yet the skeptic could well argue that the link between exposure to cold temperature and an increased susceptibility to the common cold is only apparent — it is illusory. No simple theory about temperature effects is without its apparent counterexamples, as the polar data from Spitzbergen and Antarctica have already made clear. It will take a closer look at the evidence to decide whether the apparent link between cold weather and colds is real or not. And, if it is illusory after all, then a close look will also be needed to discover how the illusion has come to exist so persuasively.

Classical Authorities Pause Briefly to Explain Our Colds

Before the time when gathering careful epidemiological records became common, when it was still very difficult to achieve such records, the healthy skepticism needed to test simple theories was often prevented by the existence of a single authoritative statement of opinion. New theories were commonly put forward with all the authority of freshly revealed law merely on the basis of a single striking observation. This tendency was facilitated in part because nature was seen as being simple at heart and transparent to the prepared mind.

By the late nineteenth century, this form of reverence for authority and precedent was fast disappearing in science, so that experimental and observational tests of every new theory began to replace unquestioned acceptance as the proper form of scientific respect to be paid to acknowledged experts. Still, the earlier legacy was such that, for instance, a reader who knew only the work of Paul and Freese could easily suppose that it had been conclusively proven once and for all that temperature plays no role in causing colds and that human carriers of cold germs (whatever those germs may be) play the dominant role. Meanwhile, a reader who knew only the work of van Loghem could easily suppose that it had been conclusively proven that carriers of germs play almost no role in causing colds, and that temperature plays the most important role in unleashing widespread epidemics everywhere at once.

Apparent conflicts between a contagion theory of colds versus a theory invoking the weather and chilling could of course always be reconciled, whichever side of the argument one might consider "true." A charming example of such a rationalized truth appears in Boswell's account of the life of Samuel Johnson, and it nicely illustrates how authoritative pronouncements often ruled, untested by further observations. Boswell relates how, in 1768, Dr. Johnson had renewed a promise to accompany him to Scotland and on to the Hebrides. Dr. Johnson said he did not wish to visit many of the outer islands, but he agreed to include St. Kilda on his tour because of what Macaulay had said about it. Boswell quotes Dr. Johnson, by way of explanation, as follows:

> Macaulay, who writes the account of St. Kilda, set out with a prejudice against prejudice, and wanted to be a smart modern thinker; and yet [he] affirms for a truth, that when a ship arrives there, all the inhabitants are seized with a cold.
>
> Dr. John Campbell, the celebrated writer, took a great deal of pains to ascertain this fact, and attempted to account for it on physical principles, from the effect of effluvia from human bodies.

Here Dr. Johnson is referring to germs from the arriving passengers: i.e., the contagion theory. But Johnson seemed to have put more stock in the observation of the Reverend Mr. Christian of Docking, who asserted, "The cause . . . is a natural one. The situation of St. Kilda renders a North-East Wind indispensably necessary before a stranger can land. The wind, not the stranger, occasions an epidemick cold."[1]

Thus, Reverend Christian, well over two hundred years ago, took a single observation to confirm that a contagion theory is incorrect, and that the correct theory of the common cold looks again to damp cold winds. From Boswell and Johnson, and from others of the time, there is no suggestion of the need to test any such "authoritative" conclusions, for instance to see if cold epidemics follow northeast winds even in the absence of arriving ships, or to see if visitors might not land on the island elsewhere, in different winds, and provoke colds when they do. Authoritative deduction was still the armchair fashion of Boswell's day, not epidemiological and experimental excursions into the field.

Among the classical medical authorities who first considered the subject of epidemics were the Greek physician Hippocrates and his revered Roman interpreter Galen. Hippocrates was something of an historian, a reporter of all he saw. He seems to have been the Western world's first respected (which is to say published and read, translated and conserved) epidemiologist. Hippocrates, however, did not see the laws of nature as simple. He taught that in medicine, "judgement is difficult and experience deceptive."[2] Galen, however, building on the work of Hippocrates, promulgated a general theory of all diseases, a three-factor theory that still influences our beliefs about common colds. The three factors that Galen believed were responsible for illness were (1) certain aspects of personal temperament, (2) certain habitual behaviors of a special sort that produce risk, and (3) exposures to high-risk environments.

By high-risk environments, Galen was primarily referring to places with moist and humid atmospheres; in the Mediterranean world studied by Galen and Hippocrates, this generally meant a place of warm temperatures. So Galen felt that excessive heat contributed to illness, not excessive cold. Even so, times of winter cold were supposed by later writers to produce behaviors, such as the wearing of too much clothing while congregating in overheated, humid rooms, that seemed to confirm Galen's law linking overheating to illnesses. And there was something else that Galen attributed to the wrong environment (that is, to humid, warm environments). That something was "seeds of pestilence." Not all disease is caused by the action of these "seeds" of disease (the "germs" of more recent times), but for Galen many diseases were helped along by such germs, and these too were presumed to prosper in warm and humid air.

So the idea that the weather is an important contributing cause of common diseases is a very old one, holding a respected pedigree. More interesting still, the *temperamental* characteristics that Galen saw as predisposing to illness, that were in his view the most significant of the three factors leading to disease, were also described using the language of atmospheric qualities, making reference to temperature and to humidity. Galen's psychology was essentially two dimensional, blending characteristics from one dimension anchored by "hot" and "cold" with those from another dimension anchored by "moist" and "dry." (Exactly what these words meant for Galen is not easy to describe, but, fortunately, the exact nature of that meaning need not concern us here.)

For Galen, an ideal (and healthy) temperament is one where each of the two psychological dimensions is harmonized and in balance. This produces the so-called eucrasic temperament that is neither hot nor cold, moist nor dry. But should there be an "excess" in the person's personality of hot or moist or cold or dry, or an excess of hot-and-moist, hot-and-dry, cold-and-moist, or cold-and-dry, then susceptibility to disease follows. And the particular disease that will most probably occur varies, depending on the special interaction of the temperamental excess with the environmental excess or weakness that may be present at the same time.[3]

In classical medicine, then, we literally have a psychosomatic theory of all illness. But since the time of Pasteur, and to a lesser extent even earlier, medical science typically has not felt any need for recourse to some form of psychological factor to account for the sources of illness and health. There are recent signs that this may be changing, following the discovery of links between psychological states and immune functions. Common colds too may some day be shown to depend somehow upon psychological factors, even as psychological states in their turn can be affected by the presence of a cold. Galen helped to sensitize medical intelligence to the potential importance of weather variables in any explanation for the sources of disease, including the common cold, but his parallel emphasis upon the important role of psychological variables was abandoned early and forgotten soon after.

The First Epidemiologists of the Common Cold

Modern scientific study of the roles of weather in causing common colds did not begin then with van Loghem in 1925 and it certainly did not end with Paul and Freese in 1930. The first large-scale study of the effects of weather on respiratory disease was undertaken by H. Schade, in Germany, just before and during the First World War.[4] Schade gathered statistics on illnesses, especially respiratory illnesses, among the German troops. Schade's major interest was in how chilling may affect men who are "hardened" to cold of various intensities. He invented his own measure of what today might be called the wind-chill factor, which he quantified using the number of cases of military frostbite treated in any given week.

Schade reported three findings, each clearly suggesting that cold weather does contribute to respiratory illness and, it follows, to the risk of catching a cold, since the majority of the illnesses he studied were common colds. First, Schade compared the incidence of disease seen in a division of seventeen thousand men during the severe winter of 1916–17 to that seen during the mild winter of 1915–16 that preceded it. Disease incidence was nearly doubled in the more severe winter. Second, Schade compared the incidence of disease in 2,700 veteran troops, stationed in muddy, wet trenches at temperatures close to freezing for three continuous days and nights, to the same incidence in 5,300 controls stationed in their barracks behind the lines. Schade reported respiratory illnesses and certain other illnesses were four times more prevalent in the exposed troops, *after* returning to their barracks, than they were in the group of control troops. But Schade did not report whether the cold-stressed soldiers had any higher incidence of illness while still in the trenches.

The third study reported by Schade was similar to the second. In this study, 4,500 men were exposed to three days and nights of extreme cold, with daytime temperatures below minus nine degrees Celsius and with gusty winds. A control group of 3,500 men were sheltered indoors. Again, when the exposed troops returned to their barracks they had nearly four times the incidence of respiratory disease found among the controls over the same time period.

Using data from Prussian war ministry records for the years between 1901 and 1912, Schade discovered that the rates of respiratory disease very closely paralleled the rates of frostbite cases when analyzed in monthly intervals over the twelve-year period. A similar type of analysis later performed on the daily incidences of respiratory disease in eight thousand troops during three winter months seemed to show a strong parallel with the rates of frostbite seen over the same days. Schade concluded from these and similar analyses that by itself cold temperature is not as important as the wind-chill factor in causing illnesses such as the common cold. Moreover, Schade argued that the effect of chill does not act alone in causing colds, but that it is perhaps the most important single risk factor leading to an increased likelihood of contracting such illnesses.

In arriving at his conclusions, Schade put special emphasis on observations made during one particular eighteen-day period beginning December 17, 1916, when the wind chill was, episodically, quite severe in the war zone.[5] The daily incidence of common colds and the incidence of frostbite were all but perfectly correlated during this eighteen-day period. On days when the frostbite cases doubled, the other illnesses doubled, and when the frostbite cases halved, the other illnesses halved. However, Schade does not comment upon the many other days outside this eighteen-day period when the incidence of frostbite was seen to be level or dropping while the incidence of colds was shooting up and down. More significantly, if during that striking period in December the wind chill was indeed causing many colds, then it was doing so in a matter of a few hours. All other studies have suggested there is a lag of rather more than a day before exposure to cold temperatures leads to observable colds. What seems likely is that the very severe wind chill that Schade was watching during those eighteen days exacerbated the otherwise mild symptoms of existing colds (or produced the watery nasal discharge familiar to polar explorers, caused in part by condensation of the breath, which in turn stings and chaps the nose and throat) leading to many more visits to sick bay on the same days.

Should We Open Our Winter Windows After All?

Early medical scientists often speculated on the mechanism by which chilling would lead to catching a cold. There were two trends in the thinking on this question. One approach focused on what might be the consequences of physical irritations of the mucous membranes, irritations that were not confined to those caused by exposure to cold air, and that included for instance the irritating effects of chlorinated pool water up the nose, irritations caused by smoke, and the like. The general line of reasoning here was that chilling provoked nasal irritation which then compromised natural defenses, following which ubiquitous waiting germs seized their opportunity to infect the unprotected cells of the nose and throat.

The other trend in thinking on the subject focused on possible "disturbances" in internal "thermoregulation" provoked by the physiological stress of coping with marked chilling. To physiologists of the time, the warm-bloodedness of humans, their nearly constant body temperature, and the presence of fever in so many disease conditions were powerful signs that the regulation of body temperature ("thermoregulation") was a key factor in human physical functioning and health. A mechanism, thought to be based in the heart, was suggested for the express purpose of regulating body temperature. Like a great muscle, this mechanism could grow weak or strong, and if too much were asked of it too quickly, it could become "strained."[6] By proper "exercise" of the thermoregulation system, which is to say by "hardening" oneself to cold through dosed exposures to cold showers, to open windows, to the wet spray of the open sea, to mountain winds, a person (and somehow it was particularly a male person) could become immune to colds by becoming physiologically competent, a tower of strength. But if one were to strain the thermoregulation system, due to its weak state or to an overly severe challenge, then the thought was that the primary line of defense against the invasion of germs was compromised and infection generally followed, particularly infections of the respiratory system.

This idea that chilling weakens the natural defenses against colds has been widely subscribed to for many years. In 1919 and 1920 a survey of college students on three U.S. campuses was taken concerning their views about the causes of their colds.[7] More than 60 percent of the students on each campus attributed their colds to the direct result of some form of chilling, and included in this sample were more than four hundred medical students.

At the University of Chicago, a census of colds was taken and a test made of the hypothesis that "hardening" oneself helps reduce the number of colds one catches. Yet Chicago students who slept with their windows open, or who exercised regularly, apparently had no fewer colds than did students who did not do these things.

However, in support of the hardening idea, the data in this Chicago study did suggest that those students who had worn light clothing all winter might have had a slight advantage. It is not clear, however, whether the students who wore light clothing had become more resistant to frequent colds, or, whether the students who enjoyed fewer colds were just more often able and willing to wear light clothing. In addition, one form of exercise monitored in this study was found to be associated with more, rather than fewer, colds. The more colds that students reported having, the more likely it was (although only to a modest degree) that they also exercised regularly by swimming.[8] The census of colds used in these analyses was based upon student memories over a span of months, however, and slight reporting biases, affecting what the students called "regular" exercise and what they called a "cold," could have produced some of the trends reported in these data.

New Meaning to the Phrase: "I Gave at the Office"

Thus, beginning sometime before the turn of the century, and continuing on into the early decades of the twentieth century, the role of cold temperatures in predisposing one to common colds began to be examined scientifically and debated at some length. Many of the studies undertaken on this topic exploited statistical tabulations of medical records existing in files at schools, military units, and in organizations with health-care departments, such as might be found at large hospitals and at certain insurance companies. But the "colds" examined in these studies often included a mix of respiratory diseases, including cases of influenza, pneumonia, tonsillitis, bronchitis, and additional forms of infection, often bacterial in origin. Even the true colds counted in these studies were special, for they were severe enough to occasion a trip to the infirmary. In most of these studies, most mild colds went unrecorded, as did more serious colds in people who, for whatever reason, would not normally elect to see a doctor or a nurse.

The results of such studies invariably seemed to confirm an association between low temperatures and an increased incidence of respiratory diseases, particularly respiratory diseases leading to death. Generally, such studies looked at monthly summaries, and in the cases of school-based research they usually did not include data from July, August, or September.[9] None of the authors of such studies truly believed that cold temperatures were the *direct* cause of colds or other diseases. As we have seen, some believed that cold temperatures act indirectly, for instance by irritating mucous membranes, and so opening the way for subsequent infection.

Others believed that cold temperatures are associated with some other quite unrelated factor that in turn indirectly leads to infection. Some believed, for instance, that the real risk factor involved is the close and prolonged exposure to indoor crowds that people experience in cold weather.[10] Some believed that cold weather is associated with cloudy weather, and that lack of sunshine breeds vitamin deficiencies that are the source of colds.[11] It would not be too difficult to disentangle such factors, to look for instance at cloudy but warm times and sunny but cold times, or to look at cold and warm weather in places with and without crowding. But it is not usually possible to try such refined analyses with just the data available in the files at the local infirmary.

An interesting example of one of these early studies appeared in November of 1923 when the Metropolitan Life Insurance Company of New York City published an epidemiological study of colds among their office workers. The study covered a fifty-two-week period ending July 28, 1923. The subjects of this study were the clerical staff of the company's home office, numbering approximately 6,700 people in total. The company maintained a "medical division" to care for the health of the staff, and records were kept of all colds that came to the attention of this medical division. Convinced that weather has a role to play in causing colds, the actuaries in the company looked at the weekly incidence of colds reported and the weekly averages in various weather variables. They found "only slight influence on the rise and fall of the incidence of common colds" associated with relative humidities or precipitation amounts. But with average temperatures each week there seemed to be a strong association to reported levels of colds.[12]

Such simple associations can be well measured using the correlation coefficient previously mentioned. In this study, the relationship between average weekly temperatures and the incidence of colds was indeed simple, and the correlation coefficient between these variables proved to be an uncommonly strong 0.89. This value represents a degree of association which is almost 80 percent of a metaphoric "distance" from complete independence between the two variables to a perfect correspondence between them. Put differently, 80 percent of the general uncertainty about the number of colds to be expected during any given week in this study disappears once you know the average temperature seen in that particular week.

The authors of this report expressed their main finding as follows: "A drop in the weekly mean temperature of 10 degrees Fahrenheit carries with it an increase of eighteen common colds per week in this group of 6,700 people."[13] That translates to one additional cold for every thousand people in each week, if the average temperature dropped by about 3.7 degrees Fahrenheit. Thus, while the trend seen at Metropolitan Life was loud and clear when following very large numbers of people through summer and winter, the magnitude of the temperature effects described would hardly be noticed even in a "crowded" office of fifty people. In this large study, the average number of colds seen per thousand workers happened to be 8.09 per week for the year as a whole. Looked at another way then, the number of colds in any week increased by about 10 percent for each three-degree drop in average temperature. This equally correct way of describing the relationship makes temperature changes seem clearly more important than noting an increase of one case in a thousand workers.

This Metropolitan Life study does not escape the criticisms noted previously for studies at large institutions. We are told nothing about the criteria used for diagnosing a cold and for discriminating it from, say, hay fever or mild flu. Almost certainly, many mild colds went unreported and so were overlooked in this study. Nor does the presence of an overall association between temperature levels and illness rates demonstrate any causal links between these variables. For instance, average temperatures were lowest and colds were also very prominent in this study in mid-February 1923. Perhaps then both the colds and the temperatures are tied to the seasons, yet colds depend as little on those temperatures as the temperatures depend on the number of colds around. Both may depend on the time of year but not on each other. A closer look at the weekly data should give us some clue as to whether or not this may be true.

In fact, the data published by Metropolitan Life were not as simple as their summary report might imply.[14] For instance, those data showed sharply increasing numbers of colds being reported all during the first three weeks of September, 1922. Overall, the incidence of colds more than doubled in this period. But during the same period the corresponding average temperature was not falling; it actually rose for a time, and it dropped only 10 percent at the end. Another sharp epidemic of colds began early in January 1923 and continued until rates had nearly doubled by the end of that month. Yet during this same period the decline in average temperature was quite minimal, and temperatures essentially as low as in January had been around for six weeks prior to the start of this epidemic, without previously setting it off. The lowest average weekly temperature of the year came during the last week of February but the incidence of colds had been falling for some time before, and did not rise again during that record low week. The following week saw a sharp rise in temperature but no further drop in the number of colds. Thus, colds and average weekly temperatures may seem to dance back and forth in a rough concordance, but clearly they are not always dancing in each other's arms.

Close scrutiny of daily and weekly weather patterns was not a concern of the early epidemiologists, however. They were seeking clear and robust truths, apparent exceptions to which could only be hiding the deeper rule that seemed so visible in the overall data. Discoveries like those of Schade and those of van Loghem, and that impressive association reported at Metropolitan Life, all seemed to point strongly to cold weather as a cause of increasing numbers of colds. Further persuasive data implicating the possible importance of temperature *shifts* in starting colds were soon to appear as well. The antidote to such data, beginning with the work of Paul and Freese, but also looking closely at day-by-day effects in data like those from the Metropolitan Life study, was far slower to appear.

Hope Simpson Finds Evidence for Increased Colds Following Colder Weather

One of the more significant studies reintroducing weather variables as important to the epidemiology of the common cold was first reported in 1958 by R. E. Hope Simpson. Hope Simpson carried out a careful study of colds occurring during 1954, 1955, and 1956 in 350 people from eighty families living in the somewhat isolated village of Cirencester, England. Volunteers used cards to report daily any symptoms they experienced. New cards were supplied and the old ones collected every three weeks. Hope Simpson maintained a general medical practice in Cirencester, and he saw many of his volunteers as patients in his practice. But only about five percent of all the common colds reported during this study were seen in the clinic, and only about 18 percent of the volunteers who had any colds ever brought a cold to be seen in the clinic. Moreover, the numbers of colds that were reported were quite high — in 1954 they averaged seven "episodes" per person per year. The average duration of these colds was found to be ten days.

It was the weather that most interested Hope Simpson. Seasonal variations in both the number of colds recorded and the general weather patterns observed seemed particularly clear to him, and so he undertook to look more closely at weather variables. He wrote:

> We examined various meteorological components for correspondence — barometric pressure, vapour pressure, the passage of hot and cold fronts, winds, radiation, precipitation, outdoor temperature — and found that the last provided the closest relationship. The temperature taken at a depth of 1 foot in the earth gives less hectic variations than that of outdoor air.[15]

Hope Simpson then presented a figure designed to show the close correspondence between the average soil temperature one foot below the ground surface and the number of colds observed, across a three-year period from January 1, 1954, to December 31, 1956. Each line, one for temperature and one for respiratory symptoms, reflected weekly totals from daily observations.[16] The resultant graph depicted a striking visual association. Seasons with high levels of cold weather were seasons having a high incidence of respiratory disease. Without calculating a formal correlation coefficient (which would have been quite high) Hope Simpson reported:

> The correspondence between the morbidity and the [decline in] the seasonal temperature throughout the three-year period is remarkably close, in fact the name "common cold" could not be more apt. The disease is par excellence common and could not be more closely associated with seasonal decline in temperature, so much so indeed that a drop of 1 degree Fahrenheit is associated with a rise of 1 percent in morbidity.[17]

Hope Simpson is saying that for every degree Fahrenheit that his soil temperature fell, on average, about three or four additional colds were seen in his sample of 350 persons. In the Metropolitan Life study in New York some thirty years earlier, the corresponding figure had been approximately one-tenth of a cold more for each 350 persons when the average weekly air temperature fell one degree. Hope Simpson saw a considerably higher incidence of colds than had been seen previously in New York, and he used a deep soil temperature measure that was much less variable and less sensitive to small changes than was the air temperature used in New York. Consequently, there may be less discrepancy here than first meets the eye. In both studies, the association between general temperature and respiratory illness was marked and suggestive.

Hope Simpson went on to explore further how cold weather might be acting to increase colds. He knew that polio victims placed in iron lungs sometimes suffered serious respiratory infections unless the air they breathed was kept at nearly 100 percent relative humidity, that is, saturated with water vapor. Moreover, Hope Simpson had been asked to monitor the health of some workers in a special new room at a cheese factory in nearby Wales, a room where the humidity was kept constant and relatively high (at 80 percent) while the temperature was kept rather cool at 58 degrees Fahrenheit (14.4 degrees Celsius). The cool damp environment notwithstanding, and to everyone's surprise, the employees working in this new room suffered less than half the number of colds than did other employees working elsewhere, over the first year of operation. It seemed very possible then that cold weather might cause respiratory disease not because of its chilling effects on the body, but because of its associated effects upon the relative humidity of the winter air. If cold air were dry air, this might account for an increase in colds during cold weather. Normally, however, cool air is relatively more saturated with water than is warm air.

In southern England and Wales, where Hope Simpson was working, both cool air and warm air come off the Atlantic, and both are laden with water vapor. Thus, in this region, both warm and cool air tend to have high relative humidity, which is the water vapor content taken relative to the maximum possible vapor content of air at the same temperature. But because warm air can carry increasingly greater volumes of water than can cooler air, when a given package of warm air starts cooling, its relative humidity actually rises. As the temperature falls, the mass of water vapor in the air remains nearly constant, but the relative humidity rises as the cooling air nears its saturation level. When the temperature falls to the point where the water vapor in the air is as much as that cool air can carry, we say the dew point has been reached. Generally, any further fall in temperature will be accompanied by water droplets leaving the air, as dew, fog, or rain. The reverse logic is correspondingly true, and it became the basis of Hope Simpson's theory about winter colds. When cool winter air is heated, as it regularly is indoors, then its relative humidity drops, often to quite low values.

Thus, Hope Simpson took the view that it is probably the relative humidity of the air we breathe that matters to our health, not the absolute amount of water vapor in the air. The structures that form our nasal passages and bronchial passages are so constructed as to put additional water vapor into any inhaled air that will accept it. When that air reaches the surfaces of the lung it is very often at or near 100 percent relative humidity. Cool outdoor air in southwest England and Wales is also near 100 percent relative humidity, especially during the winter. But indoors, after that same air is heated, the relative humidity drops considerably because the air, being warmer, can now hold considerably more water vapor. During the summers, Hope Simpson found that the relative humidity in Cirencester, both outdoors and indoors, was similar, averaging about 70 percent. During the winters, however, the relative humidity outdoors averaged around 90 percent while the relative humidity indoors averaged about 50 percent, and sometimes it was much lower than that.

When Hope Simpson replotted his graphs, looking then at the weekly incidence of colds alongside the weekly difference in relative humidity between outdoor air and indoor air (a difference that is generally high in the winter and low in the summer) he again observed what appeared to be a very high degree of association. This time he plotted his data only for one year, 1955, and again he did not compute a correlation coefficient to quantify how strong the level of association might be between these two variables. Hope Simpson's graph revealed times of marked discrepancy between the two lines, especially in January 1955, in late April, and in December when the "index of dryness indoors" (the measure of the difference in relative humidity) is well above the index of the number of colds occurring, and also in July 1955, when the index for colds is well above the index for dryness indoors.

Still, Hope Simpson was persuaded that this evidence for the unhealthy effects of low relative humidity was strong enough to be important. Low relative humidities were produced each winter by the coal and electric fires used to warm the cottages of those participating in his study. He wrote:

It seems not unreasonable to suggest, that here in the desiccating effect of artificial heating we have a candidate for the rôle of a major culprit in the causation of colds. More than that we cannot claim, but at least here is a factor the intensity of which rises and falls consonantly with the morbidity and which, should it produce any effect at all, must do so on the respiratory apparatus itself. Can it be that in artificially heating our homes we overtax the natural humidifying mechanisms in our upper respiratory passages, and subject our bronchioles and alveoli, 16 times to the minute for

hour after hour and week after week, to the dangerous action of insuffi-
ciently moistened air?

I do not suggest that this influence alone engenders the colds.
Almost certainly there must be other agencies at work, but, whatever the
immediate precipitating factors, it may be that the influence of dry air
opens the door to them, and that moist, cool air makes it more difficult
for other harmful agencies to operate. Evaporation may increase the density
of the mucus stream, halt it by impeding ciliary action, cause crusts to
form in the passages, damage osmotically the underlying epithelial cells,
and in numerous such ways prepare the soil for a crop of evil and dangerous weeds.[18]

It is not clear why Hope Simpson was so confident that any significant
effects of relative humidity must take place upon our bodies, upon the "soil,"
rather than upon the viral agents responsible for the common cold, the
"weeds." None of the evidence he discussed bore on the question concerning
whether it might be the host or the parasite that was more sensitive to low
humidity. Moreover, all the selected evidence that he discussed was conso-
nant with his overall view that indoor humidity might be more important
than cold temperatures in explaining the seasonal changes in the incidence
of the common cold. Contrary evidence, such as might be provided by the
residents of Longyear City, Spitzbergen, or by Antarctic researchers living
out their winters indoors in warmed and very dry polar air, or by the residents of desert towns and cities around the world, was not considered.

If Hope Simpson were correct about the unhealthful effects of dry
indoor air (and he believed that he was correct) then effective humidi-
fication of homes and cottages might prove to be the best and easiest way
to reduce costly yearly losses of time and health due to common colds. Yet
overcoming the drying effects of indoor English fires seemed beyond the
current technology of the day and place. Thus, Hope Simpson concluded
his 1958 article with the following pessimistic flourish:

Fire, we may remember, was a secret of the gods until Prometheus, one of
the semi-divine Titans who attended the smithy, stole fire for the benefit
of mankind. He was punished for the theft by being stapled to a rock, and
a vulture was set to gnaw his semi-divine liver which perpetually renewed
itself. We are now suggesting that the gods, with super-human malignity,
have also punished the recipients by means of the very thing stolen, artificial

heating. The penalty inflicted upon us is not unlike that suffered by the unfortunate demigod.[19]

Oddly heroic words, these, for a disease that ordinarily feels so plebeian. And strangely fatalistic too, about the prospect of any improvement in the situation. Still, if low humidity were the culprit then there would be reason for significant optimism because artificial humidifiers have recently become so effective and so common. Unfortunately for the human race, neither natural nor artificial humidifiers appear to reduce significantly the number of colds that we suffer. And what's more, future studies were soon to suggest that cold temperature is much more important than low humidity when colds begin to multiply.

8

Lagging Behind the Cold Fronts: London and Newcastle, 1951–58

"It is a challenging fact that the most obvious feature of the epidemiology of the common cold, the seasonal variation in incidence, remains without any satisfactory explanation."[1]

— *O. M. Lidwell et al., 1965*

Interest in how the weather might affect respiratory illness was rekindled by the work of Hope Simpson during the 1950s. In the years immediately following the publication of his paper, attention began to be directed to exploring the relative importance of low indoor humidity versus low outdoor temperature in their roles as possible triggers for the common cold. And although more was soon learned, still, for a time, the mysteries only seemed to deepen.

In 1961 a review of research carried out in England was reported by Dr. W. W. Holland and two of his coworkers. Their data had been gathered between 1951 and 1958 at three large training bases for the Royal Air Force, and, during 1958, at a large London hospital.[2] These data consisted of frequency counts for diagnostic classifications of general illness made on patients admitted to the hospital, and on R.A.F. personnel who missed forty-eight hours or more of duty time due to illness. Of particular interest in this study was the incidence of respiratory diseases of all types, because the authors of this study wished to examine the relative importance of local temperature versus humidity as possible causes of more serious forms of respiratory illness.

Holland pointed out that since cold weather and low indoor humidity are both linked to seasonal weather changes, neither variable may be important in causing colds should it happen that some other aspect of the fall and winter seasons is actually starting respiratory illnesses. Later writers have suggested, for instance, that in the fall, summer vacations end and schools reopen, and colds might blossom in late September and October because of the new mixing of recently more isolated people and not because of the chilly fall evenings that come at about the same time of year. If temperature or humidity really does matter in setting off common colds then it should be possible to note the existence of early fall epidemics, following unusually early fall weather, and late fall epidemics, following unusually delayed fall weather.

Holland and his co-authors set out to look for such events, introducing their study rationale as follows:

> The object of this study was to investigate the effects of certain meteorological variables on the incidence of respiratory disease, using a statistical technique which eliminates the large-scale seasonal fluctuations.
>
> There are two main reasons for this approach. In the first place, there will always be a fairly close correlation between any two seasonally varying quantities even though there is no direct connection between them. Secondly, the large seasonal variation in the meteorological variables introduces very high correlations between them which can completely swamp their minor, short-term fluctuations. These latter fluctuations can throw much light on the independent effects of the individual variables. For example, the average temperature in August is always higher than in January, and the relative humidity always lower, and to this extent temperature and relative humidity can hardly be considered to vary independently. But there can still be warm, wet Augusts, or warm, dry ones and it is by comparison of warm and wet with warm and dry that the effects of humidity apart from temperature can be judged.[3]

Unfortunately, Holland and his colleagues did not really carry out their research in such a way as to help us to draw any clear conclusions about the different effects of warm, wet Augusts and warm, dry ones, as these may affect the common cold. Instead, the analyses they undertook were for relatively severe respiratory illnesses, not simply common colds, and their analyses were done on monthly average values that must of necessity hide most of the recent day-to-day effects of falling and rising temperatures, humidity, and rates of disease.

Still, what they found and published to the world was both suggestive and influential beyond its circumscribed sphere of reference; specifically, they found evidence that it is changing temperatures, not changing humidities, that change in turn the rates of severe respiratory illness. True, Hope Simpson and others might well have responded to this evidence, arguing that the humidity changes analyzed were not really the *indoor* humidities that earlier had been found to be associated with the common cold. But apparently no such counter argument was advanced, and the publication of Holland's findings diluted the force of Hope Simpson's earlier arguments.

A careful study of day-by-day fluctuations in the weather, and in the colds that occurred in the days that followed, was finally published in 1965 by O. M. Lidwell, R. W. Morgan, and R. E. O. Williams.[4] Between 1951 and 1957 these investigators had carried out a daily survey of colds among large numbers of volunteers in London, and in Newcastle-upon-Tyne. In Newcastle, the volunteers were all employees working in certain large offices at the U.K. Ministry of Pensions and National Insurance, or they were family members of these employees. In London, the volunteers were all employees working in similar large offices at Shell Petroleum, or in two smaller government offices. Office workers were chosen for a number of reasons, the primary reason being because this study was part of an experiment exploring whether or not changes in ventilation, and disinfecting room air, might be able to reduce winter colds among workers. (It didn't.) But another reason for choosing office workers was that it was then easily possible to visit large numbers of volunteers once each week and to obtain from them an oral history of any recent colds they may have acquired, including information on the precise dates of onset for any such colds.

In Newcastle it was possible to monitor the colds seen in 350 to 500 volunteers each year. In London the study population was between 600 and 1,100 per year. However, during each summer, from early June until late August, no data were collected. A total of more than five thousand person-years of data were gathered and analyzed in this study (a "year" being one cold season, from September through May) examining the possible effects of weather on colds.

When are Colds and Weather Unusually Severe?

Lidwell, Morgan, and Williams carried out their data analyses using a simple statistical technique that would remove, on a daily basis, any seasonal biases (linked to seasonal averages) affecting temperatures, humidity, or the normal numbers of colds for the time of year. This simple technique was based on the strategy suggested in the quotation from Holland and his colleagues appearing at the start of this chapter. Each data analysis asked, in effect, "to what extent was any day that was warmer (or colder) than average *for that time of year* followed by days that had fewer (or more) colds than average *for that time of year?*" If cold weather were a risk factor for colds, then on a day that is colder than usual for the time of year, or on a day soon after, there should be more colds than usual for the time of year.[5]

Thus, Lidwell and his colleagues set out to look at just such an association. Similar associations were examined for the amount of sunshine seen each day, the degree of air pollution each day, the daily range between maximum and minimum temperature, the amount of rainfall, the barometric air pressure, as well as for both the relative and the absolute humidity (the water vapor content of the air) outdoors.

In this long list of weather factors only two were found to be associated with the degree to which colds were increased or decreased over normal values on a particular day, and *these two variables were only found to be associated with colds between November 1 and May 31, after a dramatic autumn peak of infections had passed each year.*[6] The variables were (1) the daily average temperature, and (2) the absolute water vapor content of the outdoor air.

Although the associations found between common colds and each of these two weather variables were clear and significant, at the same time the magnitude of each association was relatively small. Changes in *relative* humidity, even though these are always partially linked to changes in daily average temperature, were not found to be associated with increases or decreases in the incidence of common colds in these data from London and from Newcastle. Surprisingly then, it was absolute humidity, not relative humidity, that seemed to matter in these cities.

However, Lidwell's most interesting findings concerned (1) the relative importance of these two factors after each had been rendered independent of the other, and (2) the timing of the observed temperature and absolute humidity effects. Relative importance can be assessed by first recalculating the degree to which temperatures are above and below normal on days having the same absolute humidity at the same time of year. Then in the same way one can calculate the degree to which absolute humidities are above and below normal for days with the same temperature at the same time of year. Then, if lower-than-average temperatures were still found to be associated with higher-than-average rates of common colds after all differences in humidity had been statistically removed, while at the same time if lower-than-average humidities were no longer found to be associated with cold incidences after temperature effects had been removed, then it would be safe to conclude that temperature changes alone explain both of the original findings, and humidity only appears to be associated with colds because of its links back to general weather effects that often include corresponding changes in temperature.

This pattern was essentially just what Lidwell, Morgan, and Williams actually found. After the combined effects of humidity and temperature had been separated and controlled, the amount of association remaining between cold incidences and absolute humidity levels was only about one-third of the amount of the association remaining between cold incidences and temperatures. It seemed to be falling temperatures then, and not falling water vapor volumes, which, in these data, were doing most of the actual work of anticipating increased numbers of future colds.

Enter the "Lag" Effect

But when was that work being done? If the temperature turns rather colder, and if that in turn raises the incidence of common colds, does this effect occur on the very next morning, or does it occur only two, or four, or seven days later? In all previous studies reporting links to cold temperatures, including van Loghem's pioneer work in Holland, and Hope Simpson's work in rural England, the data for averaged temperatures and for averaged cold incidences were combined into blocks of seven or ten days. Thus, if changes in temperature were to lead to changes in cold incidences only one or a few days later, that fact would not have been detectable in those earlier studies because the data spanned a range of time considerably greater than the brief span that may be needed for the cold to develop.

It would be of great interest indeed to discover whether any lag between a time of temperature change and a corresponding increase in the numbers of colds seen was a short or a long lag. A short lag would imply either that the disease has a very short incubation period — the period between the moment of "infection" and the moment when symptoms begin to appear — or, that cold weather brought out symptoms earlier than they might otherwise have appeared, during what would otherwise have been a longer incubation period. As will be discussed soon, in chapter 10, experimental work on cold viruses, and studies of the timing of colds among the members of families, had by the time of the Lidwell study revealed that many colds appeared to have an incubation period of approximately forty-eight hours. Few colds appear to have incubation periods shorter than thirty-six hours, and longer incubation periods, while not rare, probably exceed sixty hours only about 10 percent of the time.

The correlation observed by Lidwell and his colleagues once the September–October peak of colds had passed (that is, the correlation between abnormally lowered temperatures and abnormally rising rates of common colds) was quite insignificant for colds occurring on the *same day* as the temperature shifts. But the correlation of temperature changes with the incidence of colds appearing on the *next* day was visibly stronger. And the correlation was stronger still for colds appearing on the *second* day after temperature effects were noted. This higher level of correlation with disease rates was maintained in the data over a three-day period, i.e., during the second, the third, and the fourth days following the day of notable temperature change. On the fifth day following, the correlations began to return to baseline, and gradually over the next few days they fell back to insignificant values.

Lidwell and his colleagues interpreted these results as reflecting an increase in new colds two days after colder weather (and, a decline in new colds two days after warmer weather) exactly as would happen if during the first hours of colder weather more colds had started incubating (or, in other words, more infections had occurred). But what about the continued high correlations on days 3 and 4? If there is a two-day incubation period, shouldn't there be a weaker correlation between the drop in temperature on day 1 and the number of new colds on days 3 and 4?

Lidwell attributed the high correlations on days 3 and 4 to the common inertia seen in weather patterns, an inertia that might allow some further extra colds to be triggered on a second or third consecutive day of continuously falling temperatures following upon the first. And perhaps some colds had taken longer than the expected two days to incubate. Possibly too, some of the people who were infected on the day of temperature change were responsible for infecting others two days later, leading to a continuing rise of colds two days later than that, on day 4. With this theory, however, there is no reason to stop with day 4. By the same reasoning one might expect more colds on day 6 and day 8, yet by day 6 the correlations had retreated in size to the low levels seen on the original day of temperature change.

Thus, to explain why changes in temperature level correlate notably with cold incidences seen four days later, but not six days later, is not easy, especially given that the incubation period for common cold viruses, as later research would confirm, is generally about half as long as four days. I will have reason to suggest, presently, that the true peak effect in these data may have been occurring on day 4 (not on day 2) one or two days *after* typical incubation periods normally would have elapsed. But the reasonable assumption at the time Lidwell and his colleagues published their findings was that the arrival of colder weather must be starting more infections, while the arrival of warmer weather must be reducing the number of infections that start on that day.

Whence Arises This Lag Effect?

What then might explain this lag of two, three, and four days between changes in temperatures and corresponding changes in the numbers of new colds? It may be that (1) temperature changes act directly to affect the strength of the cold virus, or that (2) those changes may influence our physical resistance to infection, or that (3) those changes may in turn influence either our own behavior or the behavior of the cold virus in such a way as to change the likelihood of the passage of an infection from person to person. Lidwell, Morgan, and Williams did not favor any one of these possible explanations over the other two. And yet their data carried implications for all three.

If temperature changes act directly on cold viruses and if in consequence they become more contagious after the passage of a cold front, then why was the temperature effect seen consistently between November and May but never in September or October? Could it be that different viruses are active each fall, or could it be that something about ourselves, our immune system perhaps, is different after a long summer, when the living is easy? What makes autumn colds different?

Lidwell and his colleagues offered another clue to understanding the special case of autumn colds while they were plotting their graphs of the average expected colds in each city, each year. They found that the "autumn" curves for London were always higher than the corresponding curves for Newcastle. And when the same special curves were fit to Hope Simpson's autumn data from the smaller city of Cirencester, and also to some data Lidwell had gathered in the rural Chalke valley, these curves were smaller still, so much smaller that in the Chalke valley, no autumn peak of colds was to be seen at all.[7] Lidwell, Morgan, and Williams commented on this, saying:

It is interesting and, possibly, of significance that the magnitude of this autumn peak follows the size of the community concerned, that ranges from around 10^7 for London down to a few hundred only in the Chalke valley. No weather variable has a distribution remotely resembling this autumn peak in colds and this, together with its apparent association with community size, suggests strongly that it is related to the immunity state of the population at this time of year.[8]

Yet it is not immediately clear why the immunity state of people at the end of summer, and at no other time, should depend upon the population density in their nearby world. Initially, it might seem more likely that the viruses themselves are somehow affected by the summer heat or the falling humidity of fall, and/or that in the autumn, transmission of infection is typically due to personal contacts, while at other times of year colds more typically spread by other means, as commensals perhaps, or through more remote contacts with contaminated air or objects. The relationship between rates of winter colds and average winter temperatures suggests that temperature changes do moderate the transmission of colds. Except for one problem. The evidence of Lidwell and his colleagues now suggests that any such moderated transmission may be delayed by as much as two further days. Could it then be that something in our bodies takes two days to respond to temperature changes, and that this something temporarily renders us more or less likely to become infected with a cold virus and to show symptoms two more days after that?

However, before we follow up on these questions it will be useful to move to warmer climates, and back in time, to consider some of the data on colds gathered in a tropical setting. The Lidwell data tell us that in very rural areas there should be no autumn epidemics of colds, and, that the numbers of colds seen should depend on how cold the winter gets. Suppose that a winter night in the tropics only gets as cold as a warm summer evening in England. Would this mean that in a rural and tropical setting almost no colds would be seen all year?

Behind the Passing Warm Fronts: the Virgin Islands, 1929, to Charlottesville, Virginia, 1978

"We noted no correlation between changes in barometric pressure, changes in relative humidity, or total rainfall, and the incidence of colds. The people themselves were convinced that rapid cooling of the body surface such as occurred if they were caught in a night rain when the wind was blowing, or if they worked hard and then cooled their perspiring bodies quickly in the wind, would certainly result in a cold."

— *D. F. Milam and W. G. Smillie, 1931*

In 1929, just before he joined Dr. John Harlan Paul for their year of work together in Spitzbergen, the bacteriologist H. L. Freese worked under the direction of Dr. Daniel (Frank) Milam and the Harvard Professor of Public Health, Dr. Wilson G. Smillie, at a tropical field station in the Caribbean. The station was on the island of St. John, in the western half of the Virgin Islands, at the tiny harbor village of Cruz Bay. In a report of the research undertaken during 1929–30, Milam and Smillie described their project in these words:

> Early in the work, our field staff was put in charge of all medical service on the island, and two small clinics were established where free advice and treatment were given. Through these clinics we obtained a general knowledge of all illness in St. John during the year. In addition a group of 232 persons in the environs of Cruz Bay was selected for special study. By frequent regular house-to-house visits to these persons a fairly accurate census was obtained of all cases of acute colds which occurred.

... St. John, which is typical of the smaller islands of the West Indian group, is mountainous and about 12 miles in length. It has a permanent population of about 700 negroes and three or four whites. In addition, a squad of four marines lives on the beach at Cruz Bay (the port of the island) and runs the radio station. Such communication with the other islands as exists is by means of small sailboats; but there is no active commerce, and movement of population is very slight. A great many of the natives have never left the island, and virtually none of them have ever been out of the tropics. The negroes are descendants of former slaves and dwell in huts scattered about the mountains.[1]

This study of colds was the first in the tropics for which careful records of changing daily weather were kept. Weather changes were always slight at Cruz Bay and the question was, would any of these slight changes produce increases or decreases in colds? Drs. Milam and Smillie thought they might.

Just how small the temperature changes were can best be conveyed by considering the range of temperatures seen in a typical day and in a typical year. On any typical day the high and low temperatures differed by about 12 degrees Fahrenheit (about 7 degrees Celsius).[2] Twelve degrees was also the approximate difference between the highest and lowest average daily maximum (or minimum) seen over a one-year period. Thus the change in daily average temperature across the whole year was almost exactly the same as the average change in temperature over any typical day and night. By contrast, a city like London might typically show daily swings in temperature of 15 degrees Fahrenheit, and occasionally 20 to 25 degrees, and the difference between an average daily temperature in January and an average daily temperature in July could easily be as much as 35 degrees.

Gentle Colds in a Gentle Climate

However, it was not only swings in the temperature that were mild in the West Indies. Common colds tended to be mild too. After a year of research at the Cruz Bay station, one conclusion seemed clear: those colds that did occur were almost always shorter, with fewer symptoms, than colds seen during parallel research in cooler latitudes. Moreover, the total number of colds seen in all 232 participants during the year of study was 184, which is to say the incidence of colds was less than one cold per person per year. This low value, seen again one year later in the research at Longyear City,

Spitzbergen, contrasts with the more familiar incidence of two or three colds per person per year, which is typical for towns and cities in North America and Europe. Still, there were 184 colds that clearly occurred in this tropical setting, and *something* made those colds happen. What was that something?

The colds seen in the vicinity of Cruz Bay did not occur scattered randomly throughout the year. Instead they occurred in four distinct epidemic waves. In the twenty weeks of summer, between June 1 and mid-October, only fourteen colds were seen in total, an incidence that equates with an average of one cold per person every six years. Moreover, there were only three colds seen during the temperate autumn period, between September 1 and October 15, at the time when large cities in more northerly latitudes have their predictable early fall epidemics.

At Cruz Bay the average weekly temperatures had been dropping slowly all during this autumn period. Finally, in mid-October, the average night-time minimum temperature broke from 76° to 73° Fahrenheit, a distinct, if slight, departure from the warmer values seen all summer long. It was then that a small epidemic of colds first broke out. This epidemic died out before the last week of November, and then a much larger epidemic occurred, starting in mid-December. Another epidemic occurred in late February. The fourth epidemic was smaller than the others, and it had occurred earlier, in the spring of the previous year, at the beginning of the study in April.

The epidemic nature of these colds suggested that contagion from infected others was one of their causes. But the average temperatures seen in the weeks marking the start of each epidemic also suggested to Drs. Milam and Smillie that temperature factors were also involved. Thus, the authors reported:

> There is some evidence that the sharp outbreak in December . . . was introduced by a sailor in a mail boat who may have become infected in St. Thomas, the cosmopolitan center of this group of islands. His was the first case in the outbreak. Secondary cases appeared in his family and among his immediate neighbors in Cruz Bay. The disease then spread rapidly in concentric circles up over the mountains to the surrounding settlements, sometimes invading a whole family simultaneously, but more often affecting only one member of a family at first. Then, after 2 or 3 days, other members of the family developed the disease. Thus we have excellent evidence to indicate that this outbreak was spread through direct contact of well persons with an infected individual, the incubation period being 2 to 3 days in each case.

We have evidence also that these colds were due to changes in temperature. There was a distinct drop in the temperature early in December, and the colds occurred coincidentally with the decline in minimum night temperature . . . If the disease had been initiated solely by environmental factors one would have expected that all individuals in all the communities would have developed the disease simultaneously. Since the disease spread in concentric waves from a central point, with definite periods of time intervening, we are forced to conclude that the colds had a common source, probably infectious in nature, spread by direct contact and with a definite incubation period, though it seems most probable that environmental factors, such as relatively low temperature, predisposed to infection.

We noted no correlation between changes in barometric pressure, changes in relative humidity, or total rainfall, and the incidence of colds. The people themselves were convinced that rapid cooling of the body surface such as occurred if they were caught in a night rain when the wind was blowing, or if they worked hard and then cooled their perspiring bodies quickly in the wind, would certainly result in a cold. Our observations give no evidence as to whether or not this factor is of importance [to the] incidence of colds.[3]

Milam and Smillie were being more cautious in their conclusion about temperature effects than perhaps they felt. Earlier Rockefeller research in this same series of studies, research carried out in Labrador and in Alabama, had suggested that cold temperatures probably were linked to the start of some small epidemics. At the conclusion of their report on this Virgin Island study, Milam and Smillie asked:

Is the inciting etiological factor of colds an environmental one or a specific infectious agent? Epidemiological evidence from all three [studies in this series] seems to indicate that it is infectious, and spread by direct contact, with an incubation period of 1 to 3 days. Nevertheless, the evidence is very strong, particularly in Alabama and St. John, that environmental factors play a definite part in the incidence of colds. In each instance, epidemics of colds followed a drop in atmospheric temperature. Furthermore, the seasonal curve of incidence of colds in the tropics is very similar to the seasonal curve in the temperate zone. The differences are of degree only. In the temperate zone, changes in seasonal temperature are more abrupt and colds are more severe; in the tropics, the changes in temperature are mild and the colds are mild. Certainly, then, we cannot rule out environmental influences as at least predisposing if not inciting factors in the production of acute colds.[4]

It is not quite accurate to say, as they do here, that the seasonal curve of incidence in the rural tropics is the same as that in the rural temperate zone. In temperate latitudes, even without the epidemics seen in cities and larger towns, the month of September generally brings a rise in the incidence of colds, whereas in this early tropical study there were almost no colds at all right through until mid-October.[5]

One might speculate that autumn doesn't begin in these islands until long after it has begun farther north, and that the mid-October epidemic corresponded to the beginning of cooler fall weather. But during the year of this study, there was a sharp break in average nighttime low temperatures early in September, marking a temporary end to a long summer period of higher nighttime minima. The average minimum temperature during this week reached the same low values that it was to reach again in mid-October, the week preceding the first epidemic. Moreover, the average daytime high temperatures had been dropping consistently, if slowly, all through August and September. It would have been easy and quite reasonable to declare September the beginning of tropical "autumn." The absence of colds that month, not to mention the absence of any epidemic, however small, does seem significant.

In addition to the September drop in temperature, there was one other occasion during the year of study when temperatures dropped noticeably but no burst of colds followed. This second occasion occurred at the new year, two weeks following the earlier drop in temperature that coincided with the severe, if brief, December epidemic described by Milam and Smillie. Thus, at the time of this later, relatively deep drop in temperature the December epidemic was waning, and was nearly finished. Over the whole year then there were six occasions when one might have declared a noticeable if mild drop in recent temperatures, and four of these six were marked by bursts of common cold activity. At no time were any bouts of colds seen following periods of rising (or even steadily warm) temperatures, as for instance were to be seen in the Amsterdam data for September 1925 gathered by J. J. van Loghem. These findings suggest that falling temperatures may often lower our general resistance to common colds, however temporarily, so that if and when a few colds start, triggered by virus introduced from outside the community, these colds can capitalize on the lowered resistance and spread rapidly.

Two other conclusions were suggested by this interesting study of colds in a tropical setting. First, it seemed that the milder the temperatures, the milder were the colds. Of course, one might cite opposing findings. For instance the *cocongo* that Heyerdahl described on Easter Island might represent an exception to this conclusion, but as noted before, the *cocongo* probably is not a true common cold. Also, the colds that develop in Polaris submarines, in an environment of mild and hardly variable temperatures, rarely seem to be severe, yet they can hang on for a considerable period of time. These too might contradict the idea that an absence of chill, and a warm environment, will mitigate the effects of cold viruses.

Then, secondly, we can also see in Milam and Smillie's study apparent confirmation of Lidwell's much later suggestion that September cold epidemics may be dependent on the size of the population in question. In this rural and tropical setting, having only a small population, just three isolated colds were seen prior to October 15. Why the Lidwell population-size effect should occur, and only in early autumn, is not at all clear. But there is one nearly universal event in the earliest weeks of September that may be of relevance. In the northern hemisphere, schools open for the new term at this time, and large numbers of children are reassembled in close indoor contact. Milam and Smillie did not report on whether the small native population of Cruz Bay attended school in 1929, but it seems unlikely that they did given the description of the informal, subsistence lifestyles of the people on the island.

Not-So-Gentle Colds in Gentle Climates

For thirty years after 1929, no further detailed research was carried out on colds in tropical settings. Then, between 1965 and 1968, three new studies were reported, investigating outbreaks of colds and other viral illnesses occurring in the tropics. The first of these next studies contrasted cold incidences in forty-three families (314 people) living in Trinidad with those in fourteen families (fifty-nine people) living in Sheffield, England.[6] Despite certain problems with the design of this study, including uncertainties introduced by some of the small numbers and the different family compositions in the two countries, one finding was clear. In the tropical setting (Trinidad) the incidence of colds for 1961–62 was every bit as high (reported as 5.7 colds per person per year) as that seen in North America and Europe. The timing was different, however. Colds in Trinidad were observed more often in the warm summer rainy season (in June) and not in mild and sunny winter season.

A second study was carried out between 1961 and 1964 in Paraiso, a town in the tropics of the Panama Canal Zone.[7] The people observed in this study were 575 native Panamanians belonging to ninety-two different families. And in this Paraiso study too, the notable epidemics of colds occurred just after the onset of the warm summer rains (in May), a time that also coincided with the start of school for the children in the town. The highest incidences of colds were seen in the summer and fall of 1962, but much lower incidences were observed throughout 1961 and 1964. Overall, however, the incidence of colds seems to have been less than one cold per person per year.[8] There might then be some reason to question the Trinidad data suggesting that colds are as likely in the tropics as in the temperate zone. Except, a third study, also carried out in the early 1960s, suggested that at least in major urban settings colds might after all be about equally prevalent in the tropics and in temperate latitudes.

This third study was perhaps the most interesting and informative of the three. It was carried out by a research team from the University of Wisconsin that monitored and compared students attending two universities: the University of Wisconsin and the University of the Philippines.[9] The subjects in this study were all those students who elected to seek help for a respiratory illness at their local campus health service. Consequently, many minor common colds were not seen and not counted in this research. And a great many of the respiratory illnesses that were seen were not just common colds but included influenzas and other diseases as well. Still, the comparisons in this study were highly suggestive and again they implied that weather factors were correlated with respiratory illness in general, and probably with common colds in particular.

The Cruz Bay study had suggested that colds in the rural tropics are less severe than colds in rural temperate latitudes. But the Philippines data, gathered between 1960 and 1964 on the large subtropical campus at Quezon City outside Manila, showed that some colds, and many other respiratory illnesses, were just as severe and just as common as were those similar illnesses seen during Wisconsin winters in North America.[10] In fact, infirmary admission rates for severe respiratory diseases appeared to be nearly twice as high in the Philippines as on the Wisconsin campus. Some of this large difference might be due to cultural differences between the two campus groups, leading to different levels of use of the health services. Even so, however, the true Philippine incidence appears to have been higher than the true Wisconsin incidence. So much then for any theory that warm climates *always* produce benign and mild colds or other respiratory diseases.

A seasonal pattern of respiratory illnesses seen in the Philippines was clear in this study, but again it was quite different from the pattern seen with common colds at Cruz Bay in the Virgin Islands. At Quezon City, as in Trinidad and Panama, respiratory disease was most common between June and September, during the summer period of heavy rains. Average air temperatures are lowest not during these rains, however, but during the dry mid-winter months of January and February. Yet illness rates during these winter months, when Wisconsin students were experiencing considerable illness, were quite low in the Philippines.

Colds in the urban Philippines seem correlated then with rainy weather, and not necessarily with the coldest weather, although with the arrival of the rains there are also associated drops in average temperature, much like those that were to be seen at Cruz Bay later in the year, during autumn. Moreover, the arrival of the rains is generally associated with another significant event on campus: the beginning of the academic year. In one year of this four-year study, epidemics of all respiratory disease peaked just after the start of school in June (and just after the arrival of the heaviest rains); in two years the peaks came about ten weeks after school had begun (once with the arrival of the heaviest rains); and in another year the peak came about fourteen weeks after school had begun (associated with a second, but low, peak in rainfall for that year.) The conclusion favored by the authors of this research was that:

> The seasonal patterns of respiratory infections revealed the highest incidence during the rainy season in the Philippines and during the cold winter months in Wisconsin. Inclement weather is a common denominator, promoting crowding indoors and the ready exchange of pathogens.[11]

Changing Weather Versus Changing Behavior?

For the authors of this study, then, it is not so much the weather per se that turns on colds; instead, it is what stormy weather does to people's social behavior that is important. The possible relationship, between school openings in particular and the September epidemic of colds so often observed in Europe and North America, has been the object of speculation for many

years. Epidemiological studies established early on that the common cold
is most common among young children between one and five years of
age, and is still very frequent among school children between the ages of
six and twelve.[12] Moreover, primary school teachers and mothers of
school-age children typically show higher incidences of colds than do
other women of the same age. The fact that *preschool* children have so very
many colds suggests that school attendance is not the only reason for
higher cold incidences in children, but schools may indeed provide a
reservoir of infection. As we shall presently see, many of the colds suffered
by preschool children, if these are in fact contaged colds, appear to be
introduced into the home by older, school-age siblings.

It was natural then that sooner or later the relative importance of
school openings and autumn storms would need to be examined, to see
why September cold epidemics begin when they do. One major research
study undertook to do just that. This study was carried out over a sixteen-
year period, in Charlottesville, Virginia, by Jack M. Gwaltney, Jr. and
J. Owen Hendley.[13] Their study group consisted of approximately 325
insurance company employees who worked together in one large office
complex. More than half of the participants in this study worked in one
very large, partially partitioned room. Most of the participants were
younger than thirty-five years of age, and just over half of them were
women. Half these employees had children, and about 30 percent had
children of school age.[14]

In fourteen of the sixteen years of this study a distinct peak of colds
occurred among the company employees during the month of September.
In eight of those fourteen years, this peak of new illness occurred from
eleven to fourteen days following the first opening of most schools in the
area.[15] In at least one year, however, the sharp peak of colds came very
early in September, before some of the schools had even opened, only four
days after the first schools had opened. Because even four days is not
enough time to consolidate any kind of new epidemic of colds, in this
year at least, it seems safe to conclude that the school opening did not create
the epidemic of colds among in the adults of this study.

Weather changes were generally distinct each autumn, so the transition
from summer weather to fall weather, produced by the arrival of a storm
front, was not hard to define. Thus, the arrival of autumn weather (the
"weather event") was defined in this study as the first day in any period of
up to three days over which the daily maximum temperature fell by at
least 14 degrees Fahrenheit (7.8°C) and the daily range of temperatures

between at least one adjacent daily maximum and nightly minimum was less than 10 degrees Fahrenheit (5.5°C). Single weather events meeting these criteria occurred in September during twelve of the sixteen years studied. One additional year produced two such weather events, and one further year produced three of them. In two of the sixteen years, no such weather event occurred at any time during September.

It is of special interest that one of the two years in which no peak of colds was observed in the adults of this study was also one of the only two years in which no weather event occurred. The other year in which no official weather event was recorded came very close to meeting the definitional criteria for such an event, however. (In this year, a drop in temperature of 20 degrees Fahrenheit occurred, but the daily range in temperature was 4 degrees more than the required 10 degrees maximum.) An illness peak was observed in this year, but it was not noted when this peak occurred relative to the unofficial weather event.

It is also of special interest that the only year in which the peak in colds came on very early in September, before some schools had opened, was also the only year in which the first weather event occurred unusually early, before the end of August. In that year the peak in colds followed this weather event by eleven days, while it led the opening of some schools by four days. However, in two other years among the sixteen studied, the peak in common colds occurred well before the first defined weather event, so that in those years too, if weather factors had any role to play at all it was a very subtle one. Such are the complications that make the life of an epidemiologist "interesting."

In nine of the sixteen years studied at Charlottesville, the peak in colds followed the most recent weather event by five to eleven days. Even five days seems rather too brief an interval to attribute to the results of weather, since three generations of spreading colds would normally take at least six days to occur, and an epidemic produced by contagion generally implies rather more than three generations of geometrically increasing transmissions. Still, that clustering (of weather events and peaks of illness) between five and eleven days would be highly unlikely if it were caused merely by chance. Consequently, if an epidemic of colds were in the process of developing, then weather changes might well have acted to speed the peak of that epidemic some five to eight days later, and contagion, if it occurred, may have been of minor significance in creating the epidemic.

The same timing considerations apply of course to school openings and to their effects on later epidemics of colds. The clustering of epidemic peaks observed eleven to fourteen days after schools opened, during eight of the sixteen years studied (eight of fourteen years showing illness peaks) is also highly unlikely if it were merely the product of chance. Dr. Gwaltney noted the frequent occurrence of a weather event soon after school had opened, followed by an epidemic peak occurring approximately a week later, and he wrote:

> Thus, it appears that temporal relationships exist between both [a] the opening of local schools and the occurrence of weather phenomena resulting from the passage of certain frontal systems, and [b] peaks in respiratory illness rates in the Charlottesville population. While if true that the events are [temporally] related, it cannot be assumed that they are causally related. However, these observations, combined with the findings previously discussed, can be interpreted in the following way for the development of an hypothesis . . . School opening in September reassembles the viral reservoir and leads to an increase in infection rates . . . After the school term has started, the occurrence of cool, rainy days associated with the dense cloud cover of a frontal passage keeps children indoors for recess and after school play, resulting in close contact and facilitating spread of the virus. This gives added impetus to the epidemic, resulting in an additional increase in the infection rate.[16]

Gwaltney is suggesting then that it isn't cold weather per se that makes September colds more likely (that is, it isn't the falling temperatures affecting our immune systems or viral potency), but rather that the falling temperatures are associated with new forms of behavior that increase the opportunities for infection to occur. There is much to recommend this hypothesis, and we shall encounter more supportive data shortly. But the data from Cruz Bay are puzzling in this regard, and it is well to note them again now. It seems somewhat unlikely that in the West Indies the moderately cooler nights associated with the start of the four cold epidemics seen by Milam and Smillie changed the behavior of the natives, or were associated with any significant change in patterns of social contact. Thus, the effects of temperature changes on the common cold may not be simple.

The most obvious way for temperature effects to occur, which could explain the findings both from Cruz Bay and from Charlottesville, would be if catching a chill makes us more susceptible to infection, or if it makes us more able to produce highly infective virus to be spread to others. And of course the most direct way to test hypotheses such as these would be to attempt to produce experimental colds in volunteers, some of whom had, and some of whom had not, just been chilled. Recall that Schade attempted a "natural" version of this sort of experiment in 1915 when he observed soldiers in the trenches during bitter weathers and contrasted their illness rate with soldiers who had been kept behind the lines in barracks. What he found was that colds were more frequent in the soldiers exposed to chilling duty, but this was reported only for the time after these soldiers were rotated back to their barracks following four days of service in the trenches.

Perhaps then, with the cooperation of civilians who volunteer to be artificially infected with cold virus, the role of changing body and air temperatures could be clarified by a few well-designed experiments. And so, toward this end, we shall leave epidemiology for a time and turn our attention to certain very interesting *experimental* investigations into the nature of cold viruses and their various infectious attributes.

PART III

VIRAL VISITATIONS

10

Shivering, Sneezing, and Healthy Volunteers: Munich, 1914, to Houston, 1967

"Mankind collectively always welcomes simplified and unitarian explanations of complex happenings: the germ theory was one of the greatest of all scientific simplifications."[1]

— *G. T. Stewart, 1968*

Following upon the stunning bacterial discoveries and demonstrations made by Pasteur and Koch in the nineteenth century, most people working in medical intelligence at the dawn of the twentieth century understandably assumed that the common cold too would soon be revealed to be caused by bacterium. Names already awaited the expected discovery of this cold-causing bacterium, and in due course more than one such discovery was announced. The enthusiastically named *Micrococcus catarrhalis* and the *Bacillus rhinitis* already had been isolated prior to 1900.[2]

Unfortunately, however, bacteria such as these were soon found to be absent in the nasal regions of many people suffering colds. Moreover, when these bacteria were introduced into the noses of healthy volunteers they did not seem to trigger many, if any, colds. Thus, there was always reason to doubt that a bacterial cause of common colds had yet been discovered.

In 1916, the state of medical knowledge of the time was summed up as follows by George B. Foster, Jr., Harvard Professor of Preventive Medicine and Hygiene, and himself one of those who was interested in doing experimental work to look at some possible causes of the common cold. Foster wrote:

Numerous attempts have been made to demonstrate the specific cause of the extremely prevalent catarrhal affections of the upper respiratory tract, popularly known as "common colds." In reviewing the literature, however, one is struck by the multiplicity of organisms to which an etiologic relation has been ascribed . . . Some investigators believe that micro-organisms bear no relation whatever to the causation of colds; but that many factors — wet and cold, drafts, irritating vapors, overheated rooms, worry, fatigue, sexual excess, dietetic errors, alcohol, and what not — enter into the etiology. Still another group takes the stand that a number of conditions — notably chilling, sudden changes in temperature, and fatigue — act as predisposing factors by lowering resistance, and thus [these conditions] pave the way for infection by micro-organisms commonly believed to be present normally in the nasal cavities.

In short, present knowledge of the etiology of the common cold is in a most chaotic state.[3]

What Passes From a Nose and Through a "Candle"?

The first experimental evidence that the common cold might be caused not simply by chilling, but by an identifiable organism far smaller than any known bacterium, was reported in 1914 by the Munich researcher W. Kruse.[4] Kruse took nasal secretions from donors suffering natural colds, then diluted this fluid with saline, homogenized it, and finally filtered the mixture through a small Berkefeld "candle," or ceramic filter. This filtering action removed all solids larger than a certain very small size. When the resulting clear filtrate was cultured, no bacteria grew. But when a few drops of this filtrate were put into each nostril of twelve volunteers, within one to three days four of the twelve developed colds. In a second experiment, repeating this procedure, Kruse gave drops of the filtrate to thirty-six volunteers. Between one and four days later, fifteen of these people came down with colds. Kruse concluded that the infectious cause of the common cold was a "filterable virus," to which he gave the name *Aphanozoum coryzæ*.[5]

The word "virus" did not mean to Kruse all that it implies today. In 1898 the Latin word *virus* had been selected by Martinus Beijerinck to describe what appeared to be a completely new type of non-bacterial disease agent, one which Dimitrii Ivanovsky had recently discovered in carefully filtered juices from tobacco leaves suffering from what is called "mosaic disease." *Virus* in Latin simply means "poison" or "venom," and its use by Beijerinck implied a liquid chemical agent at least as much as it implied any new form of living organism. Beijerinck recognized, however, that the agent causing the tobacco mosaic disease seemed to multiply like any other infectious agent when introduced into healthy tobacco leaves, and for this reason he also referred to the filterable virus in Latin as a "living contagious liquid" or *contagium vivum fluidum.*

Then in 1935 it was discovered that viruses must be neither liquid nor living things in the usual sense because the tobacco mosaic virus can be crystallized just like some inert chemical molecules can. It is now known that viruses differ dramatically from living bacteria in that viruses have no metabolic life of their own. Viruses do not move themselves, nor do they divide themselves to reproduce like bacteria do. Instead, they are little more than latent genetic blueprints, a kind of software, ready to subvert certain cells to doing cellular work of a new sort, including the work of mass-producing more viral particles ("virions") that can be sent off to infect and subvert new cells. Although viruses contain nothing living, to be "killed," much like little time bombs they can be prevented by the immune system from firing, or they can be removed, defused, or disassembled. However, Kruse's work in 1914 suggested only that the cause of the common cold was an infectious poison (a virus) still remaining in well-filtered, bacteria-free nasal liquids drawn from persons currently suffering from a cold.

By 1916, when France, England, and America were at war with Germany, Kruse's work in Munich (soon to be repeated there by H. Dold[6]) had begun to provoke great interest abroad. Harvard's Dr. Foster, who was by this time a captain in the U.S. Army Medical Corps, carried out some experiments of his own, very much like those of Kruse, with the assistance of a number of soldier volunteers.[7] In the winter of 1915–16, Foster collected nasal secretions from three cold sufferers, including himself, and filtered them using the same procedure that Kruse had followed. He incubated the filtrate in a culture medium under both aerobic and anaerobic conditions, and he found no bacterial growth. But when he put drops of the filtrate in the noses of ten volunteers, within a few days seven of the ten showed the unmistakable symptoms of a common cold.

Having produced this syndrome with an apparently sterile filtrate drawn originally from the noses of cold sufferers, Foster then took the next step of attempting to grow the organism responsible for transmitting the disease in test tubes in the laboratory. If the organism was not a bacterium, and if it would not grow in standard bacterial cultures, perhaps it was like the organisms responsible for rabies and polio, organisms that also passed through the smallest filters of the day, and that recently had been successfully cultivated in a special medium developed by Noguchi and his colleagues at the Rockefeller Institute in New Jersey. Foster tried a number of variations on the Noguchi medium and found one that seemed to produce a fine crop of suspected cold germs. In any event, something seemed to be growing in the test tubes because there was a spreading cloudiness to be seen in the culture medium. Foster looked closely at what he had grown, and reported:

> Cultures examined under the dark-field microscope showed myriads of extremely active, minute bodies occurring singly, in pairs and in agglomerations of varying magnitude. The bodies were so active and so minute that a definite idea of their morphology could not be formed. Some showed to and fro progression, and others exhibited a tumbling type of motion — end over end.[8]

Small samples from these cultures were used to seed new subcultures until four generations had been produced and the original nasal fluid had been diluted many thousands of times. When Foster tried inoculating eleven volunteer soldiers with drops from these highly diluted subcultures — with their many microscopic "bodies" — ten of the eleven came down with colds in one or two days. And when subsequent nasal washings from these ill men were filtered by the now standard method, and then cultured as before, the same minute bodies were seen to grow in the culture. Foster was understandably persuaded that he was very probably hot on the trail of the elusive cause of the common cold.

It now seems clear that what Foster saw in his microscope was a very small species of bacillus of a type that cannot be stained using the traditional "Gram's method" — this would make it one of the so-called anaerobic gram-negative bacteria. Before very long, however, it became possible to filter out even these bacteria, and also to inoculate volunteers with them. The gram-negative bacteria did not seem to produce colds in such experiments, and they were not always found in the nasal washings from those who had colds. More impressive, nasal filtrates free of even gram-negative bacteria still appeared to produce experimental colds when given to volunteers.[9] Thus, whatever may be the germ that causes colds, it appeared to be very small indeed.

Given a modern understanding of cold viruses, it is somewhat curious that Foster's fourth-generation subcultures of gram-negative bacteria produced any colds at all in his volunteers. So far as is now known, true cold viruses will not reproduce in the environment Foster created for growing his filter-passing bacteria. And eventually there was so much dilution of the original viral sample that few if any of the original viral particles should have been expected to remain in the subculture. Moreover, after Foster's work, other experimenters tried to repeat the Kruse procedure, and to transmit colds with filtered, dilute nasal washings taken from cold sufferers, and many of them failed to find any evidence for successful transmission of colds.[10] Sometimes the experimental procedure seemed to work, and sometimes it didn't. The conclusion suggested by some experimentalists was that something other than a living organism probably triggers colds. Perhaps a chemical toxin does, or perhaps even one of the constituents of the Noguchi medium itself.

Complete and Incomplete Passes on the Nasal Field

One of the facts that complicated efforts to learn about the sources of common colds is that for a very long time no rabbit, or rat, or test-tube medium could be used in laboratory experiments to stand in for living human nasal cells and show that cold germs were there and were multiplying. Animal care workers at zoos, however, had long known that chimpanzees often catch colds if their infected human caretakers have colds. In due course this fact came to the attention of Dr. A. R. Dochez and his colleagues at Columbia University in New York, who undertook a series of studies of colds in chimpanzees that were quarantined in fully aseptic conditions, and also in chimpanzees who were exposed to unscrubbed caretakers and to other chimps.

It was soon observed by Dochez that no spontaneous colds ever occurred among the chimps in quarantine, though many such were observed among the unquarantined animals, despite the fact that caretakers who had colds always wore surgical masks when working with the unquarantined animals.[11] Since the living conditions for both groups of animals are kept toxin-free, the difference in spontaneous cold incidence must be due to an infectious organism rather than from an accidental encounter with a toxic substance. When experimenting with the transmission of colds to human volunteers, then, Dochez was led to standardize a quarantine procedure, always allowing five days for any incubating infection to appear in the person before he began to test his filtered materials on each volunteer.

Dochez was the first to report that human beings who expect to catch colds in an experiment, who in fact have volunteered to get colds for the advancement of medical knowledge, often become inappropriately convinced that they have a cold when in all probability they do not. Dochez wrote:

> It is very easy for an individual who is being used for a transmission experiment to believe that he has a mild cold although objective evidence is extremely slight or absent. Where, as in the beginning of our work, volunteers believed that we were trying to produce colds, they were self-convinced occasionally that they were suffering from a mild infection. This was much easier of belief since the filtrate in practically all the cases, negative and positive, causes some slight stuffiness of the nose, a little sneezing and occasionally slight headache.
>
> Very early in the work we recognized this willingness of our subjects to oblige us and began taking measure[s] to avoid this source of error. By various ruses, [such] as nasal injections of sterile broth, collection of nasal washings for culture and equivocal statements, we were enabled to keep the subjects in ignorance.
>
> . . . Case H4 is worthy of note as an example in this connection. It was apparent very early that this individual was more or less unreliable and from the start it was possible to keep him in the dark regarding our procedure. He had inconspicuous symptoms after his test injection of sterile broth and no more striking results from the cold filtrate, until an assistant, on the second day after injection, inadvertently referred to his failure to contract a cold. That evening and night the subject reported severe symptomatology, including sneezing, cough, sore throat and stuffiness of the nose. The next morning he was told that he had been misinformed in regard to the nature of the filtrate and his symptoms subsided within the hour. It is important to note that there was an entire absence of objective pathological changes.[12]

This case brings an interesting complication to questions concerning the causes of common colds. It had long been asserted by some that colds in particular, but also illnesses in general, are often the products of belief and expectation, or a lack of proper faith, or poor mental hygiene. But many people, and most of the medical scientists working in the shadow of Pasteur, did not hold such a view and they looked almost exclusively to outside pathogens as the causes for disease. Nearly a century later it is still not clear how or even whether psychological factors enter into the disease picture for common colds. There is currently ambiguous scientific evidence, supporting a variety of hypotheses on this question.[13]

By 1930, however, Dochez and his colleagues, with their very careful experimental work, had persuaded many (apparently including Dr. J. Harlan Paul) that the agent responsible for cold infections was probably a filterable virus. In four out of nine human volunteers, Dochez was able to demonstrate the clear transmission of common colds from carefully filtered liquids in which it was reasonable to assume that only viruses might have remained.

As the years passed, and more and more experimental trials were carried out by more and more experimenters, it began to appear that in trials of infective cold viruses, even when many of the volunteers in a study apparently had minimal antibody against the virus being used, and even when the amount of virus given was many times more than what is typically an infecting dose, only about 35 to 45 percent of volunteers developed colds. Even more curious, an additional 30 to 40 percent of volunteers in such trials, while showing no cold symptoms whatsoever, did become infected, and virus could be shown to be at work in their bodies. Virus from these so-called "silent infections" can even be harvested and sometimes they will produce active colds in others. Yet volunteers with these "subclinical" colds continue to remain symptom free. They are completely unaware that they are infected and that they may be contagious to others. Finally, in every experimental trial of any size, invariably, there were 20 to 30 percent of volunteers who were not even infected by the high dose of virus that seems so infective to others.

These findings point to a deep puzzle, one having important implications. They tell us that the observable symptoms of a common cold are not simply the inevitable mechanical side effects resulting from an infection of the cells lining the nose and throat, because some of these infections don't create any symptoms. What then does cause those oh-so-familiar symptoms? It could be that cold symptoms result from the many different ways that our bodies can respond to the presence of these viruses, and fight them off. It looks very much as if on successive trials with the same group of volunteers it is different individuals on the different trials who are the ones to avoid infection, or, although infected, who successfully avoid the symptoms of their infections. So far as we know then, it probably isn't just that some people get symptomatic colds most of the time while others get subclinical colds most of the time.

Colds Have Their Families

The picture has become more interesting still with the discovery that there is not one family of common cold viruses but instead there are several families, each with its own distinct molecular architecture and unique genetic instructions for coopting the work of the cells it infects. Most colds are caused by viruses belonging to one of eight major types, of which the most common type is the so-called *rhinovirus*.[14] (*Rhino* comes from the Greek, and means "pertaining to the nose.") The number of distinct rhinoviruses known by 1990 approached one hundred, and that number was growing slowly each year. Antibodies created after an infection with a particular rhinovirus are generally specific to that one rhinovirus only. Thus, a vaccine protecting against the common cold is very unlikely in the near future because of the very large number of different cold viruses, known and unknown, that would need to be included in such a vaccine.

In addition to the many rhinoviruses, the symptoms of colds are frequently caused by various coronaviruses, by adenoviruses, respiratory syncytial viruses, coxsackieviruses, and echo viruses. These constitute the most "common" common cold viruses. Other diseases too can, on rarer occasions, present as a simple cold, including diseases provoked by the polio virus, by the meningitis virus, by influenza viruses, parainfluenza viruses, and others. Even bacteria, such as the streptococcus, will sometimes produce cold symptoms. Thus, the common cold represents a limited and common bodily response to a wide variety of agents. Why should this be? One implication is, again, that the common cold may be the consequence of a certain kind of immune response to infections of the nose and throat, and not the direct consequence of a particular infection per se.

No one has yet determined how different individuals actually respond to natural contacts with circulating cold viruses, or even how they respond to periodic experimental exposures to the same virus. This is because it is still very difficult to detect and to isolate some cold viruses; and it is still considerable trouble to sample, culture, and identify any virus in two or three nasal washings from the same person each week over a long period of time. Yet until virus-monitoring work of this type is carried out continuously on a number of volunteers, over a period of three or more years, we cannot be certain just what individual differences there may be in susceptibility to subclinical (invisible) infections with common cold viruses, and to repeated exposures to the same virus.

There is some clear suggestion that resistance to infection and resistance to developing symptoms following infection may wax and wane in individuals just as our natural language about colds seems to assume. People speak of their resistance being "low" or "high," and often they attribute the present level of their resistance to their fatigue status, to the current stress status in their lives, to dietary considerations, and often to recent exposure to cold and chilling environments. The epidemiological evidence, from the early studies of van Loghem to the subsequent work of Hope Simpson, Lidwell, Milam and Smillie, and Gwaltney, all suggested that somehow, sometimes, cold and chill could make a real difference and would trigger something that increased the likelihood of colds. Thus, experimental tests of this idea were an obvious next step, to help clarify just how and when significant temperature stresses might be important in increasing infections and colds.

Common Colds Come to the Wiltshire Downs

The first modern experimental project concerned with the possible effects of thermoregulatory stress upon a person's resistance to catching colds was carried out shortly after the Second World War, just outside Salisbury, England. These experimental trials were held at The Common Cold Research Unit, a division of the Medical Research Council (MRC) of Great Britain. Common cold research at Salisbury began in 1946, at "Harvard Hospital." This hospital complex was donated to England by doctors at Harvard University early in 1941, in anticipation of severe infectious epidemics among the troops and civilians in the war zone. It was all arranged prior to the official entry of America into the war, although American participation was expected. At the end of the war, this cluster of Quonset huts, equipped with a fine laboratory and built to allow for the comfortable isolation of people with infectious diseases, was turned over to the MRC of Great Britain and dedicated to research on the nature and source of the common cold. It was here, after long, hard work and some rather lucky accidents, that the techniques were finally developed for culturing cold viruses outside of the human nose and throat, in continuously growing cell cultures, in the laboratory.

Harvard Hospital was built atop a large hill on the southern edge of the town of Salisbury, overlooking the local Wiltshire downs. From the very first research trials carried out there with human volunteers, strict quarantine of all participants, in small "flats," each housing two or three persons, was always standard practice. Members of each quarantine group had to observe the locally famous "thirty-foot rule" when they were on the grounds of the Unit, or when they took one of the approved walks over the surrounding downs. No one from outside their own living unit was allowed to approach closer than thirty feet, and the residents of Salisbury and the surrounding villages soon became accustomed to strangers who fled at their approach or who forbade them to come closer when met upon a path.

Trials at Salisbury were begun every two weeks and usually lasted ten or eleven days. Volunteers came to the Unit from all over England, and from all walks of life. They were given no more than a round-trip rail ticket from their point of origin in England, and a few shillings a day for necessities. Of course they also received free room and board, lots of quiet, and the chance to contribute to the advancement of medical knowledge. With help from the British media, the Unit soon had plenty of volunteers, especially during the summer vacation months. By the time the MRC closed the unit in 1989 there was a long list of volunteers who had come back for repeated visits, attending multiple trials.

Participants at Salisbury usually arrived the day before the trial officially started. Isolation began following a communal lunch the next day, at which was given an explanation from the staff concerning the particular nature of this trial together with its rules of procedure and its schedule of examinations. On the third day of the trial, each participant was "challenged" with nose drops containing either cold virus or an inactive placebo. Neither the volunteers nor the regular medical staff were aware of who had been challenged with virus and who with placebo until after the conclusion of each trial. Any cold seen prior to noon of the fourth day was usually considered to be a wild cold, caught prior to challenge, and it was not counted in the results of the trial.

Does Experimental Chilling Protect Against Experimental Colds?

In the late 1940s, a set of trials at Salisbury was devoted to examining the effects of chilling on susceptibility to colds. In 1951, Dr. Christopher Andrewes (later Sir Christopher), director of the Unit, described these trials as follows:

> We put to the test the practically universal idea that chilling induces colds, or at least increases one's chances of catching a cold. Three groups of six volunteers each were used in this experiment. One lot received a dose of

dilute virus, calculated not to produce many colds. The next lot were given no virus but were put through a severe chilling treatment: that is, they had a hot bath and were then made to stand about in a droughty passage in wet bathing suits for half an hour, by which time they felt pretty chilly and miserable. They were further made to wear wet socks for the rest of the morning. A third group received the dilute virus plus the chilling treatment. On one occasion, in a variation of the experiment, the chilling consisted in a walk in the rain, following which the subjects were not allowed to dry themselves for half an hour and were made to stay in unheated flats.

Now this experiment was performed three times. In not one instance did chilling alone produce a cold. And in two out of the three tests chilling plus inoculation with the virus actually produced fewer colds than inoculation alone; in the other the chilled people who also got virus did have more colds than the "virus only" group. So we failed to convince ourselves that chilling either induces or favors colds. Perhaps under appropriate conditions it does so, but this has never been proved, to our knowledge, by any controlled experiment.[15]

A much larger set of experimental trials on the question of temperature stress and common colds was carried out a few years later in Chicago, Illinois. The full set of Chicago studies was first published to the world in 1960, and at the time these studies created quite a stir. The experiments were carried out by a team of doctors, researchers, and nurses, under the general leadership of George G. Jackson, and with the assistance of a large number of volunteers who were primarily college students.[16] Jackson and his colleagues did not quarantine their student volunteers. Instead, in these studies, volunteers reported to the laboratory, where they too were challenged with material dropped into their noses (a solution containing either cold virus or saline placebo) and then they were free to continue with their normal schedule of daily events. Each subsequent day volunteers were checked, by a person who had no knowledge of what material had been given to each volunteer, for any cold symptoms that might have developed. Thus, as at Salisbury, neither the volunteer nor the research assistants in the laboratory knew whether or not a common cold might be expected in any given case.

The Chicago experiments on the effects of chilling involved four groups of volunteers. Members of two of the four groups spent four hours scantily clad in a room where the temperature was 60 degrees Fahrenheit (15.6°C) with 80 percent relative humidity, and then they received the "challenge" material (nose drops). The chilling treatment produced marked shivering and discomfort among both groups of participants. Members of one of these two chilled groups received a viral challenge, while members of the other chilled group received the placebo control material. Two similar groups of volunteers who were not chilled also received viral challenge and placebo, respectively. In all, 378 volunteers were chilled and challenged with cold virus, and 136 were chilled and challenged with placebo. A total of nearly two thousand volunteers were tested in the two unchilled conditions over a five-year period while taking part in other experiments.

In the two groups of volunteers receiving placebo (no virus), the results were dramatically clear. Over the seven days during which each person was monitored following challenge, about 11.0 percent of the unchilled subjects (those kept warm prior to challenge) developed natural colds, while about 10.5 percent of the experimentally chilled subjects developed natural colds. These values are as close to identical as chance differences are likely to produce, and they tell us that, at least in Chicago during the years of these chill studies, just being chilled did *not* increase the risk of catching wild colds circulating outside the laboratory.

In the two groups of volunteers challenged with active cold virus inside the laboratory, the results were also dramatically clear, and they mirrored the results that Andrewes reported from two out of his three smaller trials at Salisbury. In Chicago, during the seven days that each person was monitored following viral challenge, about 32 percent of the unchilled subjects developed colds. But among the artificially chilled subjects only 26 percent developed colds. It was as if chilling the participants helped some of them to *resist* catching colds, or perhaps it helped them to avoid having symptoms when they did become infected.

This 6-percent reduction in colds seen in the members of the chilled-and-challenged group is not easily attributable to chance or to accidents of sampling. Moreover, the 6-percent difference between these two groups represents something like a 22-percent reduction in the take rate of colds produced by the active viruses given in the laboratory, over and above those colds that would have occurred anyway due to exposures to virus outside the laboratory. This group difference, then, is both surprising and significant. One begins to wonder how so many of the epidemiological studies could have suggested that cold and chill are associated with higher numbers of colds, when the experimental work very clearly was suggesting the opposite. Could the Chicago studies have been wrong, or flawed?

Another, and more sophisticated, experimental look at the effects of chilling was carried out some years later in Houston, Texas.[17] The volunteers in this study were all prison inmates who had no detectable serum antibody to the common cold virus chosen for use in the experiment. Volunteers were chilled in either one of two ways: by standing around for two hours in a cold room, clad only in light underwear, or by spending five hours immersed in a tank of water warmed to 90 degrees Fahrenheit (32°C). The former procedure produced shivering, discomfort, and a slight compensatory rise in body temperature due to shivering. Immersion in the water at less than body temperature produced no discomfort, but eventually it considerably lowered internal body temperatures.

Participants in the Houston experiments were placed at random into one of two groups, and all participants were then challenged with cold viruses. Members of one group were chilled at some time during the experiment (sometimes more than once), usually just after challenge. Members of the other group were kept warm instead of being chilled. In this research two additional, rather different kinds of responses were monitored on each participant. First, as usual, note was taken whether or not a cold developed in each volunteer. But second, the effects of chilling upon a number of bodily processes that might reflect the status of the immune system were also monitored. Of the many variables examined this way, only one showed any change due to chilling; in particular, a temporary drop was seen in the numbers of circulating white blood cells following chilling. This drop was observed among already infected volunteers, but not among volunteers who were not infected.[18]

However, the numbers of colds seen in the two groups of chilled and unchilled volunteers were nearly equal in this experiment. There were slightly more colds seen among the chilled volunteers, but this greater number of colds was well within the range to be expected by chance if the two conditions did not truly differ in their tendency to elicit colds. And chilled volunteers were no more likely than unchilled volunteers to develop complications such as a secondary bacterial infection, in those colds they did catch.

Why Would These Experimental Data Appear to Contradict Some of the Earlier Epidemiological Data?

Each one of the three experimental studies carried out to look at the role of chill in provoking common colds, in Wiltshire, in Illinois, and in Texas, strongly implied that being chilled does not increase the likelihood of becoming infected and developing cold symptoms. While this outcome agrees with the epidemiological work of Paul and Freese at Longyear City in 1930, it is still very puzzling in light of all the other work we have considered. True, the epidemiological evidence always implied that any link there may be between temperature change and cold incidences is evanescent, and never dramatically clear. But the experimental evidence implies something far stronger. It implies that the link is nonexistent, or to be more conservative about it, that any existing links there may be are indirect links. Perhaps then something else, something correlated with changes in temperature, but not the chill factor itself, is responsible for the increased numbers of colds that follow.

Recall that, on the basis of their Charlottesville data, the University of Virginia researchers suggested a possible link between school recesses held indoors during cold, inclement weather and subsequent cold epidemics. Gwaltney had earlier suggested a theory of colds very much in accord with this model. The authors of the Philippines study did too. And yet, if colder weather changes our behavior, and if changing our behavior is what actually increases the risk of colds, then why did Milam and Smillie find colds more prevalent following mild tropical cooling spells at Cruz Bay, when behavior was very unlikely to have changed in consequence? If chilling tends merely to promote behaviors that sometimes in their turn promote colds, then the experimental tests of chilling would be expected to fail, as indeed they have done. But it should then be possible for the epidemiologist to identify the true behavioral risk factors (such as holding school recesses indoors) and to show that indeed the presence of those factors is closely linked to higher incidences of colds, even during weeks when the temperatures may be warming and the weather may be fine.

One of the most obvious behavioral changes that occurs outside tropical latitudes during cold weather is increased human crowding, and studies of this crowding ought to be able to demonstrate a strong increase in the contagion of colds. Again, however, such studies end up painting a much more subtle picture, one with surprises and puzzles of its own. When Paul and Freese found undeniable evidence for rapid and effective contagion of colds at Longyear City with the arrival of the first ships of spring, and when the citizens of Tristan da Cunha suffered such severe contagions when evacuated to England and again later when ships came to visit them back on Tristan, then the suggestion was strong that something very like crowding increases the likelihood of colds. When we see in Lidwell's data from the 1950s that September peaks of colds were extreme in London, were much less extreme in Newcastle, and were all but nonexistent in

Cirencester, then again, the effects of populations and crowds seem undeniable. We must not forget, however, data such as those of J. J. van Loghem in Holland, where city and country alike, and large families and small families equally, experienced epidemics of colds together as the temperatures fell. In data such as these, any effects of crowding, of contact with infected others, look essentially irrelevant to the process of the transmission of colds. It is not even clear that the colds themselves were "transmitted" in the literal sense.

Understanding how the common cold may be affected by temperature changes cannot be achieved, then, without a clearer understanding of the mechanisms producing the transmission of both infection and overt cold symptoms. For instance, how could van Loghem's carefully gathered data have shown no effects of family size, or, in other words, no evidence of contagion? Surely the evidence for the clear contagion of colds is too great to be dismissed. Or is it? Well, let's just see.

II

Booking Passage:
Chicago, 1921, to Salisbury, 1952

"Our experiments on a group of presumably susceptible subjects, when kept in an environment arranged for maximum comfort, and exposed to sufferers from a common cold in the early stages, suggest that the common cold is not transmissible under these conditions."

— *W. Kerr and J. Lagen, 1934*

It was only in the 1980s that medical science at last began to understand something of the complex, three-step chemical process that (1) brings a virile virion up to an appropriate cell wall, and then (2) attaches that virion to this wall, and finally (3) cleaves open a piece of the cell wall so as to inject into the cell interior the nucleic codes for building more virions. Moreover, once a common cold virus sets up shop inside a living nasal cell, there are still any number of puzzling and unpredictable results that can occur. Even as the twenty-first century approaches, these outcomes are only dimly appreciated or understood.

Recall that a large infective dose of virus, when given to a susceptible recipient, only sometimes results in an infection (that is, in successful viral replication on a large scale) and in only some of these infections does it also result in visible cold symptoms. It appears that, sooner or later, more or less frequently, everyone plays host to a "silent infection," a common cold that has no noticeable symptoms. Yet today, very late in the twentieth century, medical science still has no consistent or general reading on how often silent infection by most cold viruses may be taking place outside the laboratory. The role of antibodies in warding off some of these infections is clearly important, but antibodies alone do not seem to account completely for who becomes infected, or when. Individual differences in susceptibility to silent infections seem to shift with time, sometimes even in very short spans of time. Thus, it was the obvious, symptomatic infections, brought on by what were assumed to have been invader virions, that were the prime focus of earlier medical intelligence work.

Implicit in any talk of invader virions is the premise that colds are contagious, that they intrude from outside the body, and that we get them from other people. Still, in the many years since Paul and Freese in Spitzbergen and van Loghem in Amsterdam, there never has been a resolution of the apparent conflict between all the clear evidence for and against contagion as the primary source of colds. If to the physicist the fundamental nature of light appears (impossibly) to be both particulate and wave-like at the same time, it can similarly be said that colds appear to be both invasive and commensal at the same time. This paradox begs for an explanation, but for now we must accept that sometimes colds seem invasive, and sometimes colds seem commensal, and often, somehow, they appear to be both (or neither) at once.

We are still left with a multitude of sensible questions, however. Beyond the questions we might ask about what triggers a commensal cold, we might ask the following about contaged colds: Do cold viruses generally travel from person to person just at certain times of the year, or just at certain times of life? Research has suggested that infants are born free of most cold viruses, and if so then at least their "new" colds must be acquired, not commensal. How does this *early* contagion occur then? Moreover, new subvarieties of cold viruses turn up with some regularity throughout the world, so even if these "new" viruses eventually become commensal, they would appear to begin their time on earth spreading by contagion.

If colds sometimes do travel from person to person, how is *this* sort of transmission generally accomplished? Do the virions float through the air like so many motes of dust, waiting to be inhaled by any passing primate? Or do they rather hitchhike a ride from person to person on the rim of a drinking glass for instance, or on the coins returned to us as change, or on those hands we shake in friendship, hands that may have recently covered a cough?

Where Might a Baby's First Colds Come From?

The answers to questions such as these have not come easily and those answers that now exist have resulted only after five decades of hard work.

One very early sign that understanding the transmission of colds from person to person was going to be anything but simple appeared in a paper read at the 1923 convention of the American Medical Association, in San Francisco.[1] The paper concerned a large epidemiological study of colds in infants and their parents. One thousand Chicago area babies were seen over two periods of two months each in the winter of 1921–22. All the babies were between one and twenty-four months of age, which meant that they were not yet in school and they were not yet particularly social, except with members of their own families. Half of the babies selected for this study were suffering common colds, while the other half were currently free of colds, and had been cold-free for a few weeks. The researchers asked whether or not other members of the babies' families had recently had colds, presumably infecting some of the symptomatic babies with those colds.

The results of this study were at once interesting and suggestive. While not every "sick" baby lived in a family where someone else had recently had a visible cold, 58 percent did. Meanwhile, at the same time of year, only 36 percent of the "healthy" babies lived in families having at least one other member who had recently had a cold. In other words, 62 percent of babies caught colds when another family member had a cold first, and 40 percent caught colds when other family members were healthy. Thus, having a close family member who had an overt cold increased common cold incidence by 50 percent. Ignoring for the moment the possibility that all family members, the babies included, were infected from contact with contaminated objects or from contaminated air, quite independent of the presence of nearby cold sufferers, the natural next question to ask then becomes: were each and every one of the symptomatic family members equally likely to contribute to the increased risk for the baby? The answer turned out to be "no."

Fathers had prior colds in just 6 percent of those households where the babies developed a cold and in 6 percent of households where the babies did *not* develop a cold; clearly, the presence of a cold in the father contributed nothing to increasing the risk for colds in the babies of this study. Mothers, meanwhile, had prior colds in 29 percent of those households where the babies later did, but in only 13 percent of households where the babies did not. This means 69 percent of babies caught colds after mom did while 45 percent got sick even though their mothers were healthy. Thus, the increase in the incidence of colds for babies after the mother had first caught a cold was almost exactly the same as that for the families as a whole, that is, just over a 50 percent increase. When other children in the family had colds, there was some increase in common cold incidence in the babies, but the effect was much smaller than with the mothers.

The reasonable conclusion seemed to be that colds appearing in infants certainly are contaged to some degree, yet as a group fathers were not at all contagious to their babies, while siblings were mildly contagious, and mothers were noticeably contagious. Since the mothers of that day were traditionally seen as solo caretakers, and since fathers were seen as having little to do with caring for babies or playing with them, it made sense to conclude that if contagion is to occur from an infectious adult to a susceptible infant, then sustained contact and handling is what produces that contagion.

Does This Mean That Airborne Transmission Is Rare?

Another way to look at these same data is to note how surprisingly little contagion seemed to occur, even in the presence of infectious mothers, but especially in the case of symptomatic fathers. In fact, the implication is strong in these data that airborne routes of contagion were not at all significant in the transmission of these Chicago colds, for if the infectious virions did indeed float through the air from victim to victim, then one might well have expected that symptomatic fathers and mothers would launch equivalent viral flotillas upon the sea of air; and thus, one might also have expected that the normal circulation of air in the home would often have brought the paternal flotillas to harbor in receptive nursery nostrils. Yet apparently this did not happen. If airborne transmission was of major importance in this Chicago study, only very short viral voyages must have occurred, and multiple "landings" must have been required to initiate infection.

Other studies too, with different research designs, suggested that simple forms of contagion may not often occur with colds, or that contagion may not be airborne if it does occur. One such study, following up the experimental work with chimpanzees and humans by Dochez and his colleagues, was reported by two San Francisco doctors, William Kerr and John Lagen, in 1934.[2] They set out to study the transmission of colds in human volunteers by artificially introducing doses of cold virus directly into the nostrils of their volunteers.[3] Their experiments were carried out in a special hospital isolation room in which groups of up to five volunteers lived for well over a week in sterile conditions.

For the first five to eight days the volunteers were watched for any incubating colds that may have begun prior to isolation. All volunteers were young adult males with a history of at least three colds per year who had not recently had a cold. In each of five such groups, no spontaneous colds developed during the initial observation period. Kerr and Lagen describe what happened next as follows:

> At the end of this period an individual suffering from a common cold, with onset twelve to thirty-six hours previously, was brought in and allowed to remain for twenty-four to forty-eight hours, the contact being such as exists in normal contacts in a home, namely, eating and playing cards together, use of a common drinking glass, being sneezed at and the like. The experimental subjects were then kept another four to six days in order to have them under observation during the development of any symptoms. In one group of five the degree of exposure was carried to the point of contaminating the thermometers just before temperatures were taken. The material used for this purpose was the fresh nasal secretions that ran freely from the nose of an individual with a common cold in about the twenty-fourth hour, the secretions being allowed to dry on the thermometers. They were obtained from the same individual to whom the subjects were exposed.
>
> Nineteen subjects in five groups of three to five each were so exposed. No common colds or any symptoms referable to a cold were observed in any of the experimental subjects. Our experiments on a group of presumably susceptible subjects, when kept in an environment arranged for maximum comfort, and exposed to sufferers from a common cold in the early stages, suggest that the common cold is not transmissible under these conditions.[4]

While Kerr and Lagen were surprised by these results, they had a ready explanation for them: apparently, people who are warm, rested, and comfortable are very resistant to infection. A stronger test of this hypothesis would be to try the direct inoculation of infectious nasal secretions into the upper reaches of the nose. Thus, Kerr and Lagen next set out to do this stronger test. They added nine more volunteer subjects, in two groups, isolated as before, but instead of introducing a cold sufferer into each group at the end of the observation period, the experimenters put three drops of fresh, infectious nasal fluid into the corners of each volunteer's eyes. This procedure served to introduce the infectious fluid into the upper nasal areas, through the ducts connecting the eyes with the nasal sinuses, and it did so without any risks of physical irritation due to direct contact with nasal mucous membranes. But, as the "comfort" hypothesis would predict, none of these nine pampered volunteers developed a cold. Overall then, the various wild colds employed in these experiments were not at all contagious to any of the twenty-eight volunteers exposed to them. Again, it seemed as though colds may not be contagious after all, at least not when people keep warm and comfortable.

Surely Colds Must be Contagious; But, How?

Evidence such as this, together with van Loghem's previous discovery (contrary to what one would expect if colds are contagious) that members of large families do not seem to have any higher incidence of colds than do members of small families, might have been expected to convince many members of the medical intelligence community that colds are not usually contagious. But of course there were always data, such as those from Spitzbergen, those from Cruz Bay, and those from the viral transmission experiments of Dochez, to suggest that colds must be contagious. Many physicians and researchers, and most of the general lay community, have assumed all along that colds are contagious and that, for instance, uncovered sneezes spread infectious cold germs from those who are ill to those who soon will be.

By 1940, the advent of high-speed photography had made it possible to see quite clearly just what actually happens to the nearby air when a person sneezes.[5] In 1941 the results of a study using this technique were published, accompanied by dramatic photographs of clouds of spray, most of which came out of the mouth, flying four and five feet through the air following a normal sneeze.[6] The authors of this report placed a bacterial culture plate three feet from the face of a sneezing subject (who was not ill, and who was induced to sneeze with snuff or some other inhalant) and reported cultivating nineteen thousand tiny colonies of bacteria, following a sneeze done with an open mouth. A control sneeze, with the mouth closed and with the nose covered by a handkerchief, resulted in only one small bacterial colony on a plate of the same size. The authors concluded by saying, "While in this case the bacteria are mostly harmless ones from the front of the mouth, it is clear that very many of the droplets in a sneeze do contain living bacteria. It seems reasonable to infer that in acute infections of the upper respiratory tract droplets from sneezes are highly infective."[7]

In 1941 many of those trying to understand the common cold still assumed that viral behavior was like bacterial behavior, that viral contagion was like bacterial contagion, and even that some colds were bacterial in origin. Then in 1946, detailed work began at the Common Cold Research Unit at Salisbury. The early results of this work made it clearer that viral contagion was indeed more complex than had been assumed, and more complex than the simpler bacterial model had suggested. In November of 1949, the director at Salisbury, Dr. Christopher Andrewes, gave an address at Harvard University (which, remember, had built and staffed the Harvard Hospital in Salisbury at the start of the war) in which he recounted the work done in the first four years at the new Unit.[8] In summarizing this work, Dr. Andrewes had occasion to note:

> In many ways the setup is ideal. The volunteers are happy and they are co-operative; we obtain them without great difficulty. [Our] precautions seem to be adequate to prevent accidental infection, since our negative controls remain negative. Nevertheless, I must point out some of our difficulties. The inoculums we use are filtered or unfiltered nose washings, usually given undiluted; they must thus contain many thousands of times the virus dose one would be likely to receive in one's nose as a result of proximity to an infectious, sneezing, person. The washings we use will produce a reasonable [percentage] of colds after dilution 100 times, but that is about the limit. Even with our best washings, we [produce colds] in only about 60 per cent of our volunteers. Thus, 40 per cent of our "animals" resist our inoculations, and the others get colds only because we give them an enormous dose of virus. We strongly suspect that catching a cold in real life depends on receiving quite a small dose of virus, at a time when one's defenses are momentarily off their guard.[9]

It is interesting that Andrewes seems committed to the notion that there can be no infection without invasive virus from outside. He had good reason to be so committed because essentially none of his "control" volunteers, who were challenged with placebos, ever caught colds afterwards. Only volunteers challenged with actual virus clearly caught colds. And despite the massive dose of virus that circulated in the fresh nasal washings used to induce the colds, about half the challenged volunteers did not come down with a cold. In other words, some of the volunteers proved resistant and some of them proved susceptible at the time of challenge.

Naturally, we want to know more about the nature of that resistance and that susceptibility.

If Not the Virus, Then What About the Body's Defenses?

In the many years since 1950 when Andrewes made the comments quoted above, medical intelligence has discovered a great deal about the immune system in general, and more particularly, about some of the many different kinds of immune substances that can be found in blood, lymph, saliva, mucous, and even inside cell walls. It is easy to suppose that resistance to a disease simply means that high levels of antibody are present, and that susceptibility to disease primarily occurs when the immune system is "weak" or antibody levels are low. Unfortunately, however, things are not so simple, and the phenomenon of resistance to colds can be seen even in people who appear to have no specific antibody to the particular virus being tested, or who, by various criteria, seem to have markedly depressed immune functioning. One might always suppose that there are immune factors as yet undiscovered, factors that, once discovered, will successfully enable us to predict who will fall ill and who will resist illness when challenged with a cold virus. Yet so far the history of work on the common cold gives little hope that such a simple solution will emerge.

The post-war work at Salisbury also confirmed those earlier studies described above suggesting that little if any contagion will occur if natural mechanisms are allowed to do the work of transmission among comfortable adult volunteers. Early experiments at Salisbury isolated three small groups of volunteers and introduced into each group "donor" individuals newly suffering from laboratory-induced colds; only two of twenty-eight healthy volunteers developed colds. And later, when the same experiment was repeated, introducing into a group of five volunteers a donor who was suffering from a natural cold, none of the five caught this cold.[10]

At about the same time as these experiments were being carried out at Harvard Hospital in Salisbury, an ambitious epidemiological study of the transmission of natural colds was taking place in the nearby village of Bowerchalke, west of Salisbury.[11] The authors of this study, Drs. Lidwell and Sommerville, recorded the colds occurring each week in all but one of the households in Bowerchalke over a two-year period throughout 1948 and 1949. Approximately two hundred people, of all ages, took part in the study. Researchers visited the houses each Friday, as a rule, to obtain a weekly report on the occurrence of any colds from whoever might be home, usually a housewife. The findings from this study seemed both to confirm and to disconfirm some of the wisdom about the transmission of colds that was current at the time.

The rural village of Bowerchalke was moderately isolated in 1948. Many of the villagers did not leave it over long periods of time, while others tended to go once a week either to the nearby towns of Salisbury or Shaftsbury. The villagers were mainly agricultural workers and their families. They lived comfortably. Bowerchalke had a school, three churches, and a social hall, all of which ensured a regular social mixing among most of the villagers. And of course colds came to mix with some regularity too, albeit not always with the frequency of the colds seen in London or Salisbury.

One of the statistics that Lidwell and Sommerville computed from their rich bank of data at the end of their Bowerchalke study was the ratio of colds observed among larger and smaller households. This is the same statistic that van Loghem used to help nail down his conclusion that colds are not contagious, they are commensal. If colds are contagious, those living in larger households should show a higher incidence of colds because the more intimate association with more people should more often result in cross-infections. Recall that van Loghem found no real difference in cold incidences among those living in large and small households.

Lidwell and Sommerville found essentially the same thing. They found that those living in larger households (more than four persons) had just a 6 percent higher incidence rate than did those living in smaller households. This 6 percent difference in incidence was the smallest difference reported in their whole study, and it was less, for instance, than the difference in overall incidence between the two years 1948 and 1949. Given that larger families had, on average, more children in them, a somewhat higher incidence of colds would be expected in any event, due to the younger average age in the family. If the number of others with whom these people lived were to play a role facilitating the transmission of colds, the difference in incidence rates might have been expected to be 50 percent or more, as it was for instance between females and males. Women in this study reported many more colds for themselves and for other women than were reported for and by the men in the sample.

Thus, on the surface of it, here is more evidence that transmission from person to person is weak or absent as a means of starting colds. Lidwell and Sommerville made no comment on this evidence, however, because their plan of analysis assumed from the start, and their other data seemed to confirm, that cross-infections within families would prove to be important in their data. "Cross-infections" were defined as the excess numbers of colds seen in a household beyond the number of initial infections ("introductions") that could be assumed to have come from elsewhere either because (a) these were new colds in a previously healthy household, or because (b) the number of people in the household and the time that had passed predicted that a certain number of new colds would be coincidentally introduced into the house from outside soon after the first cold appeared. "Cross-infections" then were the colds that closely followed the first colds that came into a family, with due allowance made for subsequent colds that may have represented coincidental colds recently introduced from outside the household.

Notice that silent infections within a household, infections that presumably might trigger observable colds in someone else in the same family (which colds then would be counted as "initial infections") had to be ignored in this study, as were any of the silent cross-infections that may have followed from true initial infections. In this study, the observed *initial* infections in the homes occurred with greatest probability in children of school age, then next most probably in preschool children, and these colds occurred with lowest probability among adults. The corresponding incidence rates for colds among members in these three age groups were roughly in the ratio of 11 to 6 to 3 respectively.

As noted before, this age difference in susceptibility to colds is a commonly observed phenomenon, and is often used as evidence for the role of contagion. Colds are communicated at schools, it is said, along with spelling and math. Teachers are often said to be among the most afflicted adults. And it is the transmission of germs, not stress, that is assumed to be the cause of teachers' colds and those of their pupils.

Lidwell and Sommerville found marked age group differences in the likelihood of cross-infection, but here school children were the *least* likely to be cross-infected from an initial cold introduced by someone else in the family, while preschool children were the most likely. The probabilities of a household cross-infection were as follows: for preschoolers, .54; for adults, .26; and for school children, .17. This corresponds approximately to one chance in two for infants, one in four for adults, and one in six for school children. Lidwell and Sommerville speculated that the surprisingly low rate of cross-infection seen for school children may be because "the high risk of acquiring infection outside the household leaves only the less susceptible open to household infection."[12]

Lidwell and Sommerville mention one other finding in passing that might be very important if it proved to be reliable. When they looked at colds among those living with more than two others, Lidwell and Sommerville found that the rate of cross-infection from the second case of common cold in the house to the third case was not less than the cross-infection rate from the first case to the second. This was very significant because it suggested that resistance (to a first cold) may not be an enduring or transferable state, for if resistance were enduring, then having resisted the first cold should have predicted better resistance to the second as well. And this it did not do. Lidwell and Sommerville concluded: "These indications suggest that avoidance of infection on any given exposure is usually due to factors which have a chance variation rather than to a stable high level of immunity."[13]

Overall then, the data persuaded the researchers of something they had already suspected, something they had assumed when they selected the mathematics used in reporting their results, namely that contagion is the rule in the appearance of the common cold, and commensal mechanisms do not play a significant role. Moreover, they concluded that social mixing, especially at schools, but including more intimate contacts at home, seem to provide the opportunities for such contagion to occur.

Another Look at Touching Versus Breathing

The precise nature of those opportunities for contagion was still very unclear, however. Consequently, the staff at the Common Cold Research Unit at Harvard Hospital in Salisbury set out to look experimentally at the particular routes that viruses might be taking in their travels within the home. Is the primary route airborne? Is it by direct physical contact? Or is it by indirect contacts with previously contaminated objects, such as dishes or playing cards? To answer these questions a series of small experiments was performed under the strictly controlled conditions at Harvard Hospital. Instead of infective nasal drops from deep storage in the laboratory freezers, the infective material was supplied unconsciously (even if self-consciously) by visiting "donor" individuals suffering from natural colds. Moreover, because Lidwell and Sommerville had found evidence to suggest that children might be more effective than adults at spreading their colds, some of the visiting donors used in these experiments were children.[14]

To test the effectiveness of the airborne route, a room about sixteen feet square was divided in half by a blanket partition leaving a one-foot space open at the floor, ceiling, and walls. A fan was used to mix the air throughout the whole room. Between five and eight healthy volunteers sat on one side of this room for two hours, reading or sewing, while on the other side four or five of the donors were encouraged to talk and play together. In three of the trials, children between eight and thirteen years of age, all suffering from colds, were the donors. In one of the trials, the donors were adults. Furthermore, in the name of science, halfway through each trial sneezing powder was released into the donor area to facilitate the broadcast of germs. Then, as a check on how effective these procedures might be in producing contaminated air, samples of the air were taken during each trial and analyzed for the presence of a particular bacterium known to come from the respiratory tract. This check suggested that during three of the four trials air contamination was substantially greater than normal, but in one of the trials, with donor children who sat rather quietly throughout their time in the room, air contamination was much less, although it was still higher than normal background levels.

The results of this portion of the research were somewhat inconclusive. Only two colds were seen among the twenty-five volunteers exposed for two hours to contaminated air. Ignoring the trial on which the donor children were apparently too shy to "donate" very much, then the figure becomes two colds produced in twenty volunteers. Of course, under the conditions of isolation used at Harvard Hospital, even one cold could normally be assumed to be a successful transmission (and not due to other sources). Thus, it could be concluded that airborne transmission of colds is possible, but unusual, even under these particularly favorable conditions.

Subsequent experiments in this same series used artificially infected aerosol mists (inhaled through the nose) for half the recipients to investigate whether a cold virus would produce as many colds when delivered this way as when the same amount of fluid was dropped directly into the nose. But in each of these two conditions, approximately one in five of the volunteers developed colds. Again then, it seemed like airborne transmission could very possibly be the source of at least some natural colds, though perhaps not the majority of them.

To test the effects of direct physical contact, groups of four or five donors, suffering colds, were brought into a room containing different groups of five to eight healthy volunteers. These combined parties then intermingled. They had lunch together and played cards and other games for two hours. Five such trials were carried out, and they produced a total of just three colds in thirty-two volunteers. In this small sample of five trials, direct contact seemed to produce no greater number of colds than did exposure to "contaminated" air alone, and for this reason the researchers tentatively concluded that airborne transmission was the most likely route of infection in these trials. But in fact, neither the airborne nor the "contact" routes seemed very effective at all.

However, the Salisbury staff went further to test the possible transmission of colds from contaminated objects rather than contaminated air. After the donors and volunteers had left the lunchroom used in the study of direct physical contact described above, and after the room was given a thorough airing to cleanse the air, new groups of five to eight volunteers were brought into this room to spend two hours using the contaminated playing cards and the many other objects purposely left behind. Four trials were carried out with this procedure and twenty-five volunteers took part.

As often happens in scientific work, the gods cast a veil of mist over the results of this last experiment, making the results particularly difficult to interpret. One of the twenty-five volunteers in this study had arrived at Harvard Hospital with very slight signs of a cold, but her symptoms disappeared during the first two days of preliminary observation, prior to the test exposure to the contaminated room. Consequently, she and her roommate were allowed to participate in the experiment. However, this woman's cold symptoms reappeared the morning following her afternoon exposure to the contaminated room, rather early for any cold attributable to the new exposure of the day before. Her roommate also developed cold symptoms, on the next day. These were the only two volunteers who showed any signs of a cold following contact with the contaminated objects in the test room. It may be then that none of the volunteers in this experiment contracted a cold from contact with the contaminated objects, or it may be that two did. And, as always, if there were any silent infections produced in these experiments, the data too were silent on the topic.

But were the objects in the test room contaminated enough? Were two hours of occupancy by symptomatic donors long enough to produce any concentrated places of contamination? An earlier experiment had convinced researchers at the Common Cold Unit that, indeed, substantial contamination would inevitably occur to any objects in the experimental room. That experiment was designed as follows.

A thin rubber tube was arranged along one volunteer's nose in such a way that it would slowly drip small drops of clear liquid mixed with an invisible fluorescent dye into the frontal areas of this healthy person's nose, exactly mimicking a dripping cold. This volunteer, snuffing and wiping the time away, then played cards and socialized with a few others. Every so often photographs were taken of the room and all the participants, using ultraviolet light to illuminate the fluorescent dye and trace its travels.[15] It was not long before the dye seemed to be everywhere in the room, including all around the noses of most other volunteers. To touch is human, and to touch one's nose, while hardly divine, is sublimely hard to resist. (Try this simple experiment: having read this sentence, see how long it is before your nose calls loudly for a touch. And that other person in the room with you — is it more than three minutes before he or she next touches his or her face, near the nose or the eye?)

So if there were no colds transmitted in the experiment using contaminated objects it did not seem to the investigators at Salisbury that the fault could lie in the low quality of contamination present. Thus, in their conclusion to the report of this work, the investigators wrote:

> Though common cold infection may spread from person to person by normal social contact, and through the air in the form of droplet nuclei, the rate of clinical cross-infection is low.
>
> We found no evidence suggesting that spread by indirect contact is of major importance in the natural transmission of the common cold.[16]

If, however, it is true that common cold infections spread from person to person, whether by hand or by air, then those who have the most daily contacts with other people, particularly other people who have infections, ought to catch the most colds. Thus we might predict that on average those who work in the office of a busy general medical practitioner would catch more colds than those working in insurance offices, that school children would catch more colds than preschool children who stay at home, that elementary school teachers would catch more colds than telephone operators, that salespeople would catch more colds than housewives, and so on. Yet by 1952 most epidemiological literature lent only half-hearted support to these types of predictions. Happily, a new sort of epidemiological research soon provided rather better opportunities to examine the role of human contacts in the transmission of colds. We will examine these new studies next. Can *they* at last prove our intuition to be correct when it tells us that in natural home settings contagion of colds does occur, very frequently, via contaminated air, and even more surely if one has touched the nasal fluids of a cold sufferer?

Viral Arrival: Cleveland, 1948, to Chicago, 1960

"A few families were interested in admission to the study because of a presumed high incidence of respiratory disease among their members; this presumption was not borne out, however, on sobsequent observation."[1]

— *J. H. Dingle et al., 1953*

When techniques for viral cultivation and identification at last began to be perfected, three large-scale epidemiological studies of the common cold were undertaken in the United States. These studies were larger in scope and duration than most previous studies, and they collected some new kinds of data. The first of these three ambitious projects was initiated in January of 1948, in Cleveland, Ohio, under the overall direction of Dr. John Dingle at the Western Reserve School of Medicine.

Impressed by the increasing quality of data generated in intensive medical studies done on units of military personnel, but concerned at (1) the relatively short term over which such populations were being followed, and (2) by their unrepresentative makeup, Dingle's team decided to study "a stable group of civilian families."[2] Because they were to be "stable" families, capable of "intelligent cooperation," each household was composed of atypically well-educated and financially comfortable parents who owned their own home and were likely to stay put for many years. This was the American Family of which the Western Reserve sample was so "representative."

More than sixty volunteer families were enrolled in this project, containing nearly three hundred family members. The health of these families was followed closely for a number of years. Illness of every kind was closely monitored and regular blood samples and x-rays were taken as part of the survey process. Not surprisingly, the great majority of the illnesses seen in the Cleveland study were simple common colds. Dingle and his co-workers adopted a very liberal definition of when a new cold began (sometimes observed to be before the end of a preexisting cold, as revealed by a sudden change in general symptoms) and as a result their count of colds was quite high.[3] In general they recorded for these young families an average of 10.0 illness episodes (of all kinds) *per person* per year, including in this average the illnesses of many young children who invariably suffered the lion's share of the minor illnesses. Sixty-two percent of all these documented illnesses were uncomplicated, and presumably viral colds (which excluded streptococcal "colds," allergic "colds," pharyngitis, and other illnesses that can masquerade as colds).

Do Colds Decrease with Increasing Wisdom?

This study was the first of its type having both adequate data and the resources necessary to tabulate cold incidences as a function of age. While the overall average yearly number of uncomplicated colds seen in the Cleveland families during the first two years of study was 6.2 colds per person, the incidence rate tended to be noticeably higher before the age of seven, and rather lower after the age of seven. More particularly, children in their first year of life averaged about 6.9 colds, only slightly above the overall average. One-year-old children averaged approximately 8.3 colds, however. Children aged two developed 8.5 colds per year, and at age three the maximum cold incidence was observed to be 8.6 colds per child per year. Among the four-year-olds the incidence dropped back to an average of 7.8 colds per year. Thus, over the first five years of life cold incidences rose and then fell, following a relatively low first year during which only slightly elevated numbers of colds were observed.

Children aged six, seven, and eight showed even lower (and more nearly average) incidence levels, which were 6.2, 6.6, and 5.9 colds per year, respectively. At age nine a further drop in incidence rate took place, down to 5.1 colds per year. At age ten the rate was a little above that, at 5.6 colds per year, and among children eleven to fifteen years of age the average was 5.4 colds per year. Finally, among the adults in this family study, fathers averaged just 4.1 colds per year while mothers averaged 5.4 (the same as the teenage children).[4]

These age trends clearly do not support the hypothesis that contagion from outsiders is the main general source of transmission of the common cold. Fathers, when compared with mothers, were more often out of the house mingling with others, yet had far fewer colds. And preschool children, who are not out nearly as often among larger social groups when compared to six- and seven-year-old school children, had many more colds than did the older school children. Moreover, school experience does not change much between age six and age ten, yet there seems to be a marked drop in the incidence of colds after age seven, a drop that continues right into adolescence. Different readers will see different lessons in these data, but they suggest to me that there is a large physiological component governing the risk of catching colds, and, whatever this component may include, it is sensitive at least to lived experience (age) and perhaps to gender as well.

Does the "maturity" of the developing immune system have some role to play, or do hormonal balances and status? Dingle and his colleagues looked more closely at just such questions.

Do Colds Decrease Given Certain Doses of Testosterone?

To examine whether the gender difference seen between mothers and fathers might be apparent at earlier ages, Dingle recompiled the incidence data for each year of age, this time separately for boys and girls. No gender differences were seen prior to age two and after age eight among the Cleveland families. But between ages three and seven there was a consistent tendency for boys to average about one cold more per year than girls. Thus, it is not just their female gender that put the mothers in this study at higher risk than the fathers, for we see that between ages three and seven the risk levels for girls are less than those for boys, after which (at least through age fifteen) there appear to be no reliable gender differences until the adult years.[5]

Do Colds Decrease By Avoiding Contacts with Schoolrooms?

While the overall age incidences suggest that school attendance is associated only with *diminishing* susceptibility to the common cold, another internal analysis of the Cleveland data suggested that school exposure might matter after all. Dingle and his associates divided the data for children between ages two and six into three classifications: (1) those children attending nursery school; (2) those children staying at home who had siblings at school; and (3) those children at home with no siblings in school. Then, after making some allowance for the fact that few children younger than four years were in nursery school in this sample, the data seemed to suggest that schools do after all encourage the transmission of colds. In particular, children between one and three years of age, who had siblings in school, were likely to average almost three more colds each year than were children of the same age who had no siblings in school. Moreover, three-year-olds in nursery school had almost 50 percent more colds each year than did the three-year-olds who stayed at home. Among four- and five-year-olds this large difference shrank considerably. After age three, the children attending nursery schools had on average only about one-half cold more per person per year compared to the children staying at home.[6]

While these data seemed to provide evidence that school attendance is associated with an increase in the risk of colds at age three, the corresponding increases in risk seen at ages four and five were slight, if present at all. Thus, it seemed likely that it was not school attendance per se that produced the elevated risks of colds among these children; rather it seemed more likely to have been something associated with being in school at age three, perhaps tied to unique activities taking place at school, or to different psychological or physiological stresses associated with being at school at that age.

The noticeable drop in cold incidences after children reach school age not only implies that school contacts may not be a major new source of infectious colds, it even suggests that exposure to other school children could promote increasing *resistance* to colds with age, rather than increased susceptibility resulting from new social exposures.

Dingle and his co-workers found other evidence in their data tending to falsify this latter hypothesis, however. Looking just at five-year-old children, about half of whom had been in school the year before, and half of whom had not, they compared the incidence of colds in the two groups for that next school year in which all the children finally now attended. This analysis showed that children with school experience during the *previous* year actually had slightly more colds on average (7.2 of them) than did the children who had been at home the previous year (who had an average of 6.4 colds). The small numbers of children in these two samples (twenty-four and nineteen children in the two groups, respectively) make this difference potentially unreliable, but the data seemed sufficient to call into question the simple strong hypothesis that says general resistance to colds is the direct result of previous exposures to them.[7] Rather, acquired resistance to colds seemed to be linked purely and simply to the child's maturational level.

Revisiting the Family Size Issue: Is Bigger Riskier?

Dingle and his Cleveland co-workers also looked at family size as a moderating variable in producing common colds. To no one's surprise, family size was strongly associated with the number of children present in the home, and with their ages, and of course each of these two variables are known to be related in turn to the incidence of colds to be seen in each family member. Families of six, for instance, would be much more likely to have teenage children in them than would families of three. To purify the data of these confounding influences, Dingle's group looked at family size effects separately for children within each age range, and for parents of each sex. As had been so often reported before for families in general, they found no family size effects for children of different age groupings.

But among the parents in this study, for fathers and mothers alike, there *was* a change in incidence as a function of the family size. Both parents in families of four averaged approximately one cold more per year when compared to the corresponding parents in families of three. Another one-cold increase each year was seen in the parents of families of five when compared to the parents in families of four. From three to four to five, then, increasing family size was associated with increased incidence of *parental* colds. However, for families with six or more members, the incidence rate for parents dropped back by about one cold per year per parent to the levels seen for parents in families of four.[8]

Thus, for the very first time, the data on family size from the Cleveland study appeared partially consistent with the supposition that the transmission of colds generally takes place from person to person in family groups. Evidence consistent with this hypothesis was seen only among parents, and not in the children, and it was seen only in families having between three and five members (or, one and three children), not more. The fact that this trend disappeared in families with more than five members, and was not visible at all in the children from families of any size, remains then as another strong piece of evidence calling into question the simple contagion view of cold transmission.

Who Starts All These Colds Anyway?

Still, it is hard to give up the idea that colds are contaged. The idea is so very compelling because we think we have seen simple contagion so often in our own families. Dingle and his colleagues in Cleveland noticed that the colds they recorded seemed to show up in families clustered in time, and this synchronistic clustering understandably made any but a contagion theory seem improbable. Thus, like Lidwell and Sommerville before them, the Cleveland group decided to analyze their data according to the likelihood that each member of the family would be the source (the first person showing symptoms) of new colds seen in the family, or the secondary victim of apparent contagion from a cold introduced by another member to the family. An "index case" was thus defined as the first cold introduced into a family, and subsequent "secondary" colds, presumed to be cross-infections, were counted when they followed soon after the arrival of an index case.

An index case was counted whenever a cold appeared in a family ten or more days following the start of the last previous cold in that family. Two such colds that occurred on the same day were both counted as index colds, but if the two colds started on sequential days, despite the improbably short incubation period that could be implied if contagion were assumed for the second cold, only the first was counted as an index cold while the second was counted as a secondary cold.

The results of introduction rates analyzed this way again showed that fathers had the fewest colds, and, the lowest rate of index cases. Mothers came next, with an incidence of index colds about 25 percent higher than fathers. Preschool children, still in the home, averaged twice as many index colds per year as did the fathers, and so did school children over the age of six. School children prior to the age of six were three times more likely to develop index colds than were fathers.[9] Again then, it does not appear that colds are simply brought home by those, such as fathers, who go outside the home, and are subsequently passed around to those, such as preschool children, who stay at home. Instead it looks as if the susceptibility of young children is paramount, and that index colds find their victims without impediment, whether at home or at school or at the office.

The reader might well interrupt here to ask whether fathers might not be bringing home large numbers of "silent infections" picked up in the outside world. These subclinical colds might be the true index colds in the families, undetected by the research team or the other family members. If fathers do have more frequent subclinical infections, having somehow acquired the necessary tools for avoiding symptoms, and if, perhaps, three-to seven-year-old children are starting to learn the same trick too (the girls faster than the boys) then these Cleveland findings would have a very different caste to them. But the frequency and timing of subclinical colds occurring outside the laboratory is arguably the most crucial missing datum in the whole field of common cold epidemiology.[10] At this writing we still have no good estimate of how frequently silent infections are brought home to the family nor how frequently they may later emerge in those staying at home.

Who Gets the Cold Next?

The Cleveland group then turned its attention to secondary colds. These colds, presumably started by the index case in each family, were counted during each of the nine days following the appearance of an index case. As one might expect based on a forty-eight-hour incubation period, secondary colds occurred most often in other family members two days following the appearance of the index cold, but almost as many secondary colds were reported either one or three days following the index cold. Fully half of all secondary colds occurred within the first three days of the appearance of each index cold. This pattern strongly suggested that secondary colds were contaged from the index cases.

The incidence of secondary colds on the fourth day following an index cold was noticeably lower than the incidence during each of the first three days. And the incidence for both days 5 and 6 was lower still. Many of the colds occurring after day 6 might well have been secondary to a secondary cold (third-generation colds) but no attempt was made in this study to estimate the proportion of any such colds. Moreover, even assuming that contagion is the rule in cold transmissions, quite a few of the colds occurring throughout the nine-day secondary count period were undoubtedly new and unrecognized index cases, coincidental with other secondary cases. But the Cleveland group did not attempt to make statistical allowance for the presence of these cases in the way that Lidwell and Sommerville did. By days 8 and 9, many of the infrequent colds counted as "secondary" were probably unrelated to the index case from the week prior.

The likelihood of secondary cross-infection seen in these Cleveland data was also examined as a function of age, and here again there was strong evidence of declining susceptibility to colds as age increased. The probability of developing a secondary infection soon after the appearance of an index cold in the family was very close to one-half for babies throughout the first four years of life. The year-by-year probability of such secondary infections was seen to rise slowly to a maximum of .55 during the third year of life; thereafter, it declined slowly. By the age of eight the declining probability of catching a secondary cold levelled off at about .22 where it remained at least through the age of fifteen. Among the adults, the probability of the mother catching a secondary cold was .27 and for fathers it was .17. Thus, for mothers in this study, the risk of cross-infection was actually slightly above that for children after the age of eight.[11]

Combining the evidence from the incidence of index cases at each age and the rates of secondary infection at each age, there was little in these Cleveland data to suggest that close physical proximity, with outsiders or with family members, plays any major role in the transmission of most colds. While mothers caught more colds than did fathers or young teenagers, the most colds were caught by those who stayed and played around home, that is, the three-year-olds. And even more dramatic evidence calling into question any effects of close proximity was to be found buried in an obscure table reporting the Cleveland cross-infection rates as a function of whether each family member was the index case or the secondary case.[12]

When children under one year were exposed to an index case, there was more than a 50 percent chance that they would catch the cold if the index case was a slightly older sibling, between one and five years old, but it was only 31 percent if the mother had the index cold, and it was only 26 percent if the father had the index cold. Caretaking mothers were *less* likely to infect their babies than were other toddlers and preschool siblings in the house. Moreover, when children under one year introduced the index cold, mothers had a 20 percent chance of catching a secondary cold, whereas, as we just saw, if the mother introduced the index cold then children under one year had a 31 percent chance of catching a secondary cold. Thus, infants appeared to be 50 percent more likely to catch the mother's index cold than vice versa, even though the amount of normal contact between mother and infant was probably reduced when the mother was sick and the infant was still healthy, and it probably was increased whenever she was healthy and her child was ill.

Similarly, although one- and two-year-old children interacted with three- and four-year-old children in the home to a relatively constant degree, these younger children had a 76 percent chance of developing secondary colds to index cases among their older siblings, whereas when it was the infants who introduced the index colds the same older siblings had only a 44 percent chance of developing a secondary cold. Children under one year developed secondary colds 26 percent of the time when fathers introduced the index cold, but fathers developed secondary colds only 13 percent of the time when children under one year introduced the index cold.

Or Should We Be Asking Instead: Who Does the Virus Get Next?

Asymmetrical data such as these strongly suggested that physical proximity may be less important than the role played by the susceptibility of the uninfected person and the virulence of the index case.[13] Children between two and four years of age seemed to have had index colds that were especially contagious to others and to each other. Moreover, they seemed relatively more susceptible to the index colds seen in every other family member. While the most persuasive interpretation of these findings, and the one favored by the authors of the Cleveland study, was that as we mature we become physically more resistant to colds and correspondingly less likely to release strongly contagious virus able to infect others, other interpretations of the same data are quite possible as well.

It is also possible, for instance, that as people age it is their behavior that changes, not their physical susceptibility nor their specific contagiousness to others. By the age of eight children may wash their hands more often, they may use handkerchiefs more effectively while suffering a cold, they may rub their eyes and noses less frequently, and they may have different diets or sleeping patterns compared with younger and more susceptible children. Some of these behavioral changes may very well lower the risk of infection to oneself and to others.

The difference between the incidence of colds seen in mothers and fathers might likewise reflect a difference in the things they do at home, not their different physical resistances or susceptibilities to infection. If colds are transmitted by touching contaminated toys, for instance, then other children in the home may be most likely to be cross-infected, mothers next most likely to pick up contaminated toys, and fathers least likely to do so. Moreover, contagious mothers might indeed be far less likely to contaminate toys that children will touch than contagious children would be to contaminate toys that the mother will touch. These likelihoods match exactly the patterns of apparent transmission seen in the secondary infection data.

Or Is It All Simply a Matter of Chance, of a Thousand Unknowables?

Whether it is healthy behavior or the healthy state of the immune system that makes a person resistant to a neighbor's cold (if it is either of those) there has also been considerable interest in the question of how enduring any such "resistance" may be. Some people are said to be prone to colds and others resistant to colds over most of a lifetime. And yet, recall that Lidwell and Sommerville saw no reduction in the delayed secondary attack rate among the members of larger families who had for a time resisted catching the index cold in that family, and who later seemed to catch one of the related secondary colds, leading those authors to the conclusion that "avoidance of infection on any given exposure is usually due to factors which have a chance variation rather than to a stable high level of immunity."[14]

Of course, there may be short-term fluctuations in one's resistance to colds, around a generally healthy and high level of resistance. But it is of some importance and interest whether or not colds attack certain people more than others when the age, gender, and family compositions of these people are held constant. If there are enduring individual differences in susceptibility and resistance to colds, then there should be a noticeable correlation between the number of colds a person gets in one year and the number they get in later years. A 1947 study by a group at Harvard and Boston Universities set out to test just that.[15] The study was carried out retrospectively, using data drawn from the records of visits to the Health Center at the Phillips Exeter Academy, records that had been kept during the four academic years 1935 through 1939. Six different groups of boys were studied, all of whom sought treatment for at least one common cold during their period of residence. Each of the six groups consisted of boys who attended the academy during the same particular set of sessions (over two, three, or four successive years during the period of study).

In general the members of each group of boys sought treatment for about 2.6 colds during each of the academic years studied, with the basic range among the group averages running between 2.3 colds per year and 2.9 colds per year. But of course it was the year-to-year correlations in the numbers of personal colds suffered that was of interest in this study. These correlations were found to be considerably above the level to be expected if no enduring resistance or enduring susceptibility to colds exists. Even the correlations of cold frequencies for terms that were two years apart were significantly higher than the chance (zero) level, albeit only marginally so. However, over periods that were more than two years apart there did not seem to be many, if any, enduring individual differences in personal immunity to colds, or susceptibility to them.[16] Knowing that someone had relatively more or fewer colds than average, up until two years ago, did not help at all to predict the number of colds they might have next year.

Again, it is important to understand that any personal "consistencies" in illness rates could result from factors other than enduring levels of either resistance, or susceptibility, to colds. Rather than being physiological, the explanation for positive associations might be behavioral, or even psychological. For instance, some boys may have been ready to visit the Health Center at any small sign of a cold, while others may have sought medical assistance only for very severe illness. This might be the enduring personal trait that led to the boys' high year-to-year correlations. Then, even if colds did occur randomly among boys of both these behavioral types, there would be consistently low or high yearly counts of personal colds recorded in their health files as a consequence of their attitudes about illness and about receiving treatment.

A behavioral explanation for personal consistencies in resistance to colds might be found by examining certain of the Exeter boys' personal habits, habits that might increase or decrease their likelihood of becoming infected. Suppose, for instance, that some boys always dressed in light clothing while others always dressed in heavy clothing and this were found to result in different risks for colds. Or suppose that some were generally very clean while some were not. (Wouldn't that be a surprise!) Or, that some often touched their noses and eyes with their fingers, while others rarely did. In 1947, however, the authors of the Exeter study did not consider habitual behavioral differences to be important; they concluded with considerable assurance that an enduring constitutional factor was responsible for the year-to-year consistencies in common cold incidence, and they advocated strongly that various physiological factors be examined for the secret of immunity to colds.

However, a rather different study, also published in 1947, suggested that there may *not* be any general or enduring resistance or susceptibility to colds by people of varying physical constitutions and that there may also be little immunity to cold viruses afforded by previous exposures to the virus. Capitalizing on recently developed procedures for measuring the incubation periods of some viruses, the researchers (U.S. Army personnel) exposed isolated recruits to each of two very different respiratory viruses:

one was a common cold virus having an incubation period of less than fifty hours, and produced mostly nasal symptoms with no fever; the other was a different type of virus with an incubation period in excess of seventy hours, producing symptoms of prominent sore throat, mild fever, and only slight nasal symptoms.[17] Volunteers were "challenged" with one of these viruses on each of two occasions, approximately three weeks apart, and then were challenged with the other virus on a third occasion, approximately three weeks after the second challenge.

The results of this study were interesting and clear. Three weeks after the first exposure to the common cold virus (from which four of five volunteers developed colds), the second challenge with the same virus again produced new colds in four of the five volunteers, including this time the one person who had escaped symptoms the first time (but excluding one of the four who had developed a cold the first time.) When three weeks later these same five volunteers were challenged with the other virus, characterized by the productions of sore throat and mild fever, it too produced new illnesses (now with correspondingly changed symptoms) in four of the five people, but it was a different member of this group who remained healthy on this third trial.

Among the six volunteers of the second group, who were first challenged with the other virus, five of the six became ill. But this same virus produced no illnesses in any of these same six volunteers following rechallenge three weeks later. When three weeks after that the same six volunteers were finally challenged with the common cold virus for the first time, three of the six became ill, including the one person who had escaped illness on the first challenge with the other virus.

The authors of this study concluded that while the common cold virus apparently produced no subsequent immunity (at least within the three weeks following first exposure) the other virus did produce such immunity. The immunity afforded to the other virus seemed to be specific to that virus and was of no help in resisting the common cold virus used in the study. Moreover, a general resistance to colds was not observed in any form. The one person who resisted the common cold virus on the first challenge failed to resist a second challenge three weeks later, while one of the four who proved susceptible to the first challenge successfully avoided illness at the time of the second challenge.

We might also note parenthetically that in this study transmission of colds to volunteers proved quite easy, more so than in any of the previously discussed studies. Perhaps this was due to a more virulent virus, or to better laboratory technique, or perhaps it had something to do with the fact that these army "volunteers" already had spent three weeks in enforced isolation before these experiments even began, and the quarters to which they were confined for a total of eighty days were not particularly pleasant or comfortable.

Well Then, Is It Cleanliness That Counts?

If, as suggested by this early work, there is in fact no general physiological basis for lasting immunity to colds, one might well ask again whether or not different people truly differ in their general risk for colds. Is it just coincidence or illusion or self-deception that explains why some people can boast that they almost never get colds while some others can complain that they catch almost every cold that comes to town? If there are dependable individual differences in the risk for colds, and if these do not have their basis in physiological health, then what behavioral, psychological, or environmental factors produce those differences?

In 1956 a new study was reported, focusing on the spread of colds within families.[18] The report of this investigation was laced with references to index colds and secondary attack rates, but in particular it presented evidence bearing directly on the nature of personal resistance or susceptibility to colds. This Canadian study was carried out in London, Ontario, on 164 members of forty-five families over two successive winter periods, from November 15 to May 15 in 1952–53 and again in 1953–54. The author was Dr. Carol Buck, who discussed part of her findings with these words:

> It appears that the influence of age upon susceptibility, although demonstrable, is not as important as the effect of the age of the index case upon transmission. This fact, coupled with the observation that secondary attack rates increased with crowding only when the index case was a child, point to the significance of personal habits and therefore of transmission by direct contact.[19]

Dr. Buck is pointing out here that the children in her study were about equally susceptible to catching a parental cold from either parent even though the amounts of contact between mother and child versus father and child were usually quite unequal. Meanwhile, the risks for the two parents when the child introduced a cold into the family were not correspondingly equal. Mothers had approximately a 50 percent greater chance of catching a child's cold than did fathers. Dr. Buck assumed that colds are not transmitted through the air because she had read the studies carried out at Salisbury, mentioned earlier, and because then she would have expected the fathers in her study to catch as many colds as mothers from their young children. Of course, contrary to Dr. Buck's assumption, the transmission of some colds could still be airborne if for instance it were only at certain times of day or in certain environments (when, and from which, fathers had more often been absent) that aerosol transmissions were common.

Dr. Buck also reported further evidence that personal consistencies do exist in susceptibility to the risk of colds. She computed the correlations of the number of colds caught for the two successive winters of her study, done separately for people of different ages living in families of different sizes, thus removing any spurious effects from these two potentially confounding variables. The correlations again proved to be considerably larger than would be expected if chance alone determined the number of colds that one caught each year. And in these data, unlike those at Exeter, individual differences in willingness to report a cold were not a potential confounding variable.

Or Is It Just Colds That Protect Against Colds?

Thus, an important role for basic constitutional factors, perhaps the general health of one's immune system, could not yet be ruled out. The existence of some physiological factor that affords a temporary but effective protection against colds seemed all the more probable following the subsequent report of a study of colds carried out on 147 indoor postal workers in London, England.[20] Volunteer participants in this study were monitored at work between April of 1949 and April of 1950. In late October 1949, an acute epidemic of colds occurred during and following the first sharp decline in outdoor temperatures that fall, affecting approximately half of all those participating in the study. Among those who, during the previous summer and fall, had yet to suffer any colds at all, approximately half caught their first cold during this epidemic. But among those who had already experienced a previous cold during the study, the attack rate differed considerably depending on how recently that cold had occurred. Fall colds, occurring during the previous eight weeks, were followed by another cold during this epidemic in just one-third of the participants, whereas among those who had had their previous cold more than eight weeks prior (i.e., during the late spring or summer preceding), approximately two-thirds of the participants developed another cold.

For the first time, then, research evidence suggested that a short-term increase in resistance to colds might be produced in response to a cold. Moreover, the implication seemed to be that this temporarily increased immunity was general, protecting against all colds whatever their viral source, and not limited to a single variety of virus.

Should We Make Hormones Our Prime Suspect?

The London study of postal workers was soon followed by research suggesting that certain physical factors, this time in conjunction with exposure to chilling, might affect susceptibility and resistance to colds.[21] This new study, by Dr. Jackson's research team at Chicago, was experimental, involving challenge with infectious material recently taken from the noses of cold sufferers. The participants were female volunteers, many of them medical students and student nurses who then continued living normal lives without being isolated or quarantined in any special setting. For part of this study, some of the volunteers were chilled for a few hours immediately before being challenged with cold virus. As noted previously, chilling did not by itself produce any increase in the number of colds seen following challenge. But when the data were analyzed according to the point in each woman's menstrual cycle when chilling and challenge had taken place, there appeared to be a strong association between the monthly timing of these events and the likelihood of a resulting cold. In particular, the initial study of this phenomenon suggested that during the middle third of the menstrual cycle (just before and after ovulation) chilling and challenge produced colds in ten of thirteen volunteers (77 percent) while the first and last nine days of the menstrual cycle were associated with colds under the same conditions in only twelve of forty-one volunteers (29 percent). Thus it now seemed more likely that something hormonal could be associated with general resistance or susceptibility to colds in women.

This preliminary Chicago study was followed three years later, in 1960, by a more complete report.[22] It appeared after further work that chilling the women was not as significant as had been supposed based on the preliminary findings. Instead, it seemed that the phase of the menstrual cycle alone might account for most of what had been earlier reported. After studying 994 episodes where female volunteers had been challenged with active cold virus (without chilling) the researchers found that the incidence of colds was very significantly decreased during the first four days of menstrual flow and was significantly increased during the nine middle days of the menstrual period (as reported in the earlier study of chilling). Following the twenty-eighth day in the cycle, even when menstrual flow had not yet begun, susceptibility to the challenge virus was again noticeably reduced. Something hormonal clearly seemed to affect susceptibility to colds among females, and a good guess was that elevated levels of FSH (follicle-stimulating hormone) may be associated with increased resistance to colds, while elevated levels of lutin could be associated with increased susceptibility to colds.

So are there really physiological factors that predispose one to health and to resistance to colds, or, instead, predispose one to catch more colds than others do? Or is the short-term tendency to exhibit reliable and enduring individual differences in susceptibility due instead to behavioral or dietary habits, to one's regular work or home environment, or to some other such factor? Limited evidence can be marshalled in support of almost any answer to such questions and so additional, stronger data would be helpful to have. Fortunately, interesting additional data soon did become available, and it is to them that we will turn next.

PART IV

One if by Air,
Two if by Hand

20,000 Leagues Among the Capillaries: Chicago, 1961, to the Great Lakes, 1972

"These results conform to those of previous investigations in showing that persons acutely ill with rhinovirus infection tend to have little or no antibody to the infecting virus, [implying that] such antibody is protective against symptomatic infection. The weight of the direct evidence [from this and other studies, also implies] that serum antibody is not of primary importance in recovery from acute illness or in the immediate resistance which occurs thereafter."[1]

— *J. M. Gwaltney, Jr. et al., 1967*

U ndoubtedly you have heard an apocryphal story or two, of the desert tribe that supposedly never gets colds, of the immigrant family that seems immune to colds, or the eccentric character who thrives on garlic and has never caught a cold. With the right genes, the right diet, the right stuff, colds are said to be unnecessary. The use of vaccines has in fact rendered certain other diseases unnecessary, and it has done so by alerting the immune system, in advance, to the preparations the body needs to make to be able to ward off infection by a given disease agent. With colds too, it is easy to imagine that "better" immune systems will do "better" at warding off colds. We shall have occasion very soon, however, to note that a general vaccine against colds, using classic twentieth-century medical technology, is extremely unlikely to be developed.

When they do work, vaccines lead to the creation of so-called "antibody" factors, immune substances (proteins) that specifically target and facilitate the control of particular toxic or infective agents, be these chemical, bacterial, or viral. Antibody comes in different types. It is produced in different places in the body. And it is localized in different media, for example, sometimes in the blood, sometimes in mucous, and sometimes in the cell interior. Serum antibody, with which we shall be concerned initially, is found in the blood. And most of it is found in a particular blood fraction that is called gamma globulin.

Proper diet, proper exercise, proper rest, proper attitudes, mental tranquility, or some combination of factors such as these, all have been popularly supposed to boost levels of antibody against the common cold. Similarly, a lack of one or more of these "virtues" is often believed to lower antibody levels or immune strength.

If only it were so simple. For the role of good habits, and even the antibody production that they are supposed to facilitate, was never clear, despite the fact that by 1963 some strong evidence had been gathered suggesting that cold viruses often may trigger new antibody that will help protect (for a time) against reinfection by the same virus.

Circulating Antibody and Recent Colds

In 1960, evidence had been reported suggesting that even newborn and premature infants could possess traces of maternal antibody to known cold viruses in their blood, and that these infants were susceptible to infection by at least six known common cold viruses.[2] Moreover, upon suffering natural infections with these viruses, these newborns immediately produced their own antibody to the virus that had infected them. Their immune systems did not seem to need any warm-up or maturational period before becoming competent to respond to cold viruses, even though considerable evidence already existed showing that immune responses to bacterial infections are generally absent or weak during the first few months of life.

In 1963 much of the initial evidence concerning antibodies to cold viruses in adults was summarized in another major paper from Dr. Jackson's common cold research team at Chicago, a paper entitled "The Role of Immunity in the Common Cold and Related Viral Respiratory Infections."[3] However, this paper further underlined some continuing difficulties presented by any simple view concerning the nature of any general resistance to catching colds.

The 1963 paper opened with a report of a study of forty-four volunteers who had developed experimentally induced colds during the continuing series of experimental trials being carried out at Chicago. It had originally been presumed that these colds would, however briefly, lead to increased immune activity protecting against new common colds. Yet within twenty-two weeks each and every one of these volunteers had caught a second, natural cold. Moreover, half of these volunteers had caught a new, natural cold within *forty-four days* of their earlier cold. If antibody to colds did follow from the cure of each earlier cold, that antibody did not last long, or else it did not protect against different varieties of circulating cold virus. And if general constitutional factors were involved in the production of antibody or other protective substances, these appeared to be quite variable over time, and not as characteristic of specific individuals as might otherwise have been expected.

Still, the protective role of some form of immune response to colds could not be denied, for in another study involving volunteers who were challenged on two occasions, a prior challenge with any one of four different viruses resulted in a dramatic drop in the infection rate upon the second exposure to the same virus.[4] In this study, from 33 to 63 percent of volunteers developed colds on their first challenge to one of the four viruses. But only 8 to 18 percent developed colds when challenged a second time, a few fortnights later, with the same viruses. On average this represented an 80 percent reduction in the number of colds originally produced by these same viruses. A reduction of this magnitude (it was shown that the viruses themselves had not weakened between challenges) clearly suggests that people will typically build up specific resistance to at least some cold viruses following an infection by those viruses.

The next two questions addressed by the Chicago team were (1) where might such a protective effect come from, and (2) how well might it protect? Different types of antibody may circulate in the blood (as a constituent of gamma globulin) while other types may circulate in the lymph, and in the saliva, in the nasal mucous, and in tears. Still other immune proteins apparently originate and operate inside certain cells that are at risk for infection. The Chicago team looked only at what is called circulating antibody, and to do this they exposed cold virus to a bath of gamma globulin pooled from a number of blood donors, then administered the treated virus to their volunteers. This procedure too reduced by 80 percent the power of the virus to produce subsequent colds in previously healthy volunteers. Still, 10 percent of volunteers caught colds even from the treated virus. If the gamma globulin was previously boiled (to deactivate its antibody protein) prior to bathing the virus in it, there was no reduction at all in the subsequent power of the virus to produce colds. While antibodies clearly seem to exist in normal blood serum, weakening the cold viruses, there seems to be more involved in avoiding infection than just the possession of a sufficient level of antibody in the blood.

The Chicago team knew that new antibody does not appear in the gamma globulin immediately upon infection. Thus, the next two questions they addressed were (1) how long does it take for antibody to develop, and (2) how long will its protective effect then remain in force? By treating virus with pooled gamma globulin from blood donated by volunteers previously infected with a known virus, blood taken at different points in time after infection, the level of antibody protection at different times was assessed. For the particular virus used in this study, blood serum taken one month after initial infection produced only a 15 percent reduction in colds when used as described above to pre-treat the viral challenge material. But serum taken both six months and one year after initial infection reduced colds by 60 percent when used to pre-treat the challenge material. By eighteen months after infection, the level of protective antibody in the blood serum had dropped noticeably, and by two years there seemed to be no remaining protective effect. Thus, it appears that, following certain colds at least, circulating antibody takes about two months to develop to full strength, and it then offers maximal protection only for about twelve months.

These conclusions were further supported by a new study using the technique of repeated challenge with the same virus. When rechallenge occurred after about three weeks, the incidence of colds the second time dropped by 45 percent from the original incidence. But when rechallenge was postponed until three months after infection, the incidence of colds dropped by fully 87 percent.

Other work by the Chicago group seemed to suggest that circulating antibody (from the blood serum) is normally absent from nasal mucous but that upon the arrival of at least some cold virus in the nose, and before any cold symptoms might appear, gamma globulin does then start to show up in the nasal mucous.[5] Many of the infections studied in connection with this work were *silent* infections, underscoring the possibility that symptomless colds may differ in part from symptomatic colds according to the type and strength of antibody that is available in the capillaries at the site of infection. This observation also underscored the possibility that levels of circulating cold antibodies may be kept high for considerably more than just a year if reinfections with the same virus were to occur, creating booster effects at timely intervals.

Quite distinct from the serum and other varieties of antibody, there are still other immune agents that appear to be important in determining the rate and the symptomatic effects of viral replication inside those cells that meet the air we breathe. One among such agents is interferon. Interferon is produced in and by the same cells that are infected with the virus, and its mode of action appears to be upon the metabolism of these cells, helping them to resist the self-defeating instructions received from the virus. Antibody, by contrast, is often produced far from the infected cells (in bone marrow) or in nearby lymph nodes, and its mode of action is on the viral particles themselves, rendering them less infective, or completely inert.

With the discovery of interferon, and each such agent since, it has been easy to imagine that at last our knowledge concerning the full arsenal of the immune system is essentially complete. In fact, however, there is no reason to suppose that we are close to having any final list of immunological substances. The lesson of history suggests that it is rather unlikely that we are even halfway there, and that it would be impulsive and risky to draw any final conclusions.

Nasal Antibody and Recent Colds

Soon after the effects of circulating antibody began to be understood, new research was reported investigating the different common cold antibodies that are normally found in the nasal mucous. This research was carried out under the auspices of the U.S. National Institute of Health in Bethesda, Maryland, with the assistance of thirty-two volunteers drawn from a nearby federal prison population.[6] The volunteers were studied before and after being challenged with a rather heavy dose of a well-known common cold virus, and the levels of their antibody against this particular virus were monitored, both in blood serum and in nasal secretions. At the same time, their level of infection was measured, indicated by the number of new virus found each day in secretions that were washed from their nostrils for this purpose.

Twenty-three of thirty-two initial volunteers in this research project provided a full set of blood and nasal wash samples for analysis, and it is primarily their data that were reported by the research team in Bethesda. Six of these twenty-three volunteers (26 percent) successfully resisted infection by the challenge dose of virus. All six of these volunteers had had high levels of antibody against this specific virus already present in their blood serum before challenge; four of the six had also had virus-specific antibody present in their *nasal* secretions before being challenged. Of the seventeen remaining volunteers, all of whom became infected, eight had had preexisting serum antibody (six of them strongly so) but only two had had any preexisting nasal antibody at the time of challenge. Nine of the twenty-three volunteers (39 percent) had had no detectable antibody to the challenge virus prior to the experiment, either serum or nasal, and all nine of these volunteers were infected.

Thus, with the dose of virus used in this study, the absence of serum antibody guaranteed that infection would occur, while the presence of high serum antibody reduced the probability of infection to approximately 50 percent. In no case, however, did a volunteer have any nasal antibody present at the time of challenge without having even higher levels of serum antibody. These data suggested that serum antibody may be the more significant protector against reinfection beginning in the third month following the initial infection. But since the data from this study also suggested that the production of specific nasal antibody may begin sooner than the production of serum antibody, it might play a more significant role in the first weeks following each infection.

Not all the volunteers who became infected in this study developed symptomatic colds. It would be interesting to know whether either nasal or serum antibody seemed to play a significant role in controlling the degree of actual virus shedding (a measure of infection) that occurred, and whether or not that antibody seemed in any way to help protect against illness, given that some degree of infection did occur. To answer these questions, the infected volunteers were divided into two groups: (a) those without any prior nasal or serum antibody (numbering nine of the seventeen) and (b) those who did have some prior antibody (eight of seventeen having serum antibody, two of whom also had nasal antibody.) Once they became infected, these two groups did not differ noticeably in the rate at which they shed new virus or the duration of time over which they shed virus. The authors who reported this research were led to conclude that the level of preexisting antibody serves mainly to determine the outcome of an attempt at infection, but that once infection has occurred, then the level of existing antibody at the time of that infection does not appear to determine the severity of the subsequent infection nor the likelihood of that infection leading to a symptomatic cold.

It is worth noting here that even the fundamental precipitating causes (the physiological causes) of common cold *symptoms* have yet to be completely understood.[7] The Bethesda group reconfirmed in their research that when cold symptoms do occur, they generally begin at about the time of maximum viral replication and shedding. At about the same time, or very soon after, large quantities of protein are usually released into the nasal mucous (antibodies appear to constitute some of these proteins) and sometimes blood products appear as well.[8] Moreover, there will often be evidence of local cell damage to some of the cells lining the nose and throat. But all of these effects can also be observed without any cold symptoms present at the time, or later.

Whether it is the presence of many virions that cause cold symptoms when they occur, or whether it is the effects following from some sort of mechanical cell damage caused by these virions (or a reaction to the biochemical debris scattered about by damaged cells), is not well understood. Of course, it may be that none of the above explains cold symptoms. For instance, it has also been suggested that the common cold may be a form of autoimmune response in reaction to the presence of some of the other immune substances created to fight the local infection in the first place. And, inevitably, it has even been suggested that common cold symptoms may be psychogenic, the result of the reaction of some part of the mind to some of the effects described above.

Could Stress Really Be the Key to Turning on Cold Symptoms?

The role of both a person's immune status and that person's level of psychological stress seemed more likely to be significant determinants of general respiratory illnesses in the light of another research report that arrived in the medical literature in 1963. This report emanated from the U.S. Great Lakes Naval Training Center in Great Lakes, Illinois, and the research it described was originally motivated out of concern for the high rate of severe colds and flu that regularly afflicted new military recruits who gathered there from far and wide to receive their basic training.[9] Because of the risks of epidemic disease associated with introducing large numbers of strangers into a crowded environment that is less than fully hygienic, it has long been normal military practice to inoculate new recruits against many of the more dangerous contagious diseases as soon as possible after their arrival at camp. But it is also apparent that the six common vaccines typically administered to the recruits in the first week of basic training place some sort of strain upon the immune system.[10] The considerable number of illnesses that always seemed to occur during basic training might reflect that strain as much as they reflect the unavoidable risks associated with exposures of so many susceptible recruits to so many others who may be infected.

To test this hypothesis about a possible strain upon the immune system due to inoculations, the authors of the Great Lakes study arranged for many of the new recruits arriving in 1961 to receive most of their inoculations beginning only in the fifth week of training, while the remainder of the recruits were inoculated as usual, receiving most of their vaccine in the very first week. Recruits and their instructors were permitted to believe that the delay in inoculation for some companies and not others was the result of some sort of administrative necessity, not part of an active research project. Over the five-month course of this research, there were 5,060 recruits given the standard treatment starting in their first week of training, while 4,322 were given the experimentally delayed schedule with most of their inoculations starting in the fifth week.

These two groups differed in the amount of "severe" respiratory illness they experienced during the first four weeks of their training, but not during the final five weeks. "Severe" respiratory disease was defined as that which required hospitalization, or which was accompanied by moderate fever. On arriving at camp about 2 percent of the recruits had noticeable colds or some other moderately severe respiratory illness for which they were being treated. By their second week at camp that figure had leapt to just over 10 percent for the recruits in the delayed condition, but it was well over 15 percent for the recruits in the regular condition. Thus, severe illness was reduced by approximately one third in the delayed inoculation group (5 percent from 15 percent). By the fifth week of training the incidence of newly reported respiratory diseases was back down to about 4 percent, and by the end of training it was again at about 2 percent for both groups. Moreover, there was no overall increase in new respiratory illnesses among the recruits in the delayed condition following the bulk of their inoculations. Thus, it was not simply the fact that one group had had almost no inoculations that explained the differences between the two groups during the second week of each camp. Some extra factor, presumed to be "stress," seemed to be at work to increase the incidence of illness in the early-inoculation group.

But these findings are for moderately "severe" (febrile) respiratory disease, requiring medical attention, and are not necessarily true of more typical common colds, about which no data were gathered. Moreover, no difference was reported in the duration or the severity of illnesses (once those illnesses were seen at sick bay) between the recruits in each of the two groups. Delaying the onset of inoculations reduced the likelihood of seeing clear illnesses, but it did not seem to noticeably reduce the intensity of those illnesses that did occur.

Now there are at least two ways to interpret these findings, and both have been embraced by portions of the medical intelligence community. On the one hand it may be that inoculations do put stresses on immune functioning, stresses that render the immune system less able to cope with another impending infection or with some preexisting minor infection. In this case one might predict that the duration of illnesses in the immediate inoculation condition should perhaps be longer than similar illnesses in the delayed inoculation condition. But as we just saw, no such differences were reported. Here again, then, we have evidence that immune status prior to infection helps to determine whether or not infection occurs, but apparently not what happens next.

An alternative, but not mutually exclusive interpretation of the Great Lakes findings is that the severe psychological stresses of adjusting to military life during the first three weeks of duty resulted in stresses on the immune system as well. Thus, even the recruits in the delayed inoculation condition showed a four-fold increase in respiratory illness in the early weeks of training, and when later, beginning in the fifth week, they received their main series of inoculations, their already receding rates of new illnesses continued to drop. In contrast, the recruits who were challenged with vaccines from the very beginning showed a five-fold increase in illness over the next two weeks. The vaccines alone cannot explain this 25 percent difference, otherwise these vaccines would have made the same difference in the delayed group after inoculation. Something happening in the first three weeks of training seemed to interact with the stress of inoculations to produce significantly increased levels of moderately severe respiratory illness. That something might have been psychological, or it might have been social, or viral, and/or related to immune status. These data do not begin to settle which it may have been.

The Great Lakes data were gathered in 1961 but were published in 1963. Five years later, in 1968, some related data were published that had been gathered originally in the spring of 1943 in a study of raw recruits undergoing wartime basic training in the U.S. at Ft. Bragg, North Carolina.[11]

These earlier data, also for febrile respiratory illnesses rather than for uncomplicated common colds, made it even clearer that an increased susceptibility to a more severe variety of viral illness is associated with a soldier's first introduction to military life. Grouping the recruits who arrived at Ft. Bragg according to their length of military service prior to arrival, and then analyzing their sick bay files, produced dramatic differences in the observed illness rates.[12] For 1,544 recruits having fewer than ten days of prior military service, the incidence of notable respiratory illness was 13.3 percent. For 287 recruits having between ten and thirty days of prior service, the corresponding rate was 9.1 percent (30 percent lower). And for the 85 recruits having more than thirty days of prior service, their corresponding rate of febrile illness was a mere 2.4 percent (80 percent lower).

Dividing the Ft. Bragg recruits according to their geographical region of origin produced no such dramatic differences. But dividing them by age produced one further interesting and suggestive finding: 269 older recruits (over twenty-nine years of age), who normally would be expected to experience fewer respiratory illnesses than younger men, suffered an illness rate of 16.7 percent. The 1,546 younger men experienced a corresponding rate of only 12.1 percent (27 percent lower). It is tempting to suppose that the risk factor shared by recruits having less than ten days' experience in the military and those who are above twenty-nine years of age would not be their antibody status, but rather it would be the extra stresses they might share (one group because of inexperience; the other because of a more acutely felt loss of independence while learning to adapt to a new and regimented form of life).

Antibody Happens — Just Not Every Time

Earlier we considered evidence suggesting that protective levels of circulating viral antibody for the common cold may only reach an effective maximum eight or more weeks following the initiating infection. But it turns out that even this protective effect is far from automatic. Just as only some will become infected when they are exposed to virus, and among those who are infected only some will become symptomatic, so too only some of those who become infected or symptomatic will show any later increase in their serum antibody levels to the infecting virus.

One early report of this latter phenomenon was described in a pair of papers published in 1966 and 1967.[13] The research team used what were then recently perfected techniques for assaying the amount of circulating antibody specific to particular common cold viruses, and with these techniques they looked at changes in the level of serum antibody between a point in time prior to a naturally occurring cold and a later time three weeks subsequent to that cold. Seventy-seven percent of seventy-seven cold sufferers produced at least a four-fold increase in the concentration of serum antibody specific to the virus that had caused their colds, but 23 percent of the cold sufferers did not. This was true regardless of the initial level of antibody present, although only four of the seventy-seven people had high initial levels of antibody.[14]

Other studies done in other laboratories at about the same time found more than 25 percent of those examined did not show effective rises in specific serum antibody following infection with related cold viruses.[15] Given this evidence, it would be easy to suppose that the occurrence of infection, and illness, and a later antibody response are each matters of chance, which is to say that each might depend upon factors that are either so complex and/or so variable over the short term as to be essentially unpredictable.

How Much Protection Can The Immune System Give Us?

By 1970 techniques for assaying the concentrations of antibody in the blood, and interferon at the site of infection, were well advanced. Studies of these concentrations in volunteers who were experimentally injected with cold viruses soon confirmed that interferon production is apparently unrelated to how much (or how quickly) symptoms decline in cold sufferers. Nor does the amount of interferon produced by the volunteers predict how well volunteers will resist a different infection soon afterward.[16] The role of antibody levels in protecting against colds soon proved to be more significant, however. In 1972 the common cold research group based in the U.S. at the University of Virginia published a comparative study of two cold viruses and how these behave in the presence of different levels of serum antibody.[17] Each of the two viruses studied was found to produce fewer infections in challenged volunteers the more natural antibody to that virus was already present in their blood (from previous, natural encounters with the virus). Volunteers who had *no* detectable prior antibody were used to determine a standard challenge dose of virus that would produce infections 50 percent of the time. But when volunteers had even a low level of prior antibody in their blood the challenge dose of virus needed to produce infection 50 percent of the time was often four to eight times greater than the earlier standard. Higher concentrations of antibody required even stronger doses of virus to produce infections half the time.

It is significant too that while antibody concentration was clearly seen to be protective against infection, once infection had occurred the concentrations of antibody to the challenge virus gave no additional protection against developing the symptoms of an overt cold. In this study roughly 20 percent of all volunteers who became infected developed silent infections, with no cold symptoms. And this was true for those with little and those with lots of natural serum antibody to the challenge virus. Here then is much stronger evidence supporting the earlier conclusion that antibody levels apparently do not protect against a symptomatic common cold except insofar as they do protect against becoming infected in the first place.

These findings by the group at the University of Virginia also made it possible, retrospectively, to estimate the average concentration of wild virus that might have produced the secondary (contaged) colds seen in an earlier epidemiological study carried out on natural colds circulating among families in Virginia.[18] In that earlier study blood samples had been taken before and after colds developed, and thus it was possible to look at the probability of catching a cold given various prior antibody levels against the virus causing each cold. Sometimes the probability was near 50 percent, so that the concentration of virus received in the home could be estimated fairly accurately from the curves generated in the 1972 study just described.

The results of such estimates put the average concentration of the wild virus, when naturally encountered from another ill person at home, in the vicinity of a dose that would typically produce experimental infections (not colds) between 50 and 80 percent of the time among antibody-free volunteers. This is quite a *small* amount of virus, and it is approximately the same amount that is needed to infect 50 percent of optimally prepared tissue cultures in laboratory test tubes.

Small though this amount of virus may be, however, the low rate of transmission of colds (not infections) generally seen in home studies suggests that it is not often that even this amount of active virus will survive the journey from an infected person to a susceptible recipient so as to produce a secondary infection (and, perchance, a cold as well). The doses of virus typically given in an experimental challenge study are generally many times greater than the more modest and typical dose of virus received through normal, natural contacts with another person's cold. This makes all the more striking the fact that often one-half to one-third of all volunteers do not develop colds following the unnaturally heavy dose of virus they receive in an experimental challenge.

And again, it is also striking that even volunteers who have no circulating antibody to the challenge virus frequently succeed in avoiding colds, and sometimes even infection, from these massive challenge doses. Why? Is it true that chance plays a role? And if so, how and where does it play that role? Until we discover the sources of cold *symptoms* (as opposed to cold infections), medicine will probably be unable to answer such questions.

Yet even the natural sources of those very common cold *infections* out in the real world remained mysterious in 1972, despite all the epidemiological and laboratory advances that had been made. There was a continuing debate about the actual mode by which viral transmission was taking place from person to person to person. (Medicine was still very uncomfortable with the idea that colds really might be in some sense commensal, given the existing data on epidemics like those in Spitzbergen and in the Virgin Islands, and, given the fact that "control" volunteers at Salisbury almost never developed spontaneous colds.) For a time, then, it began to look as though experiments would very soon be able to settle the question of how cold viruses are in fact naturally transmitted. It is to these new experiments, concerned with determining the mechanism for most natural viral transmissions, that we turn next.

Cloud Babies and Cold Kisses: Wisconsin, 1960, to Salisbury, 1975

"What is needed is a carefully designed experimental approach to show how staphylococci can perform the preposterous feat of seemingly 'evaporating' from a moist surface without any hint of a sneeze. When this almost unbelievable phenomenon can be explained, the cloud baby will have a firm foundation."

— *Anonymous Editor,* American Journal of Diseases of Children, *1960*

Common sense persuades us that cold germs travel through the air because it often appears that we have caught them, with no direct contact, far across a crowded room. And yet, experience also reminds us that our first impressions can be misleading, that there could be invisible contacts, unnoticed touches, encounters that might be necessary to transmit cold viruses. We do not normally remember, for instance, when we have last put our fingers to our faces, greeting our lips, wiping our nostrils, soothing our eyes. You may notice even while reading, as you bring your attention to it, that sooner than you might have guessed, your nose has been touched, or your lips, or your eyes. These acts are frequent, but unconscious, and they have led many in medical intelligence to question whether cold viruses really do, and really need to, travel by air to reach their destinations.

Enter the Cloud Babies

In 1960, however, travel by air appeared to be the route for the transmission of germs for all the most common infections, especially in light of recent discoveries concerning "cloud babies." A "cloud baby" was the name given to *asymptomatic* newborns infected with the bacillus *staphylococcus aureus*, who shed these bacteria into the surrounding air in particles so small that they floated for days at a time in an invisible cloud surrounding the otherwise healthy infant.

The pediatrician who named cloud babies, and who first reported investigations of them, was Heinz Eichenwald.[1] Dr. Eichenwald, with the help of others, was able to demonstrate that cloud babies do not shed bacteria from their body surfaces as do babies who suffer obvious skin and other visible symptoms caused by their staph infections; instead, cloud babies shed bacteria at their heads, apparently from their mouths and noses. Moreover, Eichenwald and his colleagues were able to show that the presence of an asymptomatic cloud baby in the hospital nursery could convert other babies who were asymptomatic carriers of the staph bacteria, and who were not themselves shedding bacteria, into new cloud babies. Without another cloud baby in the nursery, the asymptomatic carrier babies remained simply as carriers, noninfective to others. But with the arrival of a cloud baby in the nursery, these carriers would often become cloud babies themselves one or two days later.

Further observations by Dr. Eichenwald and his colleagues suggested that the presence of some undiscovered transmissible factor, separate from the staph bacterium itself, turns normal carriers of the bacterium into cloud babies who begin broadcasting staph bacteria to others through the air. The recipients of these floating bacteria can then become infective themselves, either as symptomatic sufferers or as new asymptomatic cloud babies.

Infants who became cloud babies did not stay that way forever. Typically, they contaminated the air around them for less than two weeks. The question faced by Dr. Eichenwald was, what could the mysterious "factor" be that changes babies from quiescent carriers into cloud babies, and back again? There was some reason to suppose that a virus might be responsible. So the research team attempted to cultivate any nasal virus that might turn out to be present in cloud babies and/or in those carrier babies who were not broadcasting bacteria into the air.

Three separate epidemics of staph infection were studied in a hospital nursery. In one of the three epidemics, no viruses could be observed in the nasal samples taken from either type of baby. But during both of the other two epidemics, a particular virus was found in every one of five cloud babies, and in none of five carrier babies. Moreover, the two different viruses that were isolated, one from each of the two epidemics, were both common cold viruses; in one epidemic it was adenovirus type 2 in every case, while in the other epidemic it was always ECHO Virus type 20.

If a common cold virus really was converting newborn babies into devices for broadcasting minute staph bacteria into the aerial sea, it would be easy to imagine a virus causing infected children to broadcast the far smaller particles of the cold virus itself in the same manner. Thus, aerosol transmission of cold viruses seemed very likely to be *the* important route for the transmission of cold viruses.

Exit Cloud Babies; Exit Airborne Transmission Too?

Still, we must not ignore the early experiments at Salisbury, and how difficult it was to get infection to cross from the "donors" on one side of a room to the susceptible volunteers waiting on the other side.[2] Even in the experiment where donors and volunteers mingled and ate together, fewer than one in ten of the volunteers caught colds, about the same small percentage as in the no-contact (air only) experiments. By the mid-1950s the Salisbury researchers had concluded that most contagions probably occur via airborne transmission, but that even under nearly ideal conditions this route is not often favorable to successful transmissions.

Ten years later, in 1965, the group at Harvard Hospital, Salisbury, tried again, this time using a different cold virus.[3] The cold virus on this occasion was coxsackievirus A21, chosen because few volunteers had existing antibodies to it, and because techniques for tracking this virus were by then well advanced. Infected volunteers with cold symptoms were asked to sneeze into air-sampling bags and into handkerchiefs for the purpose of seeing to what extent they may shed and broadcast virus. Large variations were found between individuals, and from moment to moment within individuals. Even so, any one sneeze put very few virus particles into the air, and those that were broadcast seemed to lose their infective powers rather quickly. Eleven volunteers who inhaled air from the air-bags into which infected "donors" had just sneezed and snorted did not become infected.

When infected donor volunteers shedding virus were then assigned to live for nine days in an isolated hospital apartment with one or two other susceptible volunteers, contagion of the exposed recipients took place in just three of twenty attempts. The successful transmission attempts only occurred when the donor had received very high initial doses of the virus, doses far in excess of what normally would be needed to produce infection, and when considerable time was spent in proximity together. Exposure for only a few hours consistently failed to produce any transmission of these infections. The direct placement of infectious drops of virus (1) into the nose, (2) into the eyes, (3) onto the back of the throat, and (4) on the threshold of the nostrils, generally produced declining proportions of transmitted infections, in that order. The site of most susceptibility was clearly inside the nose, and this was also the site where the great majority of infectious virus was found to be shed by the donors. Very little virus, for instance, was found in the droplets of saliva that were broadcast during some sneezes.

These findings with coxsackievirus can be construed to suggest that aerial transmission of such colds is rare since only prolonged contact of isolated roommates, or direct inoculation of the virus into the nose, produced new infections. Inhaling concentrated air exhaled by donors did not produce transmission, nor did direct exposure to donors for a few hours or even for one or two days. It is tempting to conclude that direct physical contact, by hand or object, may be required to transmit coxsackievirus. Alternatively, one might conclude that aerial transmission of this virus is the primary mode of contagion, but that a large number of virions must accumulate in the nostril before infection can occur, a process that takes considerable time spent in close proximity to an infectious person who is shedding large numbers of the virions into the air. The Salisbury team had their own reasons for preferring this latter interpretation of their findings.

Attempting a New Defense of the Aerosol Hypothesis

A study of rhinovirus transmitted by aerosol was also published in 1965 by a research team at the U.S. National Institute of Health in Bethesda, Maryland. This study too seems to provide support for the importance of either aerial transmission or direct contact with these types of colds.[4] To simulate the transmission of virus through the water vapor in the air we breathe, volunteers were asked to inhale (through the nose) a prepared aerosol spray containing exceedingly small droplets in which had been suspended particles of a rhinovirus. Normally, this virus produces a classic head cold. But administering the virus in this fashion led instead to chest colds in every case, with cough and chest pain similar to "colds" that are more commonly seen only in some military personnel suffering from rhinovirus infections. Thus, one might conclude that small-droplet aerosols are not normally the means by which this rhinovirus is transmitted naturally, because normally this virus is associated with head colds. (Larger droplets, of the type generated by coughs and sneezes, are heavier, and they tend to fall out of the air very soon after being broadcast; it is they that would typically lodge just inside the nose if they were inhaled, rather than further down in the trachea.) On the other hand, this study can be taken as further evidence for the feasibility of aerosol transmission, and especially for its possible importance in crowded military barracks.

Subsequent work by the same research team at Bethesda's NIH eventually persuaded them that aerosols are important natural vehicles of viral transmission, for certain colds at least.[5] Using the same technique described above, but this time with an adenovirus instead of a rhinovirus, similar chest colds were produced after volunteers inhaled aerosols containing virus. Volunteers who were given the same virus in an aerosol composed of somewhat larger droplets (so as to deposit most of the virus in the nasal passages instead of in the trachea) also developed chest colds, however, not head colds. These "large-particle aerosols" probably delivered less virus overall, and possibly delivered some virus to the lower respiratory system. Somewhat fewer colds were seen in the group receiving large-particle aerosols. Because aerosols composed of particles of each size produced the same lower respiratory cold symptoms that are typically seen in raw military recruits, the authors of this research report concluded that small-particle aerosols must be responsible for those transmissions that do occur in a military barracks. But why then were there no head colds at all in the large-particle condition?

Counting Coughs and Sampling Sneezes

A third study by this NIH group was carried out, this time taking careful measurements of the amount of virus put into the air when symptomatic volunteers coughed, sneezed, and breathed.[6] The virus studied was the coxsackievirus type A21, which was believed to be typically transmitted by the airborne route. Both coughing and sneezing by symptomatic volunteers was carried out into a tight-fitting mask that led to a small, collapsed weather balloon.[7] All the air put into the balloon was analyzed for the presence of virus, as was all particulate material flushed from the interior wall of the balloon. In a separate procedure, samples were taken from all expired air breathed out by volunteers for thirty minutes during the period of maximum infection and illness.

No virus at all was ever recovered from exhaled air in this study.

Coughing produced recoverable virus about 40 percent of the time, generally from the air in the balloon more than from the wall of the balloon. Sneezing produced recoverable virus about 50 percent of the time, generally from the wall of the balloon more than from the air in the balloon. The amount of virus put into the air by an average cough in this study was about the amount that would cause infection 50 percent of the time if all of it were given directly to volunteers in aerosol form. The amount of virus put into the air by the typical sneeze was twice this amount. And on a few occasions, sneezes put hundreds of times more virus into the air than this more typical amount. The presence of a stuffy nose or a dripping nose at the time of a sneeze usually increased greatly the amount of virus broadcast by the sneeze, but this was not true for coughs. It might appear then that sneezes, rather than coughs, are probably responsible for any airborne virus leading to contagion of these colds. On the contrary, however, additional data convinced the researchers that it is the coughs, not the sneezes, that are primarily responsible for those coxsackievirus found in the air of the rooms occupied by symptomatic volunteers.

Air samples were taken in the living quarters of each volunteer and it quickly become apparent that the more virus being shed in the nasal passages of the volunteer (determined by direct swabbing in the nose), the more virus particles could be found in the air of that volunteer's room. But only the amounts of virus found in cough samples correlated with the amounts being shed inside the nose. The virus broadcast by sneezes was not found to be a function of the amount of virus being produced, but depended instead on certain readiness factors such as blockage of the nose. It was further discovered that for any one individual, the more virus recovered in cough samples on a given day, the more virus was recovered from that individual's room air on the same day. Sneeze samples did not show this same relationship. So the researchers were led to conclude that coughs are more important in contaminating room air with coxsackievirus than are sneezes, despite the fact that any good sneeze put relatively more virus into the air than did an average cough. The normal relative frequency of these two events was not examined, however.

Finally, to show that the coxsackievirus put into the air by normal coughs and sneezes could be sufficient to produce transmission of these colds, the NIH researchers did an experiment in which infected and symptomatic "donors" lived in a one-room barracks on one side of a double screened barrier while susceptible volunteers (the "recipients") lived in the same room on the other side.[8] Air was constantly circulated from side to side by fans, and samples were taken of the air to confirm the presence or absence of the A21 virus in the air. On the third day after ten men had been challenged with a large dose of A21, A21 virus was first detected (for a time, only on this day) in air samples from both sides of the barracks room. (All ten of the challenged men became infected, and seven of the ten shed virus in cough and sneeze samples taken for the next few days.)

Then three days later, on the sixth day following the initial challenge, five of nineteen susceptible volunteers on the other side of the room divider became infected with A21. It seemed very clear that aerosol transmission had taken place "naturally." Of the five men who became infected on this day, three developed visible symptoms and were removed from the room within four hours of symptom onset. (The two men with silent infections would not have been identifiable until after time-consuming lab tests had been completed.) Symptomatic volunteers on the "donor" side of the room continued to be kept in the room.

Then, on day 8, for the second time only, virus was again detected in the air of the room for that one day. Four days later, on day 12, ten of the fourteen remaining uninfected recipients became infected. While physical contact with the two asymptomatic but previously infected recipients (living on the same side of the room) might arguably have produced this second set of ten infections, all on the same day, that seems highly improbable. It seemed to the authors of this research report that airborne transmission had clearly been demonstrated by this experiment on two occasions.

Is Airborne Transmission the Most Significant Kind?

As the experimental evidence mounted implicating the probable importance of airborne transmission for at least some colds, especially any colds that follow long hours of exposure to persons shedding virus, there were still those who read the epidemiological evidence to suggest that in the real world direct physical contact might be much the more important means of contagion. Foremost among those who leaned in this direction were the leaders of the research team at the University of Virginia Medical School, Jack M. Gwaltney, Jr. and J. Owen Hendley. Theirs was the study already reported (at the end of chapter 9) implicating, but then partially exonerating, school openings as the trigger for the sudden epidemics of colds that so often occur each September. Gwaltney and Hendley concluded in their earlier study (published in 1969) that it was cold weather, with its associated indoor recess times leading to more direct physical contacts among the children, that was probably responsible for the typical fall epidemics of colds. Still, it was the physical *contact* that seemed to them most likely to be producing most of the colds, not the falling outdoor temperatures per se, nor any unventilated indoor air.

In 1973 Hendley and Gwaltney reported a series of small experimental studies trying to establish whether or not physical contact is as important a mechanism of contagion as airborne transmission.[9] Their work was carried out with rhinoviruses, the most common sources of colds, and not with coxsackieviruses or adenoviruses. In a series of brief exploratory studies they traced the potential travels of type 39 rhinovirus (RV39) from the sources of virus shedding in the noses of cold sufferers to the nasal passages of susceptible others. It all began with sufferers of native colds.

Ten people suffering from natural rhinovirus colds were tested without prior warning for the presence of active virus on their hands by rinsing their fingers in a viral collecting broth. In four of the ten cases, the presence of rhinovirus on the fingers was confirmed. When tested for the presence of rhinovirus in a simple cough or sneeze, only one of four volunteers broadcast any detectable virus.[10] When an additional twenty-one volunteers with natural rhinovirus colds were tested for virus in either a cough or a sneeze, only one of thirteen persons who sneezed, and none of eight who coughed, produced detectable virus. Small amounts of rhinovirus were detected in pure saliva samples from eight out of sixteen natural cold sufferers. At the same time very large amounts of the virus were regularly detected in nasal secretions. It seemed very probable that most rhinoviruses leaving their host do so through the nose by way of fingers and handkerchiefs, rather than through droplets of saliva (and nasal fluid) from coughs and sneezes. Earlier research by the group at the Salisbury Common Cold Research Unit had shown that colds were transmitted very poorly by contaminated handkerchiefs and gauze.[11] But in this new 1973 study, fingers became the leading suspects as the primary sources of rhinovirus contagion.

The next questions addressed were: if virus is on a finger does it remain present and infective for some time, and can it then be transferred to the fingers of others? A large dose of RV39 was allowed to dry on the hands of eighteen student volunteers. In fourteen cases their test hands were kept out of use for the next three hours as would be the case during sleep. In two cases their test hands were used normally, while they studied, and in two other cases the hands were used first to eat dinner and then to study.

Each hour for the next three hours certain test areas on the hands were rinsed, and the rinse was examined for active virus. Unused hands were found to have active virus remaining after one hour in ten of the fourteen cases. And in three of four cases tested, there was still active virus remaining on unused hands three hours after deposition. (One of these four "resting" subjects soon contracted a cold and RV39 was confirmed as the cause of that cold, suggesting self-inoculation of the virus that had been put on his hand.) In the case of hands that were "active," no virus was found after three hours, but in three of the four cases infective virus was still present on the fingers after one hour.

Next, Hendley and Gwaltney looked at the transfer of virus from "donor" fingers to "recipient" fingers. A drop of liquid containing a large dose of RV39 was spread on the fingers of one volunteer and allowed to dry for twenty minutes. Another volunteer then stroked these contaminated fingers with his own, which were then rinsed to test for the presence of virus. Successful transfer of the active virus was documented in three of five such trials. Similar transfers of virus that had been deposited first on polished surfaces (such as Formica, stainless steel, and varnished wood) and on fabrics (such as nylon and silk) were also attempted. RV39 was shown to survive well for three hours and more on such surfaces. In fifteen of sixteen attempts to contaminate the fingers of recipients who stroked a plastic surface one or more hours after this surface had been contaminated, there was successful transfer. The authors concluded that contaminated fingers could well become sources of contamination to others, and in particular, to the fingers of others.

The next question was, if a recipient had active virus on his or her fingers, was self-inoculation of that virus probable or not? To begin to answer this, the researchers left their laboratories for the field and quietly began observing the unconscious behavior of colleagues seated in conference at Medical Grand Rounds (facing one way in an amphitheater). They also looked at the behavior of young students sitting around a circular table while at Sunday school. Observations on each person were continued for about thirty minutes and nasal-probing and eye-rubbing episodes were noted in these public situations. During 89 person-hours of observation done on 124 people, 29 people were seen probing their nostrils and 33 people were seen rubbing their eyes.

Many of the people under observation engaged repeatedly in these activities, although only the first episode of each activity was reported in this study. On average, in each of these public situations, touching the eyes occurred in slightly more than one out of every three persons observed for up to an hour. In the amphitheater setting, nasal probing (or rubbing) was seen even more frequently than was touching the eyes (one in every 2.4 persons), but around the circular table in Sunday school, during twenty-one person-hours of observation, only a single episode of nasal probing was observed. It seemed to the research team in Virginia that self-inoculation of virus, from fingers placed either directly into the nose or into the eyes (whence the virus would be washed through into the nose) might reasonably be expected to provide multiple opportunities for infection each day in most people, especially when the person is unobserved, in private.

It had long been clear from experimental studies that cold virus dropped into the nose or the eyes stood a good chance of producing infections, while virus placed directly onto the back of the throat stood much less chance of infecting, and virus placed directly in the mouth stood very little chance of infecting. What was not clear, however, was whether or not virus on contaminated fingers would be sufficient to produce colds if they were self-inoculated into the nose or eyes. Thus, in the final experiment in this series, the team at the University of Virginia examined the effect of deliberate nasal probes and deliberate eye-rubbing in volunteers whose fingers had been previously contaminated with RV39.

Each of the eleven volunteers selected for this final study were first shown to be free of serum antibody to RV39. Drops containing strong doses of this virus were then allowed to dry for approximately two hours on a plastic surface after which the volunteer rubbed his index finger across the contaminated surface. Immediately afterward the subject was instructed either to probe his nose with the contaminated finger, or to rub the corner of his eye with it. Four of the subjects were directed to rub their eyes, and of these, two became infected. Seven of the subjects were directed to probe their noses, and of these, two became infected. All four of these infected subjects developed typical common colds.

Transmission of at least some colds produced by physical contact, in particular by contact in the form of self-inoculation from the fingers, seemed all but proved as a result. In fact, however, there were many who still believed that aerosol transmission was the key player out in the real world of schools, stores, and recreation rooms. These data from Virginia only served to increase the interest in the question of which *was* the more important route of natural contagion: transmission by air, or transmission by hand?

Kissing (for Science) Is Not Injurious to One's Health

It was not long before further evidence was presented bearing on this question by researchers at the University of Wisconsin. One interpretation of their new evidence might have been (yet was not) that to ask which route is the more important for contagion is unrealistic. For such a question about the medium of "transmission" assumes a natural and ubiquitous contagion factor that has not always been found where we have expected to find it. If the new Wisconsin study proved to be surprising and puzzling, perhaps it was because its underlying assumption was false.

So it was that in 1972 and 1973, the team at Wisconsin reported a series of small experimental studies of colds among married couple volunteers. The researchers were intrigued by epidemiological data they had gathered in which surprisingly little contagion had been observed among married students when either one of the couple had a cold. Thus, in one early experimental study that became widely known but was documented only in the brief published abstracts of papers presented at conferences, volunteers who were free of antibody to a given rhinovirus spent time (in the name of science) in prolonged kisses with an infected donor of that virus.[12] The published abstracts tell us that only 7 percent of such contacts produced colds. It is not clear whether those few colds were necessarily transmitted by mouth or whether nasal contamination might also have been an occasional result of the kissing. But no matter; whether one holds that aerosol transmission or physical transmission of virus is the more important route, the low transmission rate seen in this study of kissing adults could be equally surprising. By 1973 it seemed clear, however, that colds are probably not transmitted by mouth.

But if aerosol transmission of rhinoviruses (the most prevalent type of cold virus) truly is the predominant mode of contagion, there were other problems with the experimental data that continued to worry prominent researchers such as Dr. Gwaltney at Virginia.[13] Gwaltney was aware of at least two unpublished studies, in addition to those published studies already described here, where experimental attempts at aerosol transmission of rhinovirus colds had failed.[14] In one such study, by members of the same NIH team that carried out the successful barracks room study of coxsackievirus A21 described earlier, symptomatic "donors" with induced rhinovirus colds resided on one side of a wire mesh barrier in a closed barracks room while susceptible recipients resided on the other. But in this study, no contagion of the rhinovirus colds occurred.[15] In a second study cited by Gwaltney, infectious and susceptible volunteers (three or more of each) were confined in a closed office room and the "donors" attempted to produce infectious aerosols by loud singing while playing cards. No contagion occurred in this study either.[16] It is not clear how long the recipients were exposed to potentially contaminated air in either of these studies. Supporters of the view that aerosols are the more important natural route of transmission would point out that long time spans spent inhaling naturally contaminated air seem to be required to produce infections.

If the experimental data made Dr. Gwaltney cautious about inferring the importance of aerosols in rhinovirus transmission, others came to similar conclusions based on the epidemiological evidence. Dr. Douglas, one of the team that carried out the two aerosol studies in the barracks room that had been divided in half by wire mesh, noted in 1970 that "rhinovirus illness does not occur in epidemics, but rather moves slowly through population groups."[17] The predominant serotype (i.e., the particular type of rhinovirus) that is circulating at any one time changes frequently, and no one serotype sweeps in and out of a given county or office building as might be expected if aerosol transmission predominated.

Contaminated Objects and Common Colds

Then in 1975, from the Common Cold Unit at Harvard Hospital in Salisbury, came the report of another study looking into the possibility of the transfer of rhinovirus by indirect contacts: from fingers to objects to new fingers and thence to a new nose. The author of this report was Dr. Sylvia Reed, and her findings were in many respects very similar to those reported earlier by the team including Hendley and Gwaltney at Virginia.[18] She too found that among sufferers of rhinovirus colds nearly half had virus on their fingers when tested without prior warning. Not surprisingly, those from whom virus was successfully recovered on the fingers tended to have (1) greater amounts of virus present in the nose, (2) more severe cold symptoms, and they were (3) more likely to remember blowing their nose in the previous five minutes and (4) were less likely to have washed their hands in the previous thirty minutes. On occasion, however, those who recently had washed their hands or who were shedding little virus still had detectable amounts of virus on their fingers. Dr. Reed also reported on the *amount* of virus recovered from the fingers of her volunteers, and sometimes that amount was not large even if it was sufficient to infect.

When various objects in the living quarters of infected volunteers were specially rinsed and tested for the presence of virus, rhinovirus was detected on six of forty objects examined, including three coffee cups, a cigarette lighter, and the handle on an iron. The amount of virus recovered from these objects seemed quite small, however, being barely enough in total to produce an infection in experimental human volunteers perhaps 50 percent of the time. When drops of rhinovirus were allowed to dry on various surfaces, Reed found, as had the Virginia team before her, that considerable infectious material still remained on most surfaces after three hours. In particular, rhinovirus placed on the handles of stainless steel spoons and left undisturbed indoors showed very little loss of infective power over as much as thirty-six hours. After four days, however, all potency of the virus had vanished.

Reed was also able to show that in order to transfer any significant amount of rhinovirus from a contaminated finger onto an object such as a coffee cup, the contaminated finger had to be damp. Once drops of virus had dried on the fingers, very little of that virus was transferred to other surfaces when those surfaces were rubbed. However, transfer in the reverse direction, from dry objects to dry fingers, or from dry fingers to dry fingers, was rather more efficient. Despite these findings, and largely because of the apparently modest quantities of transferred virus recorded in these tests, Dr. Reed was led to infer that "the chance of successful transmission to a susceptible recipient by these routes must be low." She went on to say, "It is clear that transmission of rhinovirus infection by indirect contact cannot be discounted, although our studies of the objects surrounding our volunteers and their non-infected flat-mates, suggest that it is not likely to be of paramount importance."[19] This is not to say that aerosol transmission of natural rhinovirus colds must then be supposed to be paramount. Dr. Reed went on to note that ". . . it is also hard to produce proof of the importance of airborne transmission."[20]

Thus, by the end of 1975 it seemed that certain cold viruses (for example, coxsackievirus A21) probably are transmitted primarily in aerosols, but other viruses, particularly the rhinoviruses tested in the experiments just described, probably are not. To some, the evidence seemed strong for the existence of viral transmission by direct contact (e.g., a mother wiping the nose of her symptomatic child) or by indirect contact (a clerk taking a plastic credit card from an infected customer), setting the stage for self-inoculation and subsequent infection with the virus. To others, such scenarios appeared too unlikely to explain the sources of any but a very few natural colds.

In sifting and understanding the evidence concerning avenues for the transmission of colds, the medical intelligence community had little reason to question two modest, yet very important, additional assumptions. One such assumption dealt with the equivalence of virus that had been cultivated in the laboratory to virus found out in the wild. The other assumption dealt with the equivalence of volunteers living isolated and under observation to the rest of the population. It just seemed reasonable to suppose that the minimum quantity of laboratory-assayed virus that was observed to produce colds in challenged volunteers who were quarantined during the time of study was the same amount of wild virus required to produce natural colds in non-volunteers who were busy living out a typical life while paying scant attention to any small changes felt in their noses and throats.

However, should there happen to be somewhat different rules and principles operating in the transmission of viruses, one set for instance for a real world full of children, and another set for a laboratory world full of adults and controls, then those differences could quite change the interpretation of the data from a study like Dr. Reed's. What seemed to her to be very little contamination of the objects that she examined might loom much larger in the outside world. Or, the amount of virus necessary to produce colds in comfortable volunteers (on vacation from normal routine) might be much greater than the amount needed to produce colds in stressed civilians too busy to be concerned with their health. And of course, the difference, if it existed, might also go the other way. Colds might be even harder to produce outside the laboratory than has been typically assumed. This seemed to be what Dr. Reed was thinking when she found her own experimental data about indirect contacts to be quite unconvincing. Like others at Salisbury before her, the conclusion that a majority of colds are transmitted by aerosols still seemed compelling, however uncooperative the evidence might sometimes be in helping to confirm that conclusion.

In 1975 then, common sense still argued that cold germs must be able to travel some distance through the air. Medical intelligence remained divided on the aerosol versus physical-contact question. Everyone was awaiting the arrival of new and better research evidence; and soon, that new evidence did indeed arrive.

15

Traversing Sickrooms, by Air and by Hand: Seattle, 1975, to Wisconsin, 1980

"Since person-to-person transfer of rhinovirus was so dependent upon time spent together and shedding of large amounts of virus by the donor, it seems possible that the chain of infection could be interrupted by environmental manipulation."

— *D. J. D'Alessio et al., 1976*

For centuries laypeople had been keeping watch on the comings and goings of their family colds, and, by 1965 the community of common cold researchers had been doing much the same thing, on a grander scale, over the course of a few decades. But the viruses themselves, the viruses that presumably trigger our colds, always did their coming and going invisibly, unwatched. Then, once effective techniques for isolating and typing cold viruses had been developed, a small but important set of so-called "virus watch" projects was initiated in various American communities, attempting at last to study the comings and goings of various viruses out in the natural world where humans mix together. Thus, large-scale "virus watch" programmes were carried out for a time in Cleveland, in New York City, and in Seattle, while more specialized virus watch programmes were undertaken in, for instance, Tecumseh, Michigan, in Chicago, and in Charlottesville, Virginia.[1]

Common cold viruses remain, however, masters of invisibility. The standard spy techniques of eavesdropping with parabolic microphones, of tracking with night vision telescopes, of following unnoticed in unmarked cars, or surreptitiously implanting radio tracking devices, all these techniques are out of the question when viral surveillance is intended. When watching virus, something more like big game tracking must be used, searching for signs that the beasts have been this way, heading west perhaps, about sixty hours ago. A few of the herd may be trapped for identification and measurement. But with virus there is no releasing them back into the wild, to catch up with the others, while we carefully monitor their activity. The best we can hope to do is discover who has come this way, traveling under what conditions, and where, perhaps, they seemed to be headed. Still, a virus watch can be quietly exciting, because surprises do happen. One learns to expect the unexpected.

Subclinical in Seattle

In 1975 the virus watch team at the University of Washington School of Public Health and Community Medicine reported in some detail on the epidemiology of rhinovirus infections observed among a large number of Seattle families during the period 1965–69. What made their report particularly interesting was that for the first time it provided considerable data on the number and fate of *subclinical* infections introduced into previously uninfected families, and this permitted the first rough estimates of the secondary colds and subclinical colds that followed soon after.

Among some 258 rhinovirus infections that were successfully detected as index colds introduced into Seattle families, 26 percent proved to be silent infections (of which the family was unaware) while 74 percent were symptomatic colds. Transmission of infection to other susceptible (i.e., antibody-free) family members proved to be twice as frequent when the index case was symptomatic as when the index case was subclinical. These findings held true both for the subset of those rhinovirus serotypes having "high" overall transmission rates (where secondary colds of this same viral type were soon seen among susceptible others in at least 60 percent of the exposed families) as well as with those different rhinovirus serotypes having lower overall transmission rates (where secondary infections were detected in fewer than 55 percent of the exposed families).[2]

The Seattle virus watch detected and recorded infections due to at least thirteen different rhinovirus serotypes that were occurring with considerable frequency (from among more than sixty distinct serotypes that were then known) and it found that under natural conditions these different rhinoviruses did seem to have rather different overall rates of contagion. In general, the findings in Seattle also suggested that at least 40 percent of all rhinovirus infections are subclinical infections.[3]

But most important, these first results made it clear that, at least within families, the apparent transmission of rhinovirus colds is *not* a rare and difficult event, whether that transmission may be taking place via aerosols or through direct physical contacts. Something about actually having cold symptoms, however, clearly increases the likelihood of natural transmission. For those persuaded that aerosols are the major route of transmission, that something might be seen as the presence of coughs and sneezes (but then why did so many subclinical infections also manage to get transmitted?) while for those persuaded that physical contacts provide the major route of transmission, the presence of cold symptoms might be seen as a means for providing far richer (wetter) chances for contamination of the fingers and other objects.

Fondling or Simple Togetherness: Is Either Risky?

Soon, in 1976, the authors of the widely known kissing study that had been done at Madison, Wisconsin, reported on follow-up work that looked for the probable routes of natural transmission of rhinovirus colds.[4] Twenty-four childless married couples volunteered to be subjects, all of whom were first found to be free of significant antibody to the rhinoviruses to be employed in the study. One member of each couple was then challenged with a dose of rhinovirus (either type 16 or type 55) of sufficient strength to produce infection in every case and cold symptoms in all but one case. For the next seven days each volunteer was monitored closely for infection, for symptoms, and for virus shedding, and at the same time twelve of the twenty-four couples kept records of the amount of time they spent together and what they were doing during that time together.

Four spouses from among the twelve donors who were infected with RV55 soon became infected themselves, and five spouses from among the twelve donors who were infected with RV16 also became infected. Fifteen (63 percent) of the spousal volunteers did not contage the infection of their donor spouse.

It was immediately apparent from the data on virus shedding that the likelihood of viral transmission depended strongly on the maximum level of virus produced in the nose of each donor. The twenty-four donors were divided into three categories according to the highest single amount of virus recovered from any one daily nasal wash sample (invariably a sample taken on the second or third day following challenge, at the time when symptoms were normally first beginning to appear). The richest samples from seven of the donors were found to contain at least five thousand times the small dose of virus that is necessary to infect laboratory tissue cultures with a probability of 50 percent. (This amount is usually abbreviated as the $TCID_{50}$, or simply as the TCID, the "tissue culture infectious dose.")

Among those seven strong-shedding donors, five had spouses who became infected too, a transmission rate of 71 percent. Another eight donors had maximal nasal samples with virus in amounts between 500 and 2,000 TCID. Among these eight moderate-shedding donors, three had spouses who became infected too, a transmission rate of 38 percent. The remaining nine donors all had maximal nasal samples with less than 500 TCID of virus detected in them. Among these nine lightly shedding donors, only one had a spouse who became infected too, a transmission rate of 11 percent. It seem as though successful transmission is quite unlikely unless large amounts of virus are present for a time in the nose of the donor. What then about the hands of the donors?

Finger wash samples were taken from each of the twelve donors receiving RV16, in an effort to measure contamination of the hands with virus. Five of seven donors for whom virus was detected on their fingers had spouses who became infected. None of the five donors without any detectable virus on their fingers transmitted their infections to their spouses. Put another way, in every case where the spouse was infected (in five of twelve couples) the donor was found to have RV16 on his or her fingers at some point. And in every case where the donor did not have detectable RV16 on his or her fingers (in another five of the twelve couples) the spouse did not become infected. In two other cases where the spouse was not infected, the donor did have detectable RV16 on his or her fingers at some point.

Naturally, there was also a very close association between the amount of virus shedding going on in the nose (as measured with nasal wash samples) and the likelihood that virus would be detected on the fingers of the donor. This strongly implied that since successful transmission of colds was also associated with high virus shedding scores, finger contamination provided the typical means for transmission of the virus to the spouse. But another factor proved to be strongly related to successful transmission of these colds, a factor that complicated the picture slightly, although at first it would appear to underscore the importance of finger contamination and direct contact. This third predictor of successful transmission was the total time the couple spent together in the same air space during the week of the study.

If contaminated fingers are the typical means for transmitting infectious material from one person to another, one might expect that the amount of time each couple spent directly touching, especially on days 2 and 3 following the challenge of the donor, would predict successful transmission of the virus among those donors who had virus on their fingers. But while daily records of the time spent in "direct contact" (that is, "embracing, kissing, etc.")[5] were kept by the twelve couples exposed to RV16, these day-by-day direct contact scores were not reported by the authors of the Wisconsin study. Only the *total* time spent in "direct contact" was reported, over the full seven days of observation, and that overall total proved to be quite *unrelated* to the success or failure of transmission. What was related to the likelihood of contagion, as noted above, was the total time spent together in the same air space over the full week of observation.

Here too, it would be important to know the time each couple spent in the same air space on days 2, 3, and 4, the days when it appears that all but one of the secondary infections actually took place in this study. However, we are told only that among the eleven RV16 couples for whom complete data were available, all four of the couples where the spouse became infected spent at least 120 hours together in the same air space during the week, while six of the seven couples where the spouse did not become infected spent less than 115 hours in the same air space during the week.[6]

For the authors of this research report, these observations clearly seemed to support the conclusion that time spent together was important and that direct physical contact might not be so important. It should be noted, however, that the four donors of the transmitted colds who spent rather more time than average with their spouses also had rather more severe cold symptoms than many of the other donors studied. One might imagine that because of their pronounced colds, and later those of their spouses, these donors were led to spend more time at home than they might otherwise have done. In other words, it is possible that the factors that led to successful transmissions also led to increasing the time that the couple spent together over the course of the whole week, rather than the other way around. Only the data on shared time *prior* to the appearance of the secondary cold could persuasively imply the possible importance of aerosol transmission in this study if taken in conjunction with some evidence to suggest that the amount of time the couples spent in direct physical contact with each other prior to contagion taking place was *not* of particular importance to transmission.

If in the home rhinovirus transmission normally does occur following physical contact with contaminated objects, be these other noses or fingers or coffee cups or spoons, it need not be surprising that the time recorded by spouses as so-called "direct contact" time would not quite capture or reflect the probability of contagion by a spouse. That probability would depend as well on the amount and potency of virus being spread about the body and the house, and the nature of those "direct contacts." As given to us in 1976, these married couple data would seem every bit as consistent with a theory that at home rhinovirus colds are transmitted by physical contact, as they are with a theory that in homes it is aerosol transmission, over time, that produces contagion.

The research team at Wisconsin pointed out that should most natural rhinovirus colds be transmitted via contaminated fingers, then their spread could be avoided (especially in institutional settings) by using simple virucidal products that could prevent contamination of the hands. But to prove the usefulness of any such products, only a "natural" experiment, in a natural setting, would be appropriate. The experiment with married couples at Wisconsin demonstrated nicely just how such an experiment might be performed, for it seemed to combine all the necessary experimental controls of laboratory experiments with the natural conditions of real-life environments. If natural transmissions from donor to spouse were to be cut by 90 percent, for example, through the introduction of prophylactic finger-wiping techniques with specially manufactured virucidal towels, then the evidence for the natural transmission of colds by direct contact would appear to be overwhelming. If, on the other hand, these techniques were to show no reduction in the transmission of colds, it would be hard to deny the importance of aerosol transmission. It was to be four more years before any such studies were published, however. In the meantime, other researchers were trying to solve the direct-contact-versus-aerosol dilemma, using slightly more controlled — and in a way more comical — techniques.

Fondling Versus Singing: Is Either Risky?

In 1978, Dr. Gwaltney at Virginia, together with his co-workers there, published two further papers on the mechanisms of rhinovirus transmission. One of these papers reported a new experiment contrasting attempts to produce transmissions through the air with attempts made using manual contact.[7] This experiment was carried out with the help of a number of volunteers, all of whom were found to be free of serum antibody to the particular rhinovirus employed in this study.[8] Volunteers were divided into "donors" and "recipients." On each of two successive days, those who were to be potential donors were challenged with a strong dose of rhinovirus. Twelve hours following the second challenge, each potential donor was isolated in private living quarters except for those later times when he or she might be assigned to some form of contact with the recipient volunteers.

Eleven volunteers were challenged as potential donors, and all eleven became infected with the challenge virus. Two of those infected did not develop colds, however. Among the nine volunteers who did develop colds, six "winners" were selected to serve as actual donors because they showed especially clear symptoms and distinctly runny noses. During the period when they were most symptomatic, over the first three days of their colds, each one of these six donors was repeatedly exposed to three different sets of recipients, one set for each of three different transmission conditions to be described below. Each recipient, however, was exposed in only one way to the same donor on each of the three days. Recipients were also placed in isolation during the study, but in order to minimize the time needed for this isolation it normally began twelve hours after the second of the three exposures to the donor, except in the case of those recipients who were in the "small-particle" condition to be described below.

Fifteen volunteer recipients were placed in what the authors called the "hand-to-hand" condition. In this condition the donor intentionally contaminated his or her fingers with virus using deliberately sloppy blowings and wipings of the nose. Donors then left their room (and any load of aerosol it might have contained) and went out into the hallway to meet the recipients. Recipients stroked the hands and fingers of the donor for ten seconds and then immediately left the area. Both the donors and the recipients wore surgical masks during this procedure to help reduce the amount of any aerosol transmission that might be possible during this brief contact. In another room, these recipients next attempted to inoculate themselves two or three times with any virus that may have been on their fingers by deliberately rubbing their eyes and the interiors of their nostrils in what was to each of them a normal and natural fashion. After they had done this, their hands were then lightly washed with a special broth for collecting and assaying any virus.

Twelve additional volunteer recipients were placed in what the authors called the "large-particle" condition. In this condition, groups of two, three, or four recipients spent fifteen minutes with a single donor around a small round table in a small room. Everyone wore rubber gloves while in the room to minimize the possibility of physical transmission of virus to the hands. The donor attempted to contaminate the local air by singing loudly, coughing, and sneezing while in the room. The recipients sat close by, within range to inhale any resulting large-particle aerosols before they could sink to the floor. Also, a dish of special broth was placed in the center of the table for collecting and assaying any virus that might settle out of the locally contaminated air.

Ten more volunteer recipients were placed in what the authors called the "small-particle" condition. In this condition, as in the barracks experiments discussed earlier, a large room was divided in two by a double wire-mesh barrier. For seventy-two continuous hours, save for brief absences to use separate bathrooms, or when the donor was participating in the other two conditions, one donor and either one or two recipients lived, separated, on the two sides of this room. No fresh air was allowed in the room during the whole period of occupancy. Forced air circulation in the room guaranteed that any small-particle aerosols carrying virus would be carried to the recipients in this room and that over time they would inhale a large number of these particles. Also, during the time that each donor spent in this condition, their coughs and sneezes were recorded on audio-tape for later counting.

The results of this new experiment at the University of Virginia were dramatically clear. Not one of the ten volunteer recipients exposed for seventy-two hours in the small-particle aerosol condition became infected with the rhinovirus shed by the donors. And only one of the twelve volunteers exposed during the three fifteen-minute operatic gatherings in the large-particle aerosol condition became infected. But eleven of fifteen volunteers (73 percent) in the hand-to-hand condition became infected, and nine of these eleven developed colds.

As real life would have it, it was soon discovered that the one volunteer in the large-particle aerosol condition who did become infected had spent the first night of the experiment (prior to the start of her own isolation, which followed her second visit with the donor at the small table) "in intimate contact" with a companion, another volunteer, who had that same day received his first exposure in the hand-to-hand condition with the same donor.[9] This companion was later found to be shedding virus and might have infected the volunteer in the large-particle condition during the evening they spent together.

The young woman's infection was first detected on the fourth day after she entered isolation, however, rather longer than might normally be expected if she really had been infected five nights earlier. Moreover, the experimental donor to whom she had been exposed turned out to be the only one who had detectable virus — and a lot of it — in his saliva (the source of most large-aerosol particles) on all three days of exposure to the recipients. Consequently, one might argue either that (a) large-particle aerosols are very unlikely to produce transmission of rhinovirus infection (dismissing the one case seen here as being due to contamination by earlier direct contact) or that (b) when saliva becomes strongly contaminated by the virus then perhaps as many as one-third of exposures to large-particle aerosols might result in transmission (one-third because there were only three recipients exposed to the one donor with strongly contaminated saliva, one of whom was the woman who became infected in the large-particle condition).

This experiment, using two types of rhinovirus, seemed to convince Dr. Gwaltney and his colleagues at the University of Virginia that alternative "a" above was much the more likely of the two to be correct: hand-to-hand transmission of colds seemed far more likely to explain natural contagions than did aerosol transmissions. Neither the ghost of Spitzbergen's Dr. Paul, who reported colds spreading rapidly with the arrival of the first spring mail ship even among miners who seemed to have had no direct physical contacts with symptomatic cold sufferers, nor the ghost of Amsterdam's Dr. van Loghem, who observed simultaneous epidemic outbreaks of colds in widely scattered cities across Holland, haunted the conclusion that hand-to-hand transmission is of greatest significance. But what did haunt the Virginia team was the missing datum, the key link in making the case for the central role of finger contamination and self-inoculation. This missing datum they described in their companion paper from 1978, published under the wonderful title: "Rhinovirus Transmission: one if by air, two if by hand."[10]

The All-Important Fifth Clue

In this second paper from 1978 Gwaltney and Hendley reviewed five signs that they felt ought to be present to demonstrate the truth of a given theory about the transmission of viral infection. First, it must be clear that virus really exist where transmission is proposed to start. Because it had long been convincingly demonstrated that virus *are* present in the nose whenever there is infection, this requirement presented no problem. Second, it must be demonstrated that virions really are shed into the vehicle that will carry them away. The hand-to-hand theory holds that nasal secretions will contaminate hands, and virus are regularly found in nasal secretions. The aerosol theory holds that sneezes and coughs will contaminate the air, and it is the saliva that mostly contributes to the aerosols produced from these activities. But Gwaltney and Hendley reminded their readers that most cold viruses appear in saliva much less often and at much lower concentrations than in nasal secretions.

Third, one must be able to show that virus *survive* on or in the vehicle: the hand-to-hand theory requires that virus reach and survive on hands, while the aerosol theory requires that virus are successfully broadcast into the air and survive while floating with droplets. In general, rhinovirus had often been recovered from hands and fingers in recent experiments, but much less often were they being recovered from coughs and sneezes or from air samplers placed in rooms occupied by symptomatic donors.

Fourth, one must show that the contaminated vehicle reaches an appropriate destination; for example, that it is brought into the nose of the recipient, where a new infection is possible or even likely. On this point there were no direct natural observations, but the recent experimental trials at Virginia had certainly demonstrated that infection with rhinovirus could easily occur by self-inoculation after rubbing the contaminated fingers of a donor. In the same experiment, however, near zero transmission was achieved by three fifteen-minute exposures to large-particle aerosols, or by exposures to small-particle aerosols for long periods of time. It looked to Gwaltney and Hendley as though hand-to-hand transmission (for rhinoviruses) was much more likely than aerosol transmission on the basis of these first four signs.

But fifth, Gwaltney and Hendley noted that to prove the importance of a proposed route of viral transmission, it is necessary finally to show that you can greatly reduce or eliminate the transmission that does occur if you interrupt only your hypothesized transmission route, leaving open the other possible routes. This was the sort of crucial experiment that Gwaltney and Hendley claimed had yet to be carried out for either the aerosol or the direct contact theories of transmission. In fact, there had been a few earlier attempts in England to reduce colds that may be caused by aerosols by "purifying" office air using filters or ultraviolet light, but these attempts had proven to be without effect. It would be easy to imagine an experiment that involved placing nose-and-mouth masks on some donors, to reduce the aerosol transmission of colds. And to test the theory of transmission by contaminated fingers and direct contact, Gwaltney and Hendley proposed an experiment very similar to that envisioned by the team at Wisconsin, using something like virucidal towels to prevent hand contamination. Gwaltney and Hendley wondered whether any such natural experiment using special hand-washing techniques would produce a dramatic drop in transmission rates, proving at last that hand-to-hand transmission is the most significant source of rhinovirus colds.

Enter the Killer Kleenexes

During the years between 1976 and 1980, the team at Wisconsin, under the leadership of Dr. Elliot Dick, had been attempting to carry out a study of exactly the sort previously described, testing whether the careful use of virucidal towels or handkerchiefs might indeed prevent the transmission of rhinovirus colds.[11] Dr. Dick's group decided to use their married couple research design for this work because of its close approximation to the natural conditions of cold transmission in the home. Consequently, as before, married couple volunteers were found, free of antibody to the rhinovirus used in this experiment, and one member of each couple (the "donor"), selected at random, was then challenged with a strong dose of virus designed to produce infection. Both spouses were then carefully monitored for infection and contagion.

In this new experiment couples were divided into two treatment groups. The members of one group lived their normal lives, keeping track of their time together and of any signs of a cold in either party. In the other group, the donors were instructed to use tissues moistened with a virucidal iodine solution to wipe their noses and their hands whenever they blew their noses or sneezed. Many such tissues were supplied and faithful use of them encouraged. (The iodine left a tell-tale purple stain on the skin, so donors had to be willing to put up with this cosmetic inconvenience.)

In the group that used the virucidal handkerchiefs, no transmission of any colds was detected, nor was any virus ever recovered from fingers or the opening of the nostrils. This was a very encouraging result, as it might seem to confirm that direct physical contacts usually produce rhinovirus transmission, much more than do any contaminated aerosols. But there was a problem: no transmissions occurred among any of the control couples, either.

The researchers weren't ready to give up. They tried to replicate the original published findings from the experiment with married donors and recipients, but the results here proved equally disconcerting. Dr. Dick wrote of these new findings, "Despite preparation of fresh inocula, we were never again able to obtain *any* [further] transmissions between control or test couples, presumably because the donors' colds were always mild. Apparently we were lucky in our initial married couple transmission experiment."[12] Dr. Dick also wrote, "A finding common to all these [recent Wisconsin] studies has been that respiratory viruses are not nearly as easily transmitted from person to person as was commonly believed. Others have reported similar [conclusions]."[13]

It is true that such findings echo others, beginning with the very first experimental trials in the 1930s, and extending through much of the work carried out during those first years at Salisbury, late in the 1940s and early 1950s. Once they had been isolated in the laboratory, many common cold viruses later proved to be very difficult to transmit in experimental trials with human volunteers. This difficulty came despite the direct placement of large quantities of the virus into the nostrils, and it contrasted with the high rate of secondary colds regularly reported in natural epidemiological work such as the Seattle virus watch study noted at the beginning of this chapter.

There have sometimes seemed to be important differences between the behavior of viruses cultivated inside the laboratory and those that propagate naturally in human noses out in the wild. Or, as has been suggested before, perhaps the crucial difference lies somewhere in the different mental sets of informed volunteers versus unsuspecting householders. But of course medical intelligence has usually had to assume that with these viruses no significant difference exists between the laboratory and the outside world, so that we might safely extrapolate the data of the former to better understand the latter.

All this was part of the reason that Dr. Dick and his colleagues decided to drop their studies with married couples and use instead a somewhat more natural venue to test the effects of their virucidal handkerchiefs (which soon came to be nicknamed "killer kleenexes"). The regular (if limited) bout of colds that occurs each spring in Antarctica, when a new crop of scientists and other personnel join and replace the crews that have wintered there, offered a different kind of opportunity for testing the prophylactic effects of keeping virus off of hands and faces.

Each September during the late 1970s, approximately 150 new arrivals joined approximately fifty people who had wintered over at the U.S.'s McMurdo Station in Antarctica. Among this mixed group of approximately two hundred people it was typical to see from three to six new colds develop each day. In 1979, beginning two weeks after the new group had arrived at McMurdo, Dr. Dick and his colleagues arranged to have their killer kleenexes liberally distributed to all personnel (at meals in the mess hall, and in other frequented locations).[14] During the period of this study, only these handkerchiefs were to be used for keeping one's nose and hands clean and free of virus.

The results of this intervention seemed clear. From the time of arrival of the new personnel until the time four days after the kleenexes were introduced and began to be used (that is, over the full incubation period of any previously transmitted colds), there was an average of 4.3 new colds recorded each day. Over the remaining four weeks of the study, with the treated tissues in use, there was an average of 1.7 new colds each day, amounting to a 60 percent reduction. This pattern was very much in contrast to that seen in previous years when the cold rate had continued to be high throughout the entire time that the two groups were together. Still, the implication here that the contamination of hands with active virus played an important role in the transmissions seen at McMurdo Station in 1979 would have been rather more persuasive had there been a control group of isolated Antarctic personnel who were given untreated tissues to use in a similar fashion, a group among whom the rate of transmission remained undiminished. This is precisely the form of control that the married couple study had provided, but again, in that study neither group had any transmissions to start with.

Still, these McMurdo Station data were important insofar as they offered the first positive evidence that the last, fifth, type of proof could be found to show that direct contacts between donor and recipient (or donor and doorknob) may provide the typical means for natural cold transmissions, at least for many of the rhinoviruses. Thus it is all the more ironic that, as we shall soon see, Dr. Dick and his group of cheerfully persistent colleagues at Wisconsin were soon persuaded that in fact aerosols hold the key to rhinovirus transmissions in the home and office.

16

Playing It Close to the Chest: Wisconsin, 1980–87

"The mouth is the most likely portal of viral exit and entry during kissing, with saliva serving as the vehicle for viral transfer. Our experiments with married couples revealed that 54% of the saliva specimens taken from 17 symptomatic donors . . . contained no detectable virus. In our current studies we were unable to recover virus from nearly 90 percent of specimens from donor's lips."[1]

— *D. J. D'Alessio et al., 1984*

A common cold virion hitchhiking on a "large" aerosol droplet 20 microns across (it would take fifty such droplets side by side to span one millimeter) will fall to the floor from near the ceiling of a closed room in four minutes. Particles five times larger, produced by a sloppy sneeze or an energetic cough, will fall the same distance in ten seconds. But a "small" aerosol particle only 10 microns in diameter will spend at least seventeen minutes falling to the floor, and a very small particle 3 microns in diameter can float suspended in the air for days. If the air in an enclosed room is actively circulating, all these times can be considerably longer.[2] Clearly, a hitchhiking virus can cross a crowded room through the air if it gets attached for the journey to the correct size of droplet.

If the virus in aerosols are to infect, however, they must also arrive at the site of potential infection. Very small droplets of aerosol, those that are most capable of long journeys through the air, also happen to be the most likely, when inhaled, to fly right on by the nasal cells that are the most susceptible to infection, lodging instead in the lungs where infection by most common cold viruses is thought to be rare. The aerosol droplet that is most likely to lodge in the nose, where most common cold viruses are activated, is the large (20-micron) droplet, the one that is least likely to make it across the room before falling to the floor or a table top. Still, something approaching half of all those more enduring 5-micron droplets will lodge against the cells of the nose, and any virus riding with them will be deposited where it might easily begin the process of infection.[3]

There is a time limit on the survival of a virion's infective powers, whether it be riding with a droplet of moisture or exposed to dry air. We have already seen that virus on different surfaces, including skin, often disappear or lose their infective powers after a few hours, and sometimes they will lose their infective powers in about ninety minutes. What happens to the surface of a virion capsule to render it incapable of penetrating and infecting a cell is not clear, nor is it clear what happens over time inside the virion shell, to the protein blueprints for building more virions. Only if common cold virions are stored deeply frozen in liquid nitrogen do they seem to stay infective for long periods of time.

As a rule, a single virion is generally insufficient to kindle an infectious chain reaction. Apparently, as discovered in the U.K. in the 1960s, in order to raise the probability of infection up to a modest 10 percent it will generally be necessary for a number of separate virion particles to arrive in the same nasal neighborhood. Thus, during breath after breath, many droplets of aerosol, a few of which are carrying virus presumably launched by a cough or a sneeze that occurred not long before, must accumulate along the passages of the nose in order to create the conditions conductive to infection. These conditions apparently do occur, as for instance with floating coxsackievirus given the results of the barracks room experiment described earlier. Yet when tested with rhinovirus, the same barracks room experiment proved negative, as did so many of the variations on that experimental design carried out before and since. Recall that it is from the mouth (the saliva) that the majority of aerosol droplets are broadcast during a cough and during most sneezes. Yet the rhinoviruses examined so far were often found to be absent (or few in number) in the saliva of those infected with them.

All this notwithstanding, in 1980 the evidence for the possible importance of the aerosol transmission of natural rhinoviruses could not easily be dismissed. Then, in 1984, two more investigations of rhinovirus transmission, possibly by aerosols, were published by Dr. Elliot Dick, Dr. Donn D'Alessio, and their colleagues in the Department of Preventive Medicine at the University of Wisconsin. The first of these new investigations concentrated on the effects of a series of so-called "short-duration" exposures, looking for evidence of possible aerosol transmission taking place (1) in a small meeting room, (2) in a dormitory room, and again (3) in very close proximities during kissing. The overall conclusion of this study was that "rhinoviral infections are difficult to transmit by short-term natural exposure, perhaps because the agent must be present in overwhelming numbers to reach susceptible mucosal cells."[4]

More Evidence That Rhinovirus Transmission Is Not Easy

In this new "small-room" experiment at the University of Wisconsin, either two or three infected donors were placed in a tiny unventilated room with either five or four recipients for an unspecified period of time (apparently just a few hours) spent in activities that included card playing, singing, and "talking freely" around a small table. None of the nine recipients exposed to this condition acquired the donors' previously induced rhinovirus colds.[5]

Consequently, the Wisconsin investigators decided to extend the length of time that donors and recipients were housed together and so they set up the so-called "dormitory-room" experiment. Generally, two symptomatic donors and two susceptible recipients spent each of three nights living together in a small dormitory room. A total of eleven donors and eleven recipients participated in this experiment. The dormitory room was closed, without ventilation, and the participants were together for at least twelve hours each night. Participants were instructed not to touch each other or the belongings of each other (to minimize the possibility of transmission by direct contact) and they used separate bathrooms. In this experiment three of the eleven recipients eventually developed colds, but only one of those three colds resulted from the particular rhinovirus that had been inoculated into the donors.[6] Thus, there appeared to be just one case of transmission in eleven attempts. The successful transmission occurred in the one dormitory group having the most symptomatic donors who were shedding the most virus when tested using nasal wash samples.

To look at a condition of brief but intimate exposure, the research team repeated its earlier kissing study. Ten donors kissed a total of sixteen recipients, either once, for a minute, or twice, for forty-five seconds each time. The published report of this experiment states: "Each recipient was kissed only once; the donors and recipients were instructed to use the kissing technique most natural for them."7 One instance of transmission occurred in this experiment, and this time the "success" was from a donor having only a moderate symptom score and a relatively low concentration of virus in his saliva on the day of contact.

In discussing the results of all three experiments, the authors stressed that in the dormitory-room condition, the one transmission only occurred after thirty-six hours of exposure to the most symptomatic pair of donors. They pointed out that in their previous experiment with married couples, published in 1976, transmission also occurred only in those couples who had spent the longest times together during the week of the study. In this newer "small-room" condition, the relatively shorter time that participants spent together was assumed to explain the lack of contagion that occurred there. No mention was made of the facts that (1) the score representing "time spent together" in the married couple study had been for the whole week of the study (including many days after transmission was complete) and that (2) the authors subsequently had failed in each of their attempts to replicate the level of transmission seen in that 1976 study, despite similar long times spent together by later couples.

According to the authors, it is possible that the one successful transmission in the new kissing study, a transmission from a donor with only modest levels of virus shedding, might have resulted from nose-to-nose contacts during kissing rather than from salivary mixing or exchanges of breath. Virus inoculated directly onto the outer margins of the nostrils often can result in a later infection if the challenge dose is strong enough, but it appears likely that such infection only follows if the recipient wipes his or her nose, inadvertently pushing the virus up into the nose itself soon after contamination.

Six More Trials, with Increasing Exposure Times

With the publication of this study, the Wisconsin team seemed more and more committed to the belief that rhinovirus transmission will occur only if the donor has a *strong* cold and is shedding *considerable* virus, and only if a *long* period of exposure to the donor occurs. Since direct contacts are usually brief, and in experimental studies such contacts had seemed to produce few if any successful transmissions, the Wisconsin team was becoming more persuaded that it must be indirect (aerosol) transmissions that are most important for spreading natural rhinovirus colds. The epidemiological data on the not infrequent transmission to other family members of extremely mild (subclinical) colds, as noted during the Seattle Virus Watch, for example, might have appeared to cast doubt upon this reasoning; but it might also be argued that the high Seattle figures are due to the long periods of exposure to household air experienced by the participating families.

One could conclude, then, that if "short" duration exposures do not permit contagion of colds, then experiments with longer times of exposure to donors should create higher rates of transmission. And if exposure to mild colds does not permit contagion, perhaps volunteer donors must have rather severe colds and be shedding large quantities of virus into their nasal passages to be effective transmitters. This was the reasoning behind a second set of experimental studies reported by the Wisconsin research group in 1984. The experiments in this second series were carried out over a two-year period, and they all involved exposing susceptible recipients to artificially infected donors with symptoms of various severity, over varying periods of time.[8]

Six trials were carried out for this experiment, and during each trial as many as six to ten infected donors were present in a barracks-like room of modest size. (On one trial only, a small meeting room was used for the brief time period of that trial.) The barracks room had bunk beds for twelve occupants and just enough additional room to hold a few tables, a couch, a TV, and some video game equipment. On four of the trials, there were five recipients in the room for periods ranging from a brief five hours to more than three days. Three of the trials lasted two and a half days. Each night five recipients slept in the company of seven symptomatic donors. On two trials there were nine and ten recipients in the room so some of the donors could not stay all night.

All recipients were free of antibody to the RV16 virus used to inoculate the donors. The donors were frequently rotated, with fresh donors being introduced as they became available, to ensure that only the most symptomatic of the potential donors were the ones present in the room with the recipients. Daytime interaction among donors and recipients was encouraged, and thus direct physical contacts and contacts with contaminated objects occurred with some frequency during each trial.

The proportion of recipients who became infected with RV16 during these trials ranged from zero percent for the shortest trial (five hours) to 100 percent for the longest trial (3.3 days). Trials of intermediate lengths produced intermediate percentages of transmission, but those percentages were not strictly tied to the length of the trial so much as they seemed to be tied to the variable number of donors present during each trial and how long they stayed. So the authors of this study arranged the six trials according to the number of donor-hours of exposure that the recipients received, calculated by multiplying and totalling the number of hours that each different number of donors had been present in each trial. These so-called DHE scores (Donor Hours of Exposure) ranged from a low of 45 in the brief five-hour trial (there were nine donors in that trial) to a high of 585 in the trial that ran through four evenings and that employed between five and ten donors at a time. The scores directly paralleled the transmission percentages seen in the six trials; in other words, the greater the DHE score for each trial, the higher the percentage of transmissions that occurred.

The Wisconsin team was understandably enthused about these findings, and because many of the exposure hours were at night during sleep, and because to them even the direct contacts that occurred during the day still seemed to require long times and frequent exposures to create a strong probability of producing transmission, they argued that after all it was aerosols, not direct contacts, that were producing the transmissions seen in these trials. Still, in this paper, the authors were very careful not to stress such an argument, and somewhat curiously they elected to empha-size instead what they saw as the virtues of their "new" study method (with its multiple donors and distinct trials) rather than emphasize the findings produced in their study. There are politics of getting published that can and do make such tactics strategically desirable; for instance, when reviewers are uncomfortable with some of the results claimed for a study, the journal editors will look for some additional "contribution" made by the study to help justify its publication.

In this study, the linkage seen in the reported results, between the increasing DHE scores and the increasing percentages of successful rhi-novirus transmission across the six trials, was extremely neat and orderly. One might even say that it was rather too neat. A full discussion of the potential problems for any interpretation of this observed linkage is given in the notes to this chapter.[9] A central problem, however, is the fact that the percentages of colds seen in each trial are quite unreliable given that most of them were based upon as few as five recipients. If even one person had acted differently in catching or not catching a cold, the corresponding percentage of "transmissions" seen in that trial would change by as much as 20 percent.

Perhaps the most reliable inference that could be drawn from the data generated in this 1984 Wisconsin study would be an estimate of the number of donor exposure hours that might lead to transmission of an RV16 infection with a probability of one-half. Based on just the thirty-nine participants living in the conditions created for this particular study, it would appear that approximately 170 hours of continuous exposure to donors all having quite active colds are necessary to create a 50–50 chance of contagion by this virus.[10]

One hundred seventy hours corresponds to one full week of continuous exposure to a single donor actively shedding maximum virus all week, yet the majority of natural colds, even those that for a time produce strong symptoms, are really only active, with intense virus shedding in progress, for about two days at most. And so again, one must wonder why family transmission rates have so often been found to be so "high" (frequently exceeding 50 percent) in homes into which a single index cold is naturally introduced. Is there, after all, a truly important difference between laboratory-maintained viruses used in experimental research and their wild cousins circulating in the real world? Or, is there perhaps a crucial difference between hardy and relaxed experimental volunteers and more stressed, unselected, common folk?

Bigger and Better Killer Kleenexes

Whatever doubts may now be raised about these trials carried out in the early 1980s, in 1985 the Wisconsin research team seemed to have good reason for special optimism and enthusiasm. Various members of the team were traveling down three promising avenues of investigation, any one of which might lead on to lasting fame and recognition: (1) It was possible that they could persuade the medical intelligence community that their so-called MFT (miniature field trial) technique, with its marathon poker games and legions of fresh donors, was the best and most cost-effective way to carry out experimental research on transmission of the common cold, research that would fully mimic and safely generalize to behavior in the normal home and school. (2) It was possible that they could become the first to show convincingly that rhinoviruses are, after all, transmitted primarily by aerosols, and not by direct contacts. And (3), it also seemed possible that they might share in the discovery of a financially lucrative prophylactic against colds, a spin-off from a demonstration of how the interruption of virus in aerosols may interrupt the transmission of colds. Apparently, the killer kleenexes that in 1980 had been so effective against Antarctic colds now seemed to Dr. Dick to work by inhibiting the formation of virus in aerosol form, as well as by disinfecting the face and fingers. Consequently, these tissues continued to be of special interest at Wisconsin, and this interest led to the next experiments performed there, the results of which were published in 1986.[11]

One trouble with the original killer kleenexes was that they were saturated with a solution of complexed iodine. This iodine created a number of problems: it lost its virucidal properties over time, it stained the face and hands of each user, and it had a pronounced and identifiable odor, making it impossible to run any "blind" control condition with volunteers given placebo tissues. Consequently a different virucidal agent, having none of these drawbacks, was developed by a group at Wisconsin.[12] These new virucidal kleenexes consisted of large three-ply tissues soaked in a potent solution containing citric acid, malic acid, and sodium lauryl sulfate. Thus they came to be called CMS tissues, and their prophylactic value was tested in this next experiment.

Four experimental trials in this study each consisted of a marathon poker game during which eight volunteer donors, parading active colds that had been previously engendered in the laboratory using RV16, and twelve volunteer recipients with no serum antibody to RV16, rotated among four card tables placed in a room that held them comfortably. There were two donors and three recipients at each card table, and all recipients changed tables periodically so as to ensure equal exposure to all donors. All the participants were male.

Each trial lasted for twelve hours of card playing with thirty minutes more for exercise, plus whatever time was needed for meals and for taking two nasal wash samples from the donors. Thus, each of the twelve recipients received 8 [donors] x 12 [hours] = 96 donor-hours of exposure to the rhinovirus. Given the 1984 study, this degree of exposure might have been expected to produce contagion of colds in approximately 30 percent of the recipients. In fact, however, in this study, 60 percent of the twenty-four recipients in a normal control condition became infected with RV16. No mention was made of what this new datum might do to the neat and orderly data reported in 1984. What it would do is suggest that, after all, donor-hours of exposure may not be the most important variable in determining whether or not transmission of the virus takes place.

During two of the four experimental trials in the new 1986 study, both donors and recipients were specifically instructed to use the virucidal CMS tissues liberally, frequently, and carefully. The authors stated: "Donors cleared their nasal passages gently into the tissues to avoid aerosol formation and to catch all effluent in the tissue folds. Any nasal excrement that might have escaped to the hands or to other surfaces was wiped with fresh CMS tissues."[13] During the other two experimental trials no special instructions were given and cotton handkerchiefs (not paper tissues) were used normally, as desired, by donors and recipients alike; these were the trials in which 60 percent, or fourteen, of the twenty-four recipients became infected. But in the two trials where CMS tissues were carefully used as directed, none of twenty-four other recipients became infected.

The Wisconsin team had grounds for believing that their new CMS tissues worked so well because they smothered the aerosols produced from coughs, sneezes, and nose blowing. Of course, almost any heavy paper tissue might have produced a similar smothering effect, and one desirable control to support their interpretation would have been to employ the same *supervised* use of non-virucidal paper handkerchiefs to be used by a separate subset of the participants. Another compelling explanation for any apparent effectiveness of the CMS tissues would be that such tissues were better at decontaminating the fingers and faces of the donors, preventing the spread of virus to objects and others, and/or that the CMS tissues protected the recipients from self-inoculation when they touched their eyes or nose. If this alternative interpretation were correct, however, even the careful and frequent use of non-virucidal paper handkerchiefs should have a noticeable effect in reducing the normal rate of finger contamination and subsequent transmission of the virus.

Thus, to support a conclusion that CMS tissues are effective because they interrupt aerosols, two types of tissue use would be necessary: one that prevented aerosol dispersion but allowed finger contamination, and another that somehow prevented finger contamination without preventing aerosol production.[14] In their discussion near the end of the 1986 paper, the Wisconsin authors reported that experiments were "in progress" using plain tissues and CMS tissues at different levels of intensity, under different sets of instructions. No report of the results of those experiments ever seems to have been published, however.[15]

As it happened, the research team at Wisconsin had a different idea for making what they considered to be a crucial test between the aerosol and direct contact theories of transmission. They reasoned that if self-inoculation really were the primary route of virus spreading, then if they were to prevent all facial touching, while leaving open aerosol routes of transmission, they should observe a pronounced drop in the number of infections seen among recipients who were in contact with infective donors. However, if aerosols were the important factor, then merely preventing self-inoculation during close contacts with donors should not change the continuing normal rate of rhinovirus transmission. Thus, a new experiment was carried out employing the same multiple-donor and multiple-recipient technique used before in the 1984 and 1986 studies discussed above.

Helping Recipients to Show Restraint

This new study, published in 1987 with Dr. Elliot Dick as first author, consisted of four separate experimental trials, all of which employed the same rhinovirus (RV16) that had been used in the earlier Wisconsin research.[16] Three of the four experimental trials in this study consisted of the usual twelve-hour marathon poker game, with donors and recipients arranged as before around four card tables in a small room. Again, all the participants were male.

In this experiment too, each of the twelve recipients received 8 [donors] x 12 [hours] = 96 donor-hours of exposure to active RV16 colds. And again, based on the 1984 study data, this might have been expected to produce contagion of colds in approximately 30 percent of recipients. But in this study, fully 67 percent of the eighteen normal control recipients became infected with RV16.

The recipients who took part in the first three trials were of two types, treated in two different ways. Half of the recipients (the "controls") played cards in the normal fashion, much as had the participants in the original 1984 study. But the other half of all recipients were "restrained," wearing special devices that prevented them from being able to touch any part of their faces or head while at the same time leaving them free to use their arms and hands to play cards and to carry out most other activities in a nearly normal fashion. In the first trial, this restraint was accomplished with a large clear circular plastic collar, worn rather like an Elizabethan ruff around the neck, extending about fifteen inches out in every direction. In the second and third trials, facial contact was prevented using a modified orthopedic arm brace designed so that it would not bend at the elbow more than about forty-five degrees. Thus, half the recipients were deliberately encumbered, unable to touch their faces; but half were not, nor were any of the donors.

One might well ask, how did a restrained recipient eat any food or cope with his itchy nose or eye? Food was served during lunch and dinner breaks, at which times collars and braces were removed. Still, before a restrained participant could then touch his face, his hands were immediately washed in a virucidal bath and sterile rubber gloves were placed on them. All participants wore surgical scrub suits during the experiment itself, and all the recipients had their hands and faces washed before putting on their clothes to leave at the end of the trial. Thus if there were to be any transmission of virus, it should only have taken place during the experiment itself. Donors and recipients also used separate bathrooms during the experiment. Restrained recipients had their noses blown and any urgent facial itches attended to by monitors who stood by to render just such services anytime they were not busy counting the coughs and sneezes of the donors or counting the frequency with which donors and the unrestrained recipients touched their hands to their faces.

The question addressed by this elegant research design was whether or not the prevention of self-inoculation alone would be sufficient to interrupt the transmission of this virus from donor to recipient. If it did, the important role of direct contact would seem to be all but confirmed. But if it did not, and if transmission of RV16 colds still occurred, then an aerosol route of transmission would seem to be the only existing hypothesis left to account for the contagion. Thus, in these first three experimental trials, the primary interest lay in the contrast between the number of colds seen in the "restrained" versus the "control" recipients.

In the first trial, all six of the control recipients became infected by RV16, but so did five out of the six restrained recipients. Advantage aerosol transmission. And this 92 percent overall transmission rate (so far above the value of 30 percent that might previously have been expected) could be explained, perhaps, by especially contagious donors, shedding unusually high amounts of virus.

Separate evidence gathered during subsequent trials makes this explanation seem less likely, however. On the second trial there was approximately four times more RV16 being shed by the donors, but only about half of the previous overall contagion rate was observed in the recipients. On the second trial the donors did twice as much sneezing but only half as much coughing as did the donors during the course of the first trial. And on the second trial, restrained arm movement was associated with a much reduced contagion rate. Only one of six restrained recipients became infected, while five of six control recipients became infected. In this trial, contrary to the first, it could easily appear that interrupting self-inoculation was very effective in interrupting transmission of the virus. Deuce.

Thus the third trial takes on special interest. This time, four of the six restrained recipients became infected while only one of the six unrestrained recipients did so. Since arm restraints presumably do not increase the likelihood of viral transmission, and since the lack of such restraints presumably does not protect against infection, it seemed reasonable to suppose that airborne transmission had operated in every case and that chance alone had determined who had been visited by sufficient airborne virus and who had not. With this inference in mind, it seemed reasonable to combine the data from all three trials.

Across all three trials, then, ten of eighteen restrained recipients, and twelve of eighteen control recipients, had become infected. These two proportions seemed similar enough to the team at Wisconsin to make them conclude that preventing self-inoculation played at most a minor role in lowering the rate of infection (although the sample size was so small that chance factors alone might have diluted the real effects of self-inoculation considerably). The Wisconsin group took the view that aerosols must have played the primary role in producing the infections. The fact that the infection rate in control recipients was not that much greater than in restrained recipients bolstered that opinion.

If aerosols truly do produce almost all transmissions of RV16, then interrupting aerosol transmission should prevent the spread of infection, even if one still allows physical contamination of the hands and subsequent self-inoculations. The fourth and last experimental trial reported in the 1987 Wisconsin paper attempted to demonstrate just such an effect. The design of this experiment was similar to one carried out at Salisbury years previously, and with the same result. Susceptible and unrestrained recipients played poker for twelve hours in a private room with uncontaminated air using the contaminated cards, pencils, poker chips, and furniture that were periodically introduced from eight infected donors playing simultaneously in another room. The result in this fourth trial was that no infections at all were seen in the recipients.

Now in fact this fourth experimental trial followed immediately on the heels of the third, and so the first set of contaminated objects, as well as some of the eight donors contaminating them, were the same objects and donors that had been employed during the twelve hours before, in the third trial. During this fourth trial only, the recipients in the separate room were instructed to perform what were described as "exaggerated hand-to-nose and facial rubbing, often with conjunctival and nasal mucosal contact."[17] "Rubbing" is not the same as fingering or picking at the nose, and "often" is not every time that the eye would be rubbed with the finger-tips. Still, this was meant to guarantee that self-inoculation in this group would be at least as likely as it was in the other trials, if not much more so.

Unfortunately, however, and not stressed by the Wisconsin authors, there is every reason to believe that the "contaminated" objects with which the recipients played and worked were not heavily contaminated, if at all. During the fourth trial, the hands of the eight donors were rinsed, and cultures were taken to assess the presence of any RV16. While some of the donors had virus on their hands, six of the eight had either none or very little, and the remaining two did not have the massive amounts of virus often to be expected.[18] More to the point, the hands of *recipients* were tested for virus during *both* the third *and* the fourth trials and no virus at all was recovered in either trial, in either room.

Thus, unfortunately, while viral aerosols were indeed successfully pre-vented in the fourth trial, so too were contaminated recipient fingers. In effect, the intended fourth trial did not really take place, although the out-come of that trial was interpreted as though it had. It is not possible to tell if the lack of virus on the recipient fingers reflected some natural difficulty in transmitting contamination from direct contacts in this experiment or whether it reflected something special about the behavior of these donors and recipients.

When we discover that no virus was found on the hands of any of the recipients in the *third* trial, it suddenly makes the interpretation of even those findings less clear than the Wisconsin group intended. Only in the third trial did a greater number of restrained recipients become infected than control recipients. It was only because of the data from the third trial that the overall protective effect of being restrained, (i.e., being unable to contaminate one's face) appeared to be slight. In the first two trials com-bined, where separate measures suggested that the donors broadcast a much greater amount of virus, the protective effect of restraining all facial touching amounted to a 41 percent reduction in the rate of infection.[19] Again, however, because of the small numbers of participants, we must allow for the role of unknown chance factors; the true protective effect could be either less or more than 41 percent, by a large amount.[20] Still, by 1987, the Wisconsin research team was convinced that it had strong evidence showing that rhinoviruses could be, and often were, transmitted primarily via aerosols. And the linear data from 1984 (see note 9) was now used as an important part of this "strong" evidence, supporting their conviction.

The Unobjective Author Begs a Word with You

By now it must be clear to the reader that I am not neutral here, that I cannot believe aerosols really do play a large role in the transmission of most rhinoviruses. Instead, direct contact with contaminated objects has long seemed to me to be the more likely mode of cold transmissions. For reasons that I have been unable to fathom, this is what I want to believe, at least until such time as the sifting of all this evidence and the publishing of this book may finally free me from some basic error in my intuition.

Perhaps it is simply that I prefer to believe that through cleanliness one can avoid colds. Neatness should count. And yet, apparently, in the world of the common cold, neatness often does *not* count. Nor, apparently, does neatness generally count in scientific detective work. Experiments often fail to work, despite our best efforts. Chance, error, and the workings of unsuspected causal factors act invisibly and continuously, behind the scenes. Thus our data invariably come to us full of surprises, full of apparent contradictions and logical difficulties. Added to all this are the invisible biases created by our own unique psychological makeup and temperament, biases that cause each intelligence officer to follow different leads and to prosecute different suspects, while ignoring others.

In the present case, what will remain most troubling to anyone such as myself who cannot approve the conclusions drawn by Dr. Dick and his colleagues at Wisconsin is the dilemma created by the fact that there were any colds at all (let alone ten of them) among the eighteen *restrained* participants in those first three trials reported in 1987. The reader should note well this gloss in my account of the Wisconsin research. The aerosol hypothesis remains, for the time being at least, the most powerful means of accounting for the ten colds seen among the restrained volunteers, whatever objections may be raised about other aspects of the 1987 study.

All this, of course, presupposes that one or the other of these two potential sources of rhinovirus "transmissions" must be taking place. It seems that either aerosols must play the major role, or direct contact with contaminated objects must do so. But be not deceived. Nothing requires that either one of these two routes *must* play the key role. In fact, nothing requires that the colds seen following exposure to someone else's cold have actually been "transmitted" by the movement of virus from donor over to recipient. Counter-intuitive as it may seem, it may well be that the puzzling results of the experiments designed to settle the question about the major route of viral transmission are signaling that the question itself is inappropriate as currently framed. The "answer" to our question may well be: "Tilt — Wrong Question." Keep this in mind as you begin reading the next chapter. And we will have occasion to evaluate this third, "neither-of-the-above" possibility once again, shortly before closing this book.

Tissues Aren't Trumps: Virginia, 1980–88

"Studies with technetium labelled particles have shown that material deposited in locations [near the front of the nasal passages] are moved forward, probably by secretions of the anterior nasal glands, to be incorporated in crusts which remain in the nose unless removed manually or by nose blowing. Thus, it appears that nature expects a helping hand, or at least a finger, to keep this area of the nasal cavity clean. This natural finger-to-nose contact may provide one way for cold viruses to be introduced into the nose at a site where infection can be initiated."[1]

— *J. M. Gwaltney, Jr., 1984*

In 1980 Dr. Jack Gwaltney, Jr., at the University of Virginia began a discussion of the importance of aerosol media for the transmission of rhinoviruses with these words: "The problem of studying the common cold is complicated by the many viruses involved that do not behave in the same way."[2] A greater understatement would be hard to find. For a considerable time there had existed an unspoken assumption, supported by the hope of almost everyone in the field, that viruses of the same genus (for instance, all the rhinoviruses) would be found to share the same epidemiological characteristics, with nearly identical life cycles and modus operandi. It was the viruses of differing genus (adenovirus, coronavirus, coxsackievirus, etc.) that probably demonstrated different behavior. Thus, if a given rhinovirus was not transmitted by aerosols, one might well assume that most, if not all, the other rhinoviruses also were not. In 1980 Dr. Gwaltney felt sure that at least one rhinovirus was not transmitted through the air. The unpublished study done in the enclosed space of the military barracks by Robert Couch and his colleagues, following the successful aerosol transmission of coxsackievirus in the same room, seemed to clinch that argument.[3]

Some Reasonable Doubts in Reasonable Investigators

But there were other reasons to doubt that rhinoviruses are typically transmitted via aerosols, and in his 1980 article Dr. Gwaltney went on to review some of these reasons. At the same time he acknowledged that, taken all together, these reasons were still rather less than conclusive. First there was the earlier research, using volunteers who sneezed and coughed into large balloons, suggesting that the most viable aerosols, holding the greatest number of virus, are produced by coughs, not sneezes. (Sneezes and blowing the nose tend to produce more expelled virus, but these generally fall out of the air over a short distance if they are not smothered in a handkerchief to begin with.) Coughing is common in about 40 percent of people with natural rhinovirus colds, and about 40 percent sneeze with some frequency on the second and third day of illness when most natural contagion seems to occur.[4] Thus there is a very large proportion of rhinovirus sufferers (including all those with subclinical infections) who neither cough nor sneeze, and who in consequence seem unlikely to generate infective aerosols during that limited period when their nasal cells are shedding the most virus.

Secondly, if coughing is the primary source of infective aerosols, then virus must first reach the back of the mouth and/or must pool in the saliva, to be available for broadcast. Yet rhinovirus are often absent, or they are present only in dilute quantities, when saliva is tested for their presence. And in the throat at the back of the mouth, rhinovirus usually appear to be less than one-tenth as concentrated as they are in the nose itself.[5] Perhaps there might be an unrecognized, cloud-baby-like phenomenon whereby some people produce potent rhinoviral aerosols for brief periods of time even without coughing or sneezing, but in 1980 that seemed unlikely given what was then known about these matters.

The third reason why Dr. Gwaltney doubted that rhinoviruses were generally transmitted by aerosols was that, in a study done in another laboratory, air samples taken from a room full of infected rhinovirus donors had repeatedly failed to reveal any virus in the air, although when artificially produced aerosols containing rhinovirus were broadcast in the room the same sampling equipment had been able to detect them, and it had previously detected coxsackievirus shed by infected donors as well.[6] Gwaltney's own studies, trying to detect rhinovirus in the air following simulated coughs and sneezes, all were negative, even when virus was demonstrably present in the saliva and noses of his volunteers. Only when a collecting dish was put right under the chin of each volunteer, where very large particles could land, did Gwaltney's team ever successfully detect virus, and those successes occurred only once for various sneezes and once for various coughs given out by thirteen and twelve donors, respectively. The same technique used with natural cold sufferers sneezing onto collecting dishes held close to the nose produced completely negative results.[7]

Gwaltney also alluded to a fourth reason to question the hypothesis of aerosol transmission for the rhinovirus. Rhinoviruses are known to be quickly de-activated in drier air when the relative humidity drops much below 50 percent. Yet rhinovirus colds are well represented all over the world, in dry as well as in moist regions and seasons. Thus, given the studies of hand-to-hand transmission and self-inoculation of rhinovirus that had already been reported from Virginia, it was natural that in 1980 Dr. Gwaltney and his colleagues did not espouse the belief that rhinovirus is transmitted by aerosol.

Is the Route Perhaps from Hand to Land to Hand?

Coincident with the publication of Dr. Gwaltney's review article came a report of further work showing that infectious quantities of rhinovirus can be passed from contaminated fingers to doorknobs and faucet handles, and from there they can pass to the fingers of a recipient, ready for self-inoculation into the nose or eyes.[8] This new study reported that under favorable conditions for producing contamination of these objects approximately 13 percent of the virus originally recoverable from the donor's hands could be recovered from the recipient's hands after they each had handled one of the test objects. Thus, on average, for every eight infective doses of virus detected on the hands of the donor, one dose was detected later on the hands of the recipient.

The "favorable" conditions here were of the sort that would be common with infected children as donors and not particularly uncommon after someone with an active cold wiped their nose repeatedly with a soggy handkerchief. A small drop of infected mucous was gently rubbed between the donor's thumb tip and index finger, and these were then slid back and forth on the faucet handle, or the doorknob was twisted open twice. Ten minutes later the recipients repeated these motions on the respective objects and their hands were rinsed for a viral assay. It turned out that sufficient rhinovirus was transferred in these studies to permit infection following any self-inoculation by the recipients.

A somewhat similar study was carried out soon afterward by Drs. Gwaltney and Hendley at the University of Virginia, looking a little more closely at which kinds of objects or surface materials might be most likely to facilitate the transfer of a rhinovirus from an ill person to a susceptible recipient.[9] This study went further than the previous one, in that recipients were instructed to rub their eyes and probe their noses with their presumably contaminated fingers after they had fingered the objects previously fingered by the infected donors. Infected donors initially contaminated their fingers by blowing and wiping their noses on them. The objects used in this study were ceramic coffee cups (the handles were repeatedly touched) and plastic tiles of the sort used on counter tops. The tiles were stroked for five seconds by the donors, and then some of the tiles were sprayed with a disinfectant. After the sprayed tiles dried, the coffee cups or tiles were handled by susceptible recipients and self-inoculation was then carried out.

The transmission of this rhinovirus, without any exposure to aerosols, was very effective in both the coffee cup and tile conditions. Half of ten recipients handling the coffee cups became infected, as did sixteen of thirty-six recipients handling the plastic tiles. (Ten of these latter sixteen developed clinical colds.) The disinfectant spray used did not kill all the virus on the tiles, and as a result 35 percent of the recipients rubbing their fingers on the sprayed tiles were also infected. No virus was detected in a large proportion of the samples taken either from the tile surfaces, after they were stroked by the recipients, or from the recipient's own fingers after they had probed their noses and eyes. Still, many of these same recipients later did become infected. Thus, it also appeared quite possible that the previous experimental efforts to measure the amount of virus passed on by means of direct physical contacts could have seriously underestimated the amount or the virulence of the virus actually transferred.

Disinfected Fingers and Some Disappeared Colds

During the 1980s there was an increased interest in finding some product that would prevent the contagion of colds; this interest was piqued by the recognition that a vaccine against colds was almost certainly going to be unworkable due to the existence of such a large number of different cold viruses. Of course, it would be easier to find an effective prophylactic product against colds if we knew the main routes of viral transmission, but these routes were still being debated, particularly for the rhinoviruses. In fact, the discovery of a prophylactic product might itself help to settle the debate over which route was the more important: aerosols versus direct contacts with contaminated persons or objects. Consequently, the research team at the University of Virginia, like that at the University of Wisconsin, began to investigate the possibility of creating virucidal handkerchiefs that could be used to contain the spread of colds. At Virginia, however, the assumption was that such handkerchiefs would work because they stopped the spread of contaminated infectious secretions rather than through any influence they might have on the formation of infective aerosols.

Thus, in 1985 the research team at Virginia published the first of three articles describing a series of efforts to eliminate colds by eliminating finger contamination, starting with the use of virucidal paper handkerchiefs.[10] The authors of this first report recognized that the use of common paper tissues, untreated by any virucide, might itself prevent the contamination of fingers and other objects with virus. Therefore, before full-scale testing of any virucidal tissues were carried out, it would be prudent to see whether treated tissues really were necessary; in other words, whether they were any more effective than untreated tissues of the same sort. Thus, volunteer donors who were free of antibody to a particular challenge virus were inoculated on each of two successive days with a strong dose of virus, following which they were isolated in separate rooms for five days. Donors who developed active colds and prominent runny noses were then exposed to paper tissues and to susceptible recipients, as follows.

Each donor first washed and dried his hands, and then, holding a soft paper tissue in both hands, blew his nose vigorously into one of the tissues.[11] Two kinds of tissue were used. One was virucidal (the CMS tissue with citric acid, described earlier) and one was a placebo tissue treated with an inert substance so as to resemble the CMS tissue. In a third condition, the donor blew his nose directly into his hands without using any tissue. In all, on sixty-two occasions recipients were exposed to donors who had used the *virucidal* tissues, on sixty-one occasions different recipients were exposed to donors who had used the *placebo* tissues, and on twenty-four occasions still other recipients were exposed to donors who had used *no tissue* at all. Thus, each recipient was assigned at random to just one of these three conditions, and each was exposed to a different donor in that same condition once on each of two or three days.

Exposure of the recipients took the following form. Donors and recipients, both wearing surgical masks to inhibit aerosol transmissions, came together after the donor had blown his nose according to previous instructions. Recipients then stroked the fingers of the donor with their own fingers for approximately ten seconds, following which they left the room. In another room each recipient next rubbed his eyes and probed his nose with his fingers, under supervision. The fingers of the donors and the recipients were then carefully rinsed and the rinse solution was cultured for the presence of rhinovirus. Recipients were housed in isolation after exposure on the second day, and were carefully monitored for subsequent infection with the test virus.

Virus was detected on the fingers of donors who had used no tissues at all while blowing their noses in 80 percent of twenty-four tests. When donors used regular placebo-treated tissues, virus was detected on their fingers in 42 percent of sixty-one tests. When donors used the special CMS tissues, virus was detected on their fingers in just 3 percent of sixty-two tests. It seemed clear that using regular paper tissues reduced, but did not eliminate, the presence of virus on the fingers of the donors over what it might be if no tissue were used. But using the virucidal CMS tissues all but eliminated detectable virus on the donors' fingers.

When the donors had used no tissue at all while blowing their noses 50 percent of the eight recipients, each exposed three times to this condition, were infected by the test virus. When the donors had used regular placebo-treated tissues, 13 percent of twenty-three recipients became infected following stroking of the donor's fingers and subsequent self-inoculation. But when the donors had used the virucidal CMS tissues, none of twenty-three recipients in that condition became infected. Again, it seemed clear that the use of virucidal tissues could reduce the risk of transmission to a value very near zero, while the use of non-virucidal tissues could reduce the risk of transmission to something like 25 percent of what it might have been with no tissue at all.

The low rate of transmission seen with ordinary (non-virucidal) tissues especially surprised the authors of this study. They had expected that more virus would get onto the hands of the donors using regular paper tissues, and that this would cause more infections in the recipients. Since aerosol transmission was effectively ruled out in this study because of the very brief contacts between donors and recipients, during which time all were wearing masks, it seemed clear that the noticeable prophylactic effects of using both the virucidal tissues and the non-virucidal tissues were mediated by preventing finger contamination.

The considerable value of using even non-virucidal tissues to prevent such contamination makes the conclusions of the Wisconsin study of similar CMS tissues all the more questionable. Recall that in the 1986 study by Dr. Dick and his colleagues, the CMS tissues that were used carefully and continually by symptomatic donors appeared to have prevented any infection of susceptible recipients during ninety-six donor-hours of poker game exposure. The authors of that study concluded that the CMS tissues had probably interrupted most aerosol production of virus. But of course those tissues almost certainly had prevented any finger contamination as well, so that the results from this study did not constitute the degree of support for an aerosol hypothesis that was subsequently implied.

In the penultimate paragraph of their 1985 paper, the University of Virginia research team noted, "The effectiveness of the placebo nasal tissues in blocking viral transmission . . . raises the question of whether virucidal treatment is necessary for tissues to be of use in interrupting transmission of colds."[12] Considerable time and expense was being devoted to finding a virucidal preparation that might do for a company like Kimberley-Clark (the makers of Kleenex) what the first fluoride toothpaste had done for the financial reports at Procter & Gamble.[13] But if, when conscientiously used, virucidal Kleenex proved to be little better than the existing regular Kleenex, then in addition to the obvious commercial implications there would also be significant implications for theories of viral transmission. A field trial clearly was needed, out in the real world of runny noses, sticky fingers, common glassware, and persevering parents. Just such a field trial was carried out between 1983 and 1986 by the group at Virginia, using virucidal CMS and non-virucidal paper tissues. The results of this study were published in 1988.[14]

Two field trials were actually carried out in Charlottesville, Virginia, one during the 1983–84 cold season, and another two years later during the 1985–86 cold season. In the first trial, volunteering families were assigned at random to one of three conditions. One group of families was given a plentiful supply of virucidal CMS tissues and told to use only these tissues during the twenty-four-week period of the trial. A second group of families was given a plentiful supply of placebo-treated tissues to use under the same set of instructions. These tissues closely resembled the CMS tissues although they were not in fact virucidal. A third group of families provided a baseline control condition for monitoring normal transmission rates. They were given no special instructions concerning the use of handkerchiefs or tissues, etc. Their instructions, like part of those given to families in the other two groups, were limited to the correct use of the symptom report forms and to various explanations of other research procedures. In the second trial carried out two years after the first, only the virucidal- and placebo-tissue groups were included.

The primary datum of interest in each trial was the extent to which the use of virucidal tissues might reduce the likelihood of other family members catching a secondary cold from an "index" (first) cold in a member of that family. Computing the rate of secondary colds is never easy, however, because it is sensitive to how the index colds are defined in each study and it will vary with the number and the ages of the other susceptible family members in each family. Thus, family size differences alone can lead to different apparent rates of secondary infection. During the first trial it was discovered that families of five or more members had colds so frequently that it was not possible to tell if a cold was new (an index cold) or was a late secondary cold, transmitted from someone else in the family. Consequently, the data from families this large were not analyzed in the first study, and families with more than four members were excluded from participation in the second study.

In the first of the two trials, with more than fifty families participating in each condition, the use of special tissues, virucidal or placebo, was not associated with any notable reduction in colds over what normal families were experiencing with their typical ways of coping with a cold. This was true for all colds, however, and it is the secondary cold rate that might most be affected by virucidal tissues and by the cleaner hands resulting from their use. Many colds could not be reliably categorized as either an index or a secondary cold. But among those colds that could be so categorized during the first trial, the highest rate of secondary colds was in the placebo-tissue group (0.91 secondary colds per exposed person); the second highest rate was seen in the no-tissue control group (0.75 secondary colds); the lowest rate of secondary colds was, as predicted, in the virucidal-tissue group (0.68 colds). The conclusion would seem to be that the adoption and use of virucidal tissues had only a slight effect (approximately 10 percent in this trial) upon reducing secondary colds over those normally encountered in the home.

In the second trial, carried out during the fall and winter of 1985–86, which did not include an uninstructed control group, the secondary cold rate among participants in the placebo-tissue condition was 0.94 colds per person. In the virucidal-tissue condition the corresponding rate of secondary colds was 0.84. Thus, during the second trial the rate of contagion for these two groups was closer than it had been during the first trial.

While the overall results of the two trials reported here appeared to confirm that virucidal tissues offered rather little additional prophylactic value beyond that afforded by the use of plain paper tissues, it must be remembered that by no means all of the colds in these field trials would have been rhinovirus colds. The virucidal tissues created for this field trial probably were most effective against rhinovirus. If the proportion of rhinovirus colds happened to be lower than average during these two fall trials, and if improved tissues were to be created having additional or strengthened virucidal properties against a wide spectrum of cold viruses, then it is possible that the use of some super killer kleenex might after all be shown to be highly effective in interrupting the transmission of wild colds.

Oh For a Gentle, Long-Lasting, Virucidal Hand Lotion

Our concern, however, has been with what a successful interruption of the transmission of colds, by any means, might tell us about the route(s) that such transmissions naturally follow. Neither the hypothesis of aerosol transmission nor that of hand-to-hand transmission could be disconfirmed by the data available early in 1988. And yet it was just such a disconfirmation that was needed and sought by those prosecuting these two rival hypotheses. There had been growing acknowledgement that what was most needed were studies that could show, by removing some one ingredient X (either just the virus on the fingers, or just the virus floating in aerosol form), that the transmission of colds could and would be stopped. Such a demonstration could do more than anything else to confirm ingredient X as the key ingredient in the transmission of infections.

The study of the prophylactic value of virucidal handkerchiefs appeared, on the surface of it, to be directly in this spirit. As we have seen, however, the trouble was that the use of virucidal handkerchiefs did not remove just one ingredient X, it appeared to remove both X and Y, that is, both the virus on the flesh and the virus on aerosol droplets floating out into the room air. Used as a prophylactic, some of these virucidal handkerchiefs appeared to be splendid; but used as an experimental tool for pruning back theories, they most certainly were not.

Then, later in 1988, Drs. Hendley and Gwaltney at the University of

Virginia finally published data from an earlier study of natural cold transmissions that they had carried out in Charlottesville back at the beginning of each fall between 1979 and 1982.[15] This study, together with the study carried out a few years later at Wisconsin employing restrained recipients who were unable to touch their faces, became the only two published studies that effectively achieved the removal of a single ingredient X while leaving ingredient Y operative. Moreover, this earlier Virginia study, unlike the laboratory experiment at Wisconsin, was a field trial with natural colds, carried out in normal homes over a five-week time period.

It is curious that Hendley and Gwaltney delayed the publication of their findings for more than five years, because on the surface of it their data appeared to give the strongest support yet to the hypothesis that hand-to-hand transmission is the more important route for a majority of natural colds. These field trial data were eventually published as one part of a much longer review article that summarized what was then known about the transmission of rhinovirus. Data that are finally published in this way often have first been submitted elsewhere and have met with various editorial objections, but in this case the objections came only from the two principal investigators themselves. They had delayed publication in the hope of strengthening their case with additional data, a hope that was disappointed, however, because in the end they were unable to create a pleasing, long-lasting, virucidal hand lotion of the sort that would be needed to carry out the planned additional field trials.[16]

The study reported in 1988 had been carried out in fifty homes during each September from 1979 through 1982.[17] Each participating family contained a minimum of two people, always including a mother and at least one child. The average number of people in each household was four, and most of the children in this study were under five years of age. Colds were monitored closely in each home over a five-week period by means of symptom record cards filled out daily for each family member, and by means of visits from a nurse/technician who collected viral samples during the first few days of each and every cold in any family members. They also collected samples from the mothers in each household whenever anyone else in the family was ill with a cold.

It was only the mothers who were in fact the subjects of these field trial investigations. Each mother agreed to use a prophylactic finger rinse anytime a member of her family had any symptoms of a cold. Two different finger rinse solutions were used in this study, and without their knowledge mothers were assigned at random to receive just one of the two solutions.

One solution consisted of aqueous iodine in a form that was highly virucidal against rhinoviruses, usually the most prevalent cold viruses during September. This iodine solution retained its virucidal activity for a considerable period of time after being applied to the skin, and it created a distinctive brown stain that enabled the visiting nurse to determine if the mothers had been using the solution as directed. Because prolonged use of this solution markedly dried the skin, mothers were not asked to apply it to their fingers except during times when there was a cold in the home.

The other rinsing solution was created primarily from food coloring so as to resemble closely the virucidal solution while still having no virucidal properties at all against rhinovirus. This placebo solution did have a trace of iodine in it, to help give it the smell of the virucidal solution. But the stain it left on the fingers disappeared more quickly than did that from the virucidal solution.

Mothers in both test groups were given these finger rinse solutions in wide-mouthed glass containers; they were to dip the fingers of each hand into the solution, then blot them lightly on paper towels and allow them to air dry. All mothers were instructed to use their solution on first awakening in the morning and then every three to four hours thereafter, so long as any other member of the family had a cold. Of key interest in this study was whether mothers using the virucidal finger decontaminate would have any fewer secondary colds than would mothers in the control condition who were rinsing their fingers in a placebo solution. If the virucidal solution were associated with a much lower incidence of secondary colds among the mothers, then a strong argument could be made that finger contamination and self-inoculation is an important ingredient in the transmission of colds, at least for rhinovirus colds. It is significant here that any aerosol transmission of colds would not be diminished by these finger treatments.

Because this field trial involved various wild viruses circulating naturally, not every index cold was one to which the mother was susceptible, and not every index cold was caused by a rhinovirus. Across all four years of the study, there were eleven instances in which mothers using the virucidal solution were exposed to a rhinovirus to which they were susceptible, meaning they had little or no corresponding serum antibody. *None* of these eleven mothers caught the rhinovirus index cold present in their home. There were sixteen instances in which mothers using the placebo solution were exposed to a rhinovirus to which they were susceptible. *Thirty-one percent* (five) of these sixteen mothers caught the rhinovirus index cold present in their home. In this small sample, then, there appeared to be 100 percent protection against rhinovirus transmission achieved by the prevention of finger contamination in a setting where aerosol production was being left unaffected.

Even after four years of study, however, the twenty-seven opportunities for rhinovirus transmission to susceptible mothers was not a large number, and the five transmissions that did occur were not sufficient to permit firm conclusions about the protective effect of keeping active rhinovirus off the fingers. Some might wish to argue that it was largely due to chance that the observed transmissions all appeared in mothers using the placebo solution. In fact, if aerosols alone *were* the cause of all the rhinovirus transmissions in this study, and if only chance factors caused all five of the observed infections to appear in mothers in the placebo condition, then this dramatic and suggestive result, apparently so supportive of the hypothesis of hand-to-hand transmission, could be expected to happen again, on average, approximately once in every twenty similar experiments.[18]

Looking at the incidence of *all* the colds contaged by the mothers from others in their families, without regard to viral type or to the mother's antibody status, considerably increases the number of colds available for study and it provides a corresponding increase in the reliability of the estimated protective effects of the virucidal finger treatment. For the mothers using the virucidal rinse, fifty-eight index colds resulted in four transmissions to the mothers, and a corresponding incidence of *thirteen* colds for every thousand person-days of exposure. For the mothers in the placebo condition, seventy-nine index colds resulted in sixteen transmissions to the mothers, and an incidence of *forty* colds for every thousand person-days of exposure.

Allowing for the number of index colds to which the mothers could be assumed to have been immune, overall transmissions occurred in 12.5 percent of opportunities when the virucidal finger rinse was in use and in 36 percent of opportunities when the placebo rinse was in use.[19] This secondary infection rate of 36 percent is itself slightly below the rate normally expected based on previous virus watch studies. Thus, the use of the virucidal finger rinse here appeared to reduce the transmission of all September colds by an impressive 65 percent margin. While the true protective effect might be rather more or less than 65 percent, as could be seen in a far larger study, it is very unlikely that this true effect is near zero or that differences like those observed in this study would be seen in any situation where chance alone would cause them.

Concluding their delayed report of this four-year field trial of virucidal finger treatment, Drs. Hendley and Gwaltney were noticeably cautious, however. They expressed some concern over the fact that while 60 percent of mothers in the virucidal condition thought they probably had been using a virucidal solution, only 42 percent of the mothers in the placebo condition thought they had been using a virucidal solution. It is known that beliefs about one's treatment condition can sometimes influence the willingness of a participant to report mild cold symptoms, and can lead them to try to "help" a study by behaving as expected. But the mothers were asked their impressions about their treatments only after the end of their trial and by that time their illness experience could have made them aware of (or willing to guess about) their true treatment condition.[20] Moreover, beliefs the mothers may have held would almost certainly have no effect upon virus shedding nor on the hard evidence of infection that was gathered independent of what the mothers were saying about their own health.

Consequently, despite the modest number of rhinovirus colds occurring in the families of susceptible mothers, and despite the moderate group differences in the mothers' beliefs about their treatment condition, the data from the Charlottesville field trials early in the 1980s were, and still are, further strong evidence that hand-to-hand transmission of many cold viruses may be more important than aerosol transmission for producing apparent contagion in natural settings.

And so, by the end of 1988 and for some time following, there appeared to be contradictory research evidence available, some of it favoring the aerosol hypothesis and some favoring the hand-to-hand hypothesis, to explain the transmission of colds, especially rhinovirus colds. Could *both* these hypotheses be correct? Or neither? In 1990 it still seemed unlikely that either question would ever be answered in the affirmative. And yet . . .

PART V

MEDICAL INTELLIGENCE IN THE GOLDEN AGE

Lagging Behind on the Cold Trail: Toronto, 1983, to Salisbury, 1988

"Human respiratory viruses are among the most successful animal viruses in the world. Many show regular antigenic variation, and because of assured increases in human numbers and density, this group of viruses are perhaps entering their golden age, with an almost unlimited supply of susceptible hosts in the foreseeable future, and poor chances of control by vaccination."[1]

— *C. A. Mims, 1976*

As we have seen, late in the 1980s two great paradoxes commanded the attention of medical intelligence personnel trying to understand the common cold. One of these paradoxes was that sometimes colds seemed to be contagious only if the recipient had been in direct physical contact with an active cold sufferer, while at other times they seemed to have been contagious only if the recipient had inhaled virus-laden aerosols over a long time period. Of course these are not mutually exclusive possibilities, and both could be important and correct. Yet for any one virus, only one of these two possible routes of transmission was thought to be typical in the chaotic everyday world outside laboratory doors.

The hypothesis of airborne transmission frequently presented difficulties given the existence of earlier epidemiological studies suggesting that variations in crowding and in the degree of indoor ventilation had little effect upon observed rates of cold transmission. Among office workers there usually seemed to be much less contagion of colds than was seen in equivalent air spaces at home or in school classrooms. Moreover, an hypothesis of aerosol transmission did not fit easily with the pattern of secondary colds seen in many virus watch studies. For instance, most secondary colds in the home show up within three days of the outbreak of an index cold. Yet in experimental studies, particularly those done at Wisconsin, significantly longer time periods appeared to be required, spent in the same air space as multiple, highly infective donors, in order to produce apparent aerosol transmission. Recall too that mothers are much less likely to catch an index cold in a child than vice versa, even though mother and child spend similar amounts of time in each other's air space. And yet, certain experimental studies have seemed to rule out everything except the aerosol route as being the probable source of contagion. The paradox here lies partly in the fact that experimental results and the data from naturalistic field studies so often appeared to lead to contradictory conclusions.

The second notable paradox about common colds late in the 1980s also resulted from an apparent contradiction between data gathered in experimental laboratories and data gathered in the field. The experimental data were unanimous in showing that chilling a person before or soon after they are challenged with a cold virus does not increase the likelihood of a subsequent infection. On the other hand, the epidemiological data frequently suggested that when temperatures outdoors fall noticeably (or sometimes, rise noticeably), there is an increased incidence of new colds. Not that this means the temperature change itself must cause the new infections, for as we saw earlier the temperature change might be associated with some change in risk behavior, such as holding school recess periods indoors, or more frequent wiping or blowing of weeping noses, and so on. In 1980 what seemed clear and very puzzling was that in all the experimental studies, and in many of the epidemiological studies (beginning with Paul and Freese in Spitzbergen), there was no evidence that colder temperatures increased the risk of colds. Yet other epidemiological studies kept showing a very clear relationship between temperatures and illness.

Delayed Susceptibilities to Infection

I am persuaded that at least this second paradox has an interesting and simple resolution. If I am right, both the negative experimental findings and the episodic positive findings from epidemiological work, findings that implicate temperature changes as one factor leading to the outbreak of colds, are "true," at least in part. However, I believe that there are two simple reasons for the apparent "contradictions" seen in previous research studies. First, only some viruses, perhaps only under certain circumstances, will cause colds following significant temperature changes. Other viruses appear to infect, or not, independent of all recent vicissitudes of the local temperature. If correct, this may explain why different epidemiological surveys, in different places at different times, sometimes did and sometimes did not detect a link between recent temperature changes and the incidence of colds.

Secondly, and rather more surprising, it appears that in cases where temperature change does alter the risk of infection and colds it may do so only for a brief time period, one that does not begin until something like twenty-four to sixty hours *after* the occurrence of the temperature change. That is, the increased time of risk is not immediately coincident with the temperature change. This may explain why the experimental studies, in which the time of challenge has always been closely associated with the time of chilling, have observed no increases in the apparent risk of infection. If these experimental challenge studies were to be repeated, with different cold viruses applied at various times beginning twenty-four hours after prolonged chilling, I would predict that a more consistent and strong relationship between temperature change and cold incidence would be observed.

A lag of time between exposure to some temperature change and a period of increased risk for infection would also make the role of temperature changes (and the existence of the lag) hard to notice in any epidemiological study that did not look at day-by-day changes in both temperatures and the incidence of colds. But of course all the early epidemiological surveys looking at colds and temperature effects were "blocked" (that is, summarized by a single average number) week by week or even month by month, obscuring any daily or delayed time dependencies. This made it virtually impossible for the authors of those studies to recognize a lag effect. Instead, the authors of the early studies, following in the steps of van Loghem, assumed there would be an immediate link between temperature changes and the altered risk of infection. And the later experimental studies of chilling and viral challenge were all based on the same assumption.

I have come to my two hypotheses, about (1) the different effects of temperature change for different viruses and (2) the delay to changes in the risk of infection following certain temperature shifts, as the result of two research studies of my own carried out between 1983 and 1988. One of my two studies involved an epidemiological survey monitoring the health of approximately one hundred different first-year university students during each of the four academic years between 1983 and 1987. The other was a retrospective study of experimental trials held at Harvard Hospital in Salisbury between 1983 and 1988. I looked at their "success" rate in producing experimental colds as a function of local temperature changes leading up to the day of challenge.

When Do Undergraduate Colds Choose to Enroll?

The first study, a large-scale epidemiological survey carried out at the University of Toronto, required significant assistance from many people, all of whom volunteered their time to make that study possible.[2] During the four summers between 1983 and 1986 approximately two thousand entering first-year students at Toronto were invited by letter to participate in the research trials to be held during that year. We explained that our study would require about one hour of time filling out two long questionnaires prior to arriving on campus for the September start of classes, and that later it would mean filling out brief nightly reports of the previous day's moods and stress levels, plus reports of any symptoms of illness experienced during that day.

Approximately one hundred fifty volunteers initially agreed to participate in this study each year, and complete records were obtained from about one hundred of them. Each volunteer participant was supervised by one of a dozen volunteer student research assistants each year. The research assistants met periodically with the participants, supplied them with daily report forms, monitored their understanding and correct use of the report scales, and collected the completed research forms week by week, during trials lasting between sixty and ninety days.[3]

While volunteers contributed their personal data on illness, moods, and daily stressors, Climate Canada provided local weather data each day from its weather monitoring station on the University of Toronto campus. Thus local temperature data, rainfall data, humidity levels, hours of sunshine, and wind speed information were collected and analyzed for any role that they might play in the outbreak of colds among our volunteers. It is these data that are central to the hypotheses under consideration here (although the personal data proved interesting in their own right).[4] During the first two years of the study, the only weather data that showed a relationship with subsequent illness were those of temperature, so I set out to examine this relationship in detail for all four academic years of this study.

The presence of common colds was diagnosed from information on detailed symptom report forms. Only clearly "uncomplicated" common colds were included in the analyses of temperature effects. "Uncomplicated" colds were those that (a) did not last more than ten days, and (b) were not accompanied by any reports of fever, chest pain, nausea, or other gastrointestinal symptoms, and (c) were seen by the reporting volunteer as being a common cold (however mild) and not as any form of allergic reaction. All such colds had to be accompanied by an unusually runny or stuffy nose during at least one day of the episode. Colds were defined as beginning on the first day of any symptoms following a day of no symptoms of any kind. Very few of the participants in this study knew any others in the study or had regular contact with them, except rarely and by chance. Thus, the uncomplicated colds documented in this study were, in this sense, "independent" of each other.

Changes in average daily temperature were computed for each day of each trial. Each daily change score consisted of the average temperature on that day, minus the average temperature on the day before. Positive change scores, then, reflected increasing average temperatures while negative change scores reflected decreasing temperatures. These change scores removed any links to the absolute temperature and the time of year. In previous chapters we have seen that colds will occur readily at both warmer and colder times of year and at warm and cold absolute temperatures. It has been the "sudden chill" in the air that has traditionally been associated with colds, both in the minds of the public and also in many of the epidemiological studies recounted in earlier chapters. That is why temperature *change* was the variable of most interest in this study.[5]

With the notable and interesting exception of the Lidwell study described in chapter 8 (to be reviewed again, below), all previous epidemiological studies of possible temperature links to the incidence of common colds tended to combine and condense the data week by week. In our Toronto study, however, new colds and temperature changes were studied day by day. In particular, all the uncomplicated colds reported during any one trial were "lined up" for analysis according to the day on which the symptoms first appeared for each cold. Then, an *average* temperature change score for this first day of *all* colds was generated by averaging the individual temperature change scores applying to each first day of symptoms for each reported cold during the trial. Then a similar average score was computed for the day *prior* to the onset of the symptoms of each cold. Next another such average change score was computed for the day before that, and so on up to the day nine days prior to the onset of symptoms. Thus there were ten temperature change averages generated in this study, one for each of the nine days prior to the start of the colds that developed, plus one for the first day of the colds themselves. The question was, would these average change scores be notably negative (or positive) two days prior to the onset of the colds (at about the presumed time of infection and the beginning of incubation), and would they average near zero on all other days?

Were Any Temperature Changes Seen Prior to Infection?

Ten trials were carried out over the four years of this study. Each year there was a trial in the early fall lasting approximately sixty days. A second trial, with most of the same participants, was held in mid-winter and lasted between fifty-five and ninety days. In 1986 and 1987, the numbers of participants and the numbers of available new colds permitted a third trial to be analyzed in the late winter or in the spring. Typically, each trial was characterized by a period during which colds were in progress in approximately 10 percent of the one hundred participants, and in most cases each trial concluded with a final week in which no new colds were reported.

The results of the first two trials, during the first year of this study, were very interesting and suggestive. The first trial, carried out during the fall of 1983, yielded twenty-eight uncomplicated colds. The average change in daily temperature proved to be near zero on the days that the various cold symptoms were first noticed during this trial. On the day before the first day of symptoms the average temperature change was slightly negative (i.e., slightly cooling). On the second day before symptoms started, the day when many of these colds presumably were initiated due either to self-inoculation or to contagion from contaminated aerosols, the average change in temperature was truly zero. Three days before the symptoms began, at the start of most of the remaining incubation periods, the average change in temperature was still close to zero. However, *four* days prior to the onset of colds, there was a sharp drop in the average temperature change scores, and *five* days prior there had been a sharp rise in average temperatures. If temperature effects were involved in starting some of the colds seen in this first trial, those effects appeared to take place one or two days *prior* to the start of incubation, which is to say four or five days before the onset of overt symptoms. In the period from six through nine days before the start of cold symptoms the average change scores were again all back in the vicinity of zero.

During the second trial, carried out two months later during the winter early in 1984, twenty-two uncomplicated colds were documented. When these colds were "lined up" according to the day that symptoms began in each case, and when average temperature change scores for these start days and the nine days previous were computed, an even more dramatic picture emerged. During this trial, all the average temperature change scores were very close to zero except on one day *five* days prior to the onset of symptoms. On that day there was a marked *drop* in the average temperature. Again it appeared that any possible temperature effects were taking place at least two days *prior* to the start of incubation, or five days prior to the onset of symptoms.

In the second year of the study two more trials were held, one in the fall and one in the early winter, exactly as in the year before. Each of these trials yielded forty-four uncomplicated colds. During the fall trial the only non-zero changes seen in the average daily temperature were modest in size. One such change consisted of a small average drop in temperature two days prior to the onset of symptoms (at about the time of infection, presumably), while the other consisted of a small average rise in temperature four days before the onset of symptoms. During the winter trial, however, again there was a notable change in average daily temperature, and again it was only for a single day. Five days prior to the onset of symptoms there was a sharp, clear drop in the average temperature.[6]

To review then, in three of the first four trials, notable temperature shifts tended to occur on the fifth day prior to the start of overt colds. In the fall of 1983 the shift consisted of a distinct rise in temperature (a distinct drop came on the following day) while in each of the two winter trials this shift consisted of a distinct drop in temperature.[7]

During each of the next two academic years, three trials were carried out and data were collected on a somewhat greater number of colds. During four of these final six trials there were no notable shifts of average temperature observed on any day prior to the onset of cold symptoms. However, in the trial carried out during the early spring of 1986, there was a marked drop of temperature two days prior to the onset of symptoms (at about the presumed time of infection) as well as a marked rise in temperature on the day that symptoms were first reported. In the fall of 1986, a notable rise in average temperatures was seen three days before the onset of symptoms. All other days during this trial had near zero changes in temperature, on average.[8]

Thus, during the four years of this study, four trials showed no notable temperature changes at all, while six trials produced suggestive shifts of temperature either two, three, four, or five days prior to the onset of symptoms. *In none of the ten trials was there ever a notable temperature change during the four-day period six, seven, eight, or nine days in advance of the onset of cold symptoms.*

Because the temperature effects seen during these ten trials were episodic, sometimes there, sometimes weak, and sometimes absent, it might be tempting to dismiss them as unreliable coincidences and statistical artifacts. However, two reasons suggest that indulging such a temptation would be a mistake. First, the analyses of a number of other weather variables, including changes in indoor humidity, did not show anything like these suggestive findings. Why would only the variable of temperature show such suggestive patterning? Secondly, the clustering of all the notable average temperature change scores in just that period from two to five days before symptom onset, with no *maximum* average change scores on any trial occurring zero or one day before onset and none occurring six through nine days before onset, is extremely unlikely in any world where chance alone determines the occurrence of notable, maximum, scores.[9] Something is happening as a result of those temperature changes, and that something clearly seems to be complicated by additional factors.

Have We Seen Such Temperature Effects Before?

It is interesting that when prior temperature shifts did seem to matter, sometimes (but only in the fall) it was *increasing* temperatures that were involved, while on other trials only *decreasing* temperatures appeared to be involved. We have seen this fall warming effect previously, particularly in the very early data from Holland by van Loghem (in chapter 3) and in the data from England by Lidwell (in chapter 8). Is there some particular virus that is more common in the fall and that is able to capitalize on something resulting from a marked warming at times when the days are generally getting cooler? In virus watch studies it is often the rhinoviruses that are seen most prominently each fall. Could certain rhinoviruses have been prominent in the Toronto trials carried out in the fall of 1983 and 1984 but not the fall of 1985?

The research done during the ten trials held at Toronto had certain advantages, primarily because it dealt with wild colds transmitted naturally in the field. But for that very reason it had two distinct disadvantages as well. First, the particular viruses that may have been responsible for each of the 390 uncomplicated colds recorded by our volunteers were unknown to us, so we could not tell if different viruses were causing different visible effects. Second, we were blind to the exact timing of any naturally occurring challenge, or, in other words, to the moments when "infection" presumably had begun. If the times of infection were known, and the species of virus as well, it would be possible to see with far greater certainty whether or not the potency of certain viruses is related to temperature changes, and just how much of a delay occurs before the risk of infection increases following any significant changes in the temperature.

Experimental studies involving challenge with different viruses offer an opportunity to avoid these two problems. By looking at temperature shifts leading up to the day of challenge in such studies, together with the incidence of colds that followed, it might be possible to identify certain viruses for which temperature changes are sometimes linked with subsequent illness. To this end, in 1988 I decided to approach the director of the Common Cold Research Unit in Salisbury, requesting permission to examine the records of the many experimental trials carried out there between 1983 and 1988. Permission was granted, and just before the few final months of operation at Harvard Hospital I was able to complete an analysis of the relevant data from these trials.[10]

English Weather: Is It as Powerful as They Say?

Seventy-six trials were carried out at Salisbury over the five-year period in question. Four different challenge viruses were repeatedly employed at various times over these years. Thus it was possible to look at the relationship between cold incidence and temperature changes in the days leading up to the day of challenge with each of those four different viruses.

Temperature data for the Salisbury area were collected at Boscombe Down, a nearby meteorological station located approximately twelve kilometers north of Harvard Hospital. These data consisted of minimum daily temperature readings only. No hour-by-hour data were recorded, and so daily temperature averages were unavailable. Since participants on each trial at Salisbury were typically challenged on their *third* day following arrival at the Unit, and since participants came to trials from all over Great Britain, the weather they experienced four and five days prior to challenge may have varied in some cases from that recorded at Boscombe Down. Often, however, significant changes in temperature at Boscombe Down marked passages of large frontal systems oriented SW–NE. These fronts generally involved much of the country over an eight-hour period, and usually they would similarly affect all who lived in or near the major centers of population lying north and east of Salisbury.

The four challenge viruses used in the trials at Salisbury were rhinovirus type 2 (RV2) employed on fourteen trials; coronavirus LP (229E), employed on fifteen trials; rhinovirus type 14 (RV14), employed on twenty-two trials; and rhinovirus type 9 (RV9), employed on twenty-five trials. Parallel to the Toronto study, daily temperature change scores (today's low minus yesterday's low) were computed. One such score was generated on each trial, for each one of the five days leading up to challenge, for the day of challenge itself, and for the first three days of incubation and outbreak of symptoms that followed the day of challenge. But whereas in the Toronto study all colds had been "lined up" according to the first day of visible symptoms and the nine days prior to that, the data at Salisbury were always "lined up" with respect to the day of challenge with active cold virus.

Each of the nine temperature change scores computed for each trial was matched to (and later correlated with) the *percentage* of the volunteers who developed colds on that trial after being challenged with virus. For any one type of virus having no links to temperature change, all nine measures of association would be expected to average near zero, with random fluctuations above and below zero according to the random vicissitudes of both the weather and the general health of the trial volunteers. However, if rising temperatures or falling temperatures did affect the later incidence of colds for a particular virus, we would then expect one or two of these daily measures (correlations) to be far from zero, either negative (for days when falling temperatures were associated with higher numbers of subsequent colds) or positive (for days when rising temperatures were associated with higher numbers of colds).[11]

Historical epidemiological work had led to the inference that for some, but certainly not all, of the viruses, we might expect to see notable negative (or perhaps some occasional positive) associations showing up for the day of challenge, but only for that day. However, my Toronto study data suggested that if unusual positive or negative associations were to be found they would probably be found one, two, or three days *before* the day of challenge, while the estimates of association would be near zero for the day of challenge itself, consistent with the universally negative results from previous experimental studies of chilling carried out at the time of challenge. In general, data from these Salisbury trials did indeed prove to be consistent with the Toronto findings, and inconsistent with the view that temperature matters at the time of initial challenge or infection.

It turned out that each of the four different cold viruses provided evidence of quite notable associations, either for one or for two of the nine days examined. There were no notable associations for the day of challenge itself or for any of the three following days of incubation and symptom onset.[12] In what follows I will describe the associations that were seen in percentage terms, from zero percent association (complete independence) to one hundred percent association for perfect correspondence. (These percentages derive from the squared correlation coefficients, as described in note 11.)

For the trials with coronavirus 229E there was a single notable association (–19.4 percent) seen on the day two days *before* challenge. For the RV2 trials there was also a single notable association (–17.6 percent), and it too was on the day two days *before* challenge. For RV14 trials there were two notable associations, one positive (+25.0 percent), this coming two days *before* challenge, and one negative (–22.1 percent), which came on the following day, one day before challenge. Finally, for the RV9 trials there was one highly significant and positive association (+47.6 percent) that occurred four days prior to challenge. However, one day prior to challenge there was another very suggestive (if not quite "notable") index of association, and this time it was again negative (–15.2 percent).

Thus, for three of the four viruses studied, the day two days before challenge was characterized by a notable correlation, indicating that temperature changes on that day would predict, to a degree, the subsequent percentage of volunteers who would develop colds on that trial some four or five days later. But temperature changes on the day of challenge itself were generally far less predictive.[13] The strongest predictive effect came with RV9. For the twenty-five trials using this virus, nearly half (47.6 percent) of all the uncertainty about the percentage of volunteers who would later develop colds on each trial could be removed by knowing the degree of temperature change four days before challenge (when many of the volunteers were traveling to or arriving in Salisbury). A distinct warming on that day predicted many more RV9 colds developing on the trial, while a distinct cooling on that day predicted many fewer such colds on the trial.

What Do These Findings Mean?

On the basis of these two studies, one at Toronto and one at Salisbury, two conclusions seem likely. First: temperature changes can indeed be one important factor predicting the onset of some colds. Second: whatever effects temperature changes may be having, they increase the risk for colds that generally will appear four or five days after those changes take place.

It would have been nice to be able to tell whether the temperature changes at Salisbury led to a higher proportion of *infections* one or two days later (among which would be some number of *silent* infections), or instead to a higher proportion of observable (i.e., symptomatic) colds, with no real impact on the overall rate of infection. I was unable to extract sufficient data on the percentage of subclinical colds seen in the trials at Salisbury to suggest a conclusion on this matter. However, from some of the virus watch studies and experimental studies we've seen previously, it seems more probable that a higher proportion of colds on a given trial reflects a higher proportion of *infections* occurring from one to three days prior.

Were Temperature Lag Effects Seen in Other Studies?

The data from Toronto and Salisbury suggest as well an interesting reinterpretation of the previous data from the north of England reported by the Lidwell group.[14] Lidwell and his colleagues generated eighteen correlations, between (1) the amount of daily temperature change on a given day and (2) the incidence of colds occurring on each of the next eighteen days. Averaging over many months and a great many colds, they found that, only after October, their strongest correlations were for cold incidences occurring two, three, and four days following the day of temperature change. Before and after those three days their observed correlations returned smoothly to zero.

Fixing on two or three days as the typical transmission time for the common cold, the Lidwell group interpreted their data to show that colder temperatures immediately and directly affect transmission and infection. But their data are equally consistent with the conclusion that temperature change is important one or two days prior to the time of infection. Moreover, like the September data rationalized away many years before by van Loghem, their data suggested that in the early fall a day of marked warming will sometimes lead to the appearance of colds from three to five days later. It does appear then that some viruses, including perhaps RV9, are more likely to prove infective after a time of sudden autumn warming.

The hypothesis of a delayed susceptibility to virus after exposure to falling temperatures also fits well with another puzzling observation in the previous research literature. Recall that in 1973, T. R. Allen reported a curious epidemic of colds among men who had been under total isolation for seventeen weeks in Antarctica.[15] No triggering cause was found for this epidemic, nor was the virus identified. However, exactly four days prior to the first appearance of any symptoms, a very striking plunge in outdoor temperature had occurred, producing a drop of twenty-five degrees Celsius in thirty-six hours. Four days before the onset of symptoms would be one or two days prior to the presumed start of incubation. Sharply falling temperatures seemed very likely to have been a contributing cause of this unusual epidemic.

Even that classic early study by Schade, of colds among German soldiers serving in the freezing winter trenches and warm barracks of World War I (discussed in chapter 7) gave strong suggestion of a four- or five-day delay in illness after chilling. Recall that colds were four times more prevalent among soldiers stationed three days in cold trenches after they were rotated back to warm barracks, in contrast to soldiers stationed in the barracks the whole time. But the surplus of colds apparently did not break out in the trenches, where they might have been expected if there were no great delay in the start of incubation following a day of exposure to cold.

Could it then be the case that marked changes in temperature (perhaps in interaction with something else) change the virulence or potency of certain viruses, which in turn have more infective power one or two days later? For instance, does that sudden warm day amid the first cooling days of fall trigger something in type 9 rhinovirus, something that makes that virus better able to find a new host, or harder to resist after it does find one? To me this seems very unlikely in view of the data gathered at Salisbury. Viruses there hibernated comfortably, insulated under deep refrigeration, until prepared for challenge a few hours before use. These viruses knew nothing of the weather outside during the days leading up to and beginning each trial. No, the Salisbury data suggest that it is the hosts, and not the parasites, that seem to be affected by certain temperature changes.

What then happens with the hosts? Does thermoregulation have some as yet undetermined link to immune function? For instance, does a body that is busy responding to unaccustomed chilling temporarily cease to produce new nasal antibodies that will protect it against certain colds, so that one or two days later these antibodies reach a dangerously low level for a time? Or, perchance, does the immune system itself temporarily *overreact* to the presence of commensal cold virus, creating the very symptoms that we attribute to the virus? Or, is it instead our *behavior* that changes at times when the temperature is changing, rendering us more at risk for infection and the symptoms of a cold?

As we have already seen, the hypothesis of some important behavioral change has long been appealing because it provided another way to explain away previous failures to find any *experimental* evidence that chilling increases the risk of colds. Experimental chilling, in the laboratory, would not lead on to those typical behavioral changes (such as more frequent riding in more crowded buses, or more touching of children's dripping noses) that might facilitate new colds outside of the laboratory, among social groups. Prior to carrying out my study of the experimental trials at Salisbury I had private doubts about any such behavioral theories, if only because my Toronto survey data gave no hints that colds are associated with any changes in, for example, the variable numbers of "crowd contacts" that students reported having each week, or any of a number of other such individual differences in potential risks of exposure that I tried to measure. Moreover, data such as those of Milam and Smillie from the Virgin Islands,[16] or those of the Evans group from the Philippines,[17] suggesting that rather slight but unusual changes in temperature have been associated with significant epidemics of colds, make it seem as though a behavioral change is an unlikely candidate to account for at least these subtropical colds.

Now, with both the Salisbury data and the Toronto survey data, behavioral explanations for temperature links to later colds seem to be improbable. If risk behavior is changed, that behavior must take place reliably during a brief time period that is delayed by approximately two days from the time of the temperature change that triggers it. Such a reliable delay seems unlikely, particularly in the controlled environment of Harvard Hospital. It seems much more likely that some cascading series of immunological events occurs in the body and that these events take between one and three days to work themselves out. In the trials analyzed at Salisbury, nearly everyone was inoculated with a dose of virus, whatever had been the recent weather. Yet the temperature dependencies seemed to be at least as visible in the Salisbury data as they were in the epidemiological data from the students at Toronto.

Whatever the reason for the lag of four days between certain temperature changes temperature and cold onset, this lag is both long enough and elusive enough that many people working in medical intelligence have found it easy to dismiss. I have been unable to discover information about any relevant physiological process that takes four days to unfold, one that might offer a ready explanation for the mechanisms at work causing the lag effects that I believe sometimes operated in my research data. And yet if the mechanisms are unclear, the existence of various other lag effects, similar to those found in the data from Toronto and Salisbury, are not totally unknown in medical research. There have been reports, for instance, of increased catecholamine activity, reflected in sudden spikes of vanillyl-mandelic acid (VMA) excretion, observed three (and possibly more) days prior to the onset of respiratory illness in thirteen of nineteen such illnesses studied.[18] These brief spikes occurred on a single day only. Similar spikes of corticosteroid and catecholamine levels have been observed two, three, and four days before adenovirus illness in army recruits.[19] Brief spikes in reported psychological stress, occurring just three and four days before minor illnesses, have been described as well.[20] In none of these studies were the different "stressors" identified directly, but a one- or two-day lag between the time of stress and a subsequent susceptibility to infection seems common to all of them.

It is even less clear what may account for the episodic nature of observed temperature lag effects. Is it that some cold viruses, more prevalent in certain years, remain unaffected by the bodily consequences of temperature change? Or are there as yet unidentified variables interacting with temperature changes, variables that come and go, variables that are necessary ingredients in the mix of factors leading to a much elevated risk of infection and/or to symptoms? One might speculate that individual differences could be playing such an interactive role. Yet in our Toronto survey we had one hundred and more new volunteers each year. This number is large enough that the proportion of a more susceptible type of individual would be expected to be approximately equal in the samples participating each year. The fact that some trials (even some with the same individuals) showed temperature lag effects, while others did not, suggests that the missing ingredient is not tied to personal physiology so much as it is tied to environmental factors other than the temperature effects. This same line of reasoning would seem to render less likely any putative role for psychological stresses as the missing ingredient because the stresses (and the timing of the stresses) of first-year university life are (on average) quite similar from year to year, while the temperature lag effects came and went over the years.

Perhaps then it is again time for medical intelligence to look more closely at the possibility that many colds (particularly "index" colds) are commensal, and to look at the interactions possible among different viruses all present in our bodies at the same time. Perhaps unwittingly we may become our own "cloud babies" and so infect ourselves, as much through multiple, chronic, commensal organisms and various subclinical infections as through our probing, social fingers and our ubiquitous inhalations. Perhaps van Loghem was on the right track after all, so many years ago. But if so, why then were all those colds at Longyear City so clearly linked to the arrival of the first ships each spring? And why did the colds seen at Cruz Bay in the Virgin Islands spread in expanding circles out from the initial site of infection? These are some of the questions that will inform the final chapter of this book. Along the way, however, we must also ask after the health of medical intelligence work, as it existed at the start of the last decade of the second millennium.

19

Resolution: Arriving Home, 1990

"As the work of [Salisbury's Common Cold] Unit comes to a close it is to be hoped that others interested in [these] mild but important infections will continue the studies elsewhere. There is much more to be done."[1]

— *D. A. J. Tyrrell, 1988*

One of the reasons why medical intelligence and public health personnel have sought for so long to discover the true causes of the common cold has been in the hope that they might one day develop a reliable and effective prophylactic for colds. Whenever the common cold is a serious health threat (as indeed it can be if infants or seniors are in fragile health) or whenever the immense social and economic costs of colds are assayed and compared unfavorably against the GNP, then achieving the prevention of all colds becomes an unquestioned good deserving of a Nobel Prize. By 1990, however, it had become abundantly clear that the common cold reflects a very complex, diverse, and mysterious set of phenomena. There seemed to be no danger that colds would soon become entirely preventable.[2]

For myself, I cannot help but wonder whether the successful prevention of all colds (should that ever become feasible) might later prove to be rather like the successful prevention of all sunlight. In the end it might just prove to be another entry in man's long and dubious honor role of so-called "improvements" upon nature, on that growing list of ill-judged interventions recording everything from the careless deforestation of the Earth, or the creation of multiple zones of radioactive desert, to the introduction of rabbits into Australia and gorse into New Zealand.

A "cure" for the common cold would undoubtedly mean one of three things: it would mean (1) the eradication of all the various viruses that create colds in man, or (2) the creation of a personal buffer to keep cold viruses from infecting particular people, or (3) the introduction of some chronic mechanism or chemistry that permits cold infections, but in every case stops the development of the symptoms of a cold. I hold that, in different ways, each of these three possibilities might just be risky gambles for the future of our species, but particularly the first one of the three.

We are a species that has been subject to common colds since the dawn of recorded history. Moreover, our direct primate ancestors probably shared cells in their bodies with close relatives of these viruses many thousands of generations before humans appeared on Earth. It would be well to remember that there is much we still do not know about viruses. Even more, perhaps, there is much we do not know about ourselves and about the complex interdependencies that rule the functioning of our immune systems. And what we do not know *can* hurt us. As a species, we have probably had no more than a few dozen thousand generations to accommodate to the viral environment into which we are born. Any radical changes in that environment, or in our exposures to it, or in our normal reactions to it, can be expected to bring unwelcome surprises to most of us, if not sooner, then later. Those surprises might involve a loss of general immune competency in ourselves or our descendants. Or, they might involve an increased risk of later infection by altered viruses that pose greater dangers to our health than do colds.

Keeping cold viruses out might also risk the loss of something good, something not yet appreciated, something that these viruses may quietly be bringing to us. In this connection, a few years before his death, cancer researcher and bestselling author Dr. Lewis Thomas was musing on viruses, and on some of the things that people have done to the Earth and to each other. He had occasion then to write as follows:

> Our microbial ancestors made use of quicker ways for bypassing long stretches of evolutionary time, and I envy them. They have always had an abundance of viruses, darting from one cell to another across species lines, doing no damage most of the time ("temperate" viruses, as they are called), but always picking up odds and ends of DNA from their hosts and then passing these around, as though at a great party. The bits are then used by the recipients for their betterment — new tricks for coping with new contingencies.

I hope our species has a mechanism like this. Come to think of it, maybe
we do. After all, we live in a sea of our own viruses, most of which seem to
be there for no purpose, not even to make us sick. We can hope that some of
them might be taking hold of useful items of genetic news from time to
time, then passing these along for the future of the species. It makes a cheerful footnote, anyway: next time you feel a cold coming on, reflect on the
possibility that you may be giving a small boost to evolution.[3]

And alongside Dr. Thomas's cheerful note some fascinating questions
remain. We have now learned that for every cold we feel coming on, there
is probably another occasion when we feel nothing while a subclinical
infection develops, thrives for a few days, and then retreats. Why do we
have symptoms on some occasions but not on others? In 1990 medical
intelligence was only beginning to appreciate what might become a full
and satisfactory answer to this question. For most of the previous half
century, considerable research effort had been concentrated in a different
direction: on working out the main mechanisms of cold transmission. Are
colds contaged through the air we breathe or from the things we touch?
Or do cold viruses live commensally and blossom into infection when
their environment is changed in some important ways? If there is to be
any hope of reconciling the various conflicting studies recounted in this
book, studies that dealt with how colds are transmitted, then I believe that
medical intelligence must look afresh at this third, commensal, possibility.

Some Problems with a Commensal Theory of Colds

A commensal hypothesis brings with it many problems, to be sure. Foremost among these is the lack of any satisfactory commensal theory to
explain, for instance, why so many of the colds studied by Paul and Freese
on Spitzbergen appeared to be triggered by the arrival of the first ship each
summer, or why experimental colds are sometimes so easy to produce in
the laboratory following a challenge with a known cold virus. In all the
years of trials carried out at the Common Cold Research Unit at Salisbury
there were virtually no colds reported among isolated volunteers who had
been challenged with saline placebo. Only exposure to active cold viruses
produced some colds, colds that invariably followed an infection with just
that particular challenge virus employed on the trial. If natural colds really
are caused primarily by commensal viruses, then why do challenge studies
seem to suggest otherwise? And again, if colds are commensal why should

they always tend to die out in small isolated populations, and why would they often spring back into epidemic life when the isolation is broken?[4] If we really do carry with us the viruses that cause many of our colds, why don't colds simply occur with almost uniform regularity, independent of the surrounding social and seasonal environment?

One answer to these problems is to invoke one or more additional (interactive) ingredients necessary to trigger an initial infection, and perhaps still others necessary to produce the symptoms of a clinical cold. Just as guns can be found in two states (loaded and unloaded), only one of which ever produces projectiles that can injure, so too commensal viruses may come in two states (infective and non-infective). Viruses gathered from an active cold sufferer and then prepared to become the challenge dose in an experimental study may come in the "loaded" (infective) state much more often than the benign virus normally circulating among the members of a small, isolated community, or the members of a large community enjoying a summer holiday from colds.

In an epidemic of natural colds, perhaps what is contaged far more often than any loaded virions themselves is the infective agency (the ammunition) that converts already commensal viruses into infective viruses. Such a possibility has important if subtle ramifications, ramifications affecting the interpretation of many past studies of viral transmission as well as the design of new ones.

When, for instance, a sample of air, or a door handle, is examined for the presence of virus in a transmission study, it may be that what really matters is missed. Looking for a gun, we may not see the ammunition. Overlooking the ammunition, and finding no gun in plain view, we may cease searching before we have found the gun that is hidden inside the cellular drawer. Or, finding a gun in plain view, we may fail to notice that it isn't loaded. The virus that are commensal, in a non-infective state, may not propagate under the conditions that have been standard for laboratory viral cultures. Thus they may fail to be counted, or they may not infect when they are employed in challenge studies, leading us to conclude that they have not been present. Virus residing in a commensal state (inside nasal cells) may not even get sampled in the nasal wash (surface) collections typically employed in virus watch studies.

Still, there are problems even with a two-factor theory of commensal virus and an activating agent. We have seen in the previous chapter, for instance, that when temperature changes appear to trigger colds, they probably do this by affecting people rather than affecting the viruses themselves. It seems likely that if commensal viruses are rendered infective by the introduction of some critical ingredient, that ingredient is first found outside the virus, in the cell environment, and it probably has its own sources in normal body functioning. It is hard to imagine how any such ingredient would be transmitted from person to person. Yet without a theory of such transmission, family epidemics of colds, and the epidemics studied at Longyear City, Spitzbergen, cannot reasonably be attributed to commensal viruses.

Historically, the favorite two-factor theory of colds has placed immune substances in the role of the second factor. In this view it is not that some form of ammunition is loaded into a viral gun that soon explodes into infection, but rather that the immune system temporarily fails, thereby taking the gun off its safety and allowing it to fire. We have seen in chapter 13 some of what may be problems with this view. Infections can be avoided even by some who have little apparent antibody protection against a specific virus, even after a massive challenge from that virus. And infections occasionally occur with just a small challenge dose of virus, even in people who have very high concentrations of antibody to that virus.

It is quite likely, of course, that we have yet to discover the full complement of antibody substances needed to understand resistance to colds. Moreover, it is likely that some of the relevant immune factors can oscillate dramatically in their concentrations over short periods of time, a possibility yet to be carefully examined. Most researchers working in this field in 1990 were already persuaded that the strength of existing antibody will determine when infection will and won't occur. So it would be premature to rule out antibodies as important factors in stopping and starting epidemics of colds. Again, however, we must face the data of Paul and Freese. If creating antibodies strengthens resistance, explaining why colds died out in Longyear City over the winter, why then was the population so ripe for a new epidemic when the first ship arrived in the harbor the following spring? And if the answer is that the new ship brought with it a new virus, why then was that virus so much more virulent among the residents of Longyear City than it had been among those aboard the ship, or among those in the southern cities in which the ship's passengers had embarked?

There appears to be but one compelling answer to questions such as these. Each new virus brought to Longyear City in the spring must have been circulating in the larger, external population where fewer people were still susceptible to it, perhaps because most of the people living out there would be experiencing periodic encounters with the virus, and thus they would receive booster doses of antibodies to it.

Something about even this answer doesn't sit right, however. The Antarctic data and the laboratory data suggested that immunity does not wane so very quickly under isolation, if it does at all. Specific antibodies to a given cold virus seem to take more than a year to wane (see chapter 13) and if there are non-specific substances, they appear to wax and wane over very short time periods indeed. If the answer is that a brand new virus (or one that hasn't been around for a few years) is now circulating in the big cities, but it cannot come to Longyear City until spring, then why isn't there an equally dramatic epidemic of this new virus in those cities too, whenever it hits? Perhaps there is, but perhaps in the big cities, on first appearance, this novel virus produces a higher proportion of silent infections than it would in a population that has experienced no other colds at all for six months. Perhaps, then, some symptom-prevention factor decays with time, and in Longyear City the lack of new winter infections prevents both silent and overt colds. With the arrival of the first ship of summer, and with it an accumulation of the latest in circulating viruses, infections leading on to colds are very common. Later, infections from newer viruses might still be very common, but no longer would observable new colds be so frequent.

This is all very well, save for two major problems. First, the same logic should have applied in Antarctica, when each new crew arrived in the spring to join the isolated wintering-over group (see chapter 6). But as we saw, the rate of colds among newcomers and previous isolates was not notably unequal, and in fact it tended to be higher in the new recruits. And in both groups the incidence of colds was less than it was in the cities to the north, from which these personnel had come. Then, secondly, most epidemiological studies find no good evidence of any general symptom-prevention factor following an overt cold. Each next cold seems to come at random, and it can come within a few days of a previous one.

Now I recognize that among my readers there will be some who cannot remember when they last had a cold, readers who employ something close to a sure-fire prophylactic for preventing colds. To them, this assertion about the random arrival times of colds may seem strange. Such readers are more likely to be over fifty years old, I submit, more likely to ignore and forget the few brief colds that do visit them, and more likely to attribute any colds that they can remember to dramatic omissions in their prophylactic regime. This is neither the volume nor the time to explore the evidence for and against such hypotheses. I can only confess that I now enjoy many fewer colds than I once did (being well over fifty years old) and no prophylactic that I know about seems to make those fewer colds stop coming.[5]

At the moment then, for every hypothesis that might make sense of any one set of data, those gathered for instance by Paul and Freese in Spitzbergen, or by van Loghem in Holland, there are problems presented by conflicting data gathered in different settings using different methods. How shall we reconcile these apparently conflicting data? The answer will probably require a kind of research that we have yet to see, together with more of the types of research that we have been seeing for a full century. (But of this, more in a moment.)

What Have We Learned to Help Us Avoid Colds?

Given that we are in no danger of soon being freed of all our colds and all our uncertainties about how colds manage to make their rounds, what can we then take away from this historical journey of ours? First, if exposure to certain temperature changes does increase the risk for colds, as I believe it does, and if it does so only after a lag in time following an exposure to that change, we may then have to change some of our folk warnings about colds. No longer can parents solemnly deny their children the thrill of under-dressing in inclement weather. They will instead have to exact a price from their children, namely that beginning about one day later, the child would be well advised to stay home from school for a day or two, keeping warm and comfortable, wearing a fancy gauze facemask perhaps, and taking time every few hours to dip the fingers of each hand into a solution that leaves lovely purple stains on the hands and on some of the many things those hands touch. As adults, perhaps we can practice a more realistic but similar caution after being exposed to marked temperature shifts: doing whatever we think prudent, but not until the time between twenty-four and forty-eight hours following our exposure. This may involve more attention to washing hands, taking a favorite medicine against colds, avoiding contact with people who have visible colds, and so on. But of course, the "danger" of exposure to any marked temperature change can still be reduced in the old-fashioned way: by avoiding exposure to that change to begin with, or by dressing appropriately, or by other means of buffering the felt temperature shifts.

There is a counter folk wisdom going around which insists that (1) exposures to chilling and to marked temperature shifts in fact produce no increased risk of colds, and (2) that it is merely retelling an old wives' tale to claim otherwise. One thing I hope the reader will take from this book is that while often this "wisdom" is probably true, the denial of any increased risk following exposure to temperature shifts is sometimes misguided. The many different epidemiological studies, all suggesting a link (even though lagged) between temperature shifts and the incidence of colds, cannot be dismissed. But note, this is not to say that the chilling itself triggers the colds. Given especially the uniformly negative experimental evidence on colds after chilling, it is safe to say that the chill itself is not what produces any increase in our risk of a cold. Perhaps then we should stop saying to each other "I caught a chill" when what we mean is that we have a new cold. Instead, we might say: "Apparently I neglected to pay for my chill when billed a little later."

The relative importance of aerosol transmission versus direct physical contacts in promoting infections by common cold viruses remains less clear. The reader can arrive at his or her own judgment on this matter, having seen the evidence on both sides. The practical importance of the chosen view may not be great however. By wearing gauze masks, as the Japanese often do, aerosol exposure (at least to larger aerosol droplets) can be minimized. Less recognized is the happy fact that a nose covered by a mask is also a nose that cannot be probed with the fingers. (True, the eyes can still be rubbed. But perhaps goggles will also come back into fashion, as they were in the early days of the automobile.) If, on the other hand, one holds, as I currently do, that most of the contaged colds we catch are likely to be self-inoculated colds, then the importance of keeping the hands clean, or keeping them away from the nose and eyes, seems increased. Such habits may be hard to modify. But not impossibly hard. And like so much in life, it is always worth a try, keeping an open mind about the possible good that may result. Research into how to reduce the likelihood of colds, like the earlier research involving the use of killer kleenexes and the virucidal hand rinse, might yet provide new inspiration to those who seek to reduce the number of colds they suffer. But such research is currently unlikely in the absence of a commercial incentive and a commercial, rather than a scientific, curiosity.

What Do We Need to Know Next?

In the modern study of colds, basic epidemiological research seems to be disappearing. It is becoming more and more expensive and harder and harder to justify such research when there are no strong reasons to expect dramatic and predictable new findings. But should we really suppose that there are no longer important facts about wild colds that remain unsuspected, unpredicted, and undiscovered? (Of course not.) The loss of new virus watch studies and other new epidemiological projects means the loss of fresh clues about colds.

How else, for instance, might we ever discover, *if it were true*, the significant fact that the immediate removal from a family of a person with an index cold (just at the start of infection) would produce no drop at all in the probability of seeing what we previously called a "secondary" cold occurring in the same family? How else, *if it were true*, might we ever discover that informing a family as soon as one of its members developed a silent cold (a subclinical infection) significantly increased the rate of secondary infections seen in the rest of the family over that same rate when families were kept in the dark about the silent cold? If there are few studies, there can be few surprises. And right now, medical intelligence needs rather more surprises.

We can count on laboratory work to bring us some new surprises, of course, and such studies are somewhat more likely to be continued despite the increased attention now being given to more serious illnesses, particularly those resulting from the AIDS viruses. Suppose it were discovered, however, that among the cold viruses, primitive though they may be, many actually come in something like sexed or multiple specialized forms, i.e., as "male" and "female," or as "gun barrel," "ammunition," and "trigger." What if infections are caused only by the conjunction of a full set of these forms, forms that differ only slightly, and that invariably in the past have all been propagated together in laboratory test tubes as well as in challenged nasal cells? What if the immune system typically suppresses only one of these forms, perhaps selected at random, a different form in each individual, so that the remaining, unsuppressed form(s) become "commensal"? And then, what if a new epidemic of colds represents the spread or activation of the missing one of the forms, which had been suppressed only in some proportion of the previously infected population? Ah yes, wouldn't we then be in for some real surprises! And wouldn't a few of our remaining puzzles start then to make more sense?

If, as I still suspect (despite all the problems noted earlier) commensal colds are quite common in everyday life, then techniques need to be developed for finding and experimenting on commensal viruses wherever they are normally lodged inside their host cells. And if cold viruses differ when they are infective from when they are merely commensal, then we are almost certainly going to have to map the viral DNA and RNA that may cause or express such differences. This will have to be done for very many of the cold viruses, if not all of them. And once we have their genetic codes, we still need to work out the meaning of those codes and the various implications of the instructions they embody. If cold viruses only differ in their effects as a function of the cell environment itself, then we are also going to have to map that environment very closely. Each of these tasks is likely to be as daunting as finding the proverbial needle in a haystack, that is, until we can invent the equivalent of a magnet for pulling out just the needle, the better to examine it closely. Such inventions have been made before; with luck (and public support) they can and will be made again.

Once the relevant human cell environments, together with the nucleic hearts of the many differing cold viruses, have all been successfully mapped, and while the meanings of those maps are being worked out, it will probably become desirable to test the implications of any new discoveries by performing new challenge studies, carried out with the help of isolated volunteers. With the closure of England's Common Cold Research Unit at Salisbury, such studies will not be as easy as they once were. Poor old Harvard Hospital was falling down in 1990, and it had been closed in large part because of the high cost of duplicating its facilities, whether on the old Salisbury site or on any another. The finances involved in pursuing common cold research have always limited what could be done, but never more so than today. The Rockefeller Foundation support that financed a productive year in Longyear City in 1930, and the government grants that enabled the work of the world's Medical Research Councils in 1970, had each become victims of the times by 1990. Research funds were diluted, and a kind of anemia began to erode the health of that portion of the medical intelligence community working on the case of the common cold.

Big Science and Big Money

Or so it has seemed. Common cold research projects, like those in almost every other field of science, have tended to become more and more technical and specialized over the years. This shows up clearly, for instance, in the number of authors' names attached to common cold research articles, a number that has grown steadily over time. Where an article would have had either one or two authors in 1930, it was typical for it to have five or more authors in 1990. The varied technical skills needed to work with viruses today, with samples of immune protein, with machines that sort, count, weigh, and compute, and with volunteers who may not wish to spend significant portions of their lives donating both information and tissues during a long sequence of scattered colds, all combine to require more and more complex (and expensive) teams of research talent. The lone detective, patiently gathering viral intelligence and piecing together the great secret of how colds are transmitted, is fast becoming (or more probably, always was) a fiction. Instead everyone seems to be looking for the big break in this case, the discovery of a smoking gun, followed by a dramatic surprise confession. Raw intelligence work appears to be slipping out of fashion, while bigger research is marching in. I cannot help but see this as a loss.

I hope I exaggerate, but I don't know that I do. That is why I worry about the continued health of medical intelligence and our rate of progress in understanding the common cold. When in 1983 I applied for a small amount of money to enable my own epidemiological cold research at the University of Toronto, I was turned down. The national granting agency to which I had applied reported that their main reason for so doing was because there appeared to be very little chance that I would get more than a few of the required volunteer participants who would keep decent daily track of their health and moods. When I easily succeeded at doing so, in the first year of my project, I was then told (off the record) that without special training in the field, and without laboratory technicians, I was unlikely to discover anything of use or importance with my continuing study.

Then, four years later, I submitted for publication the first fruits of my research in Toronto and at Salisbury, describing the evidence for a one- or two-day temperature lag effect. Four different medical journals declined to publish my article, for four different reasons and for one common reason. The one common reason was that because no bodily mechanism was currently known that might explain a lag between the timing of temperature changes and any later susceptibility to infection, it seemed highly doubtful to the reviewers that any such lag truly existed. The four differing reasons given were in part mutually contradictory from journal to journal. In every case they seemed to me (naturally) to be focused on matters quite tangential to my one main point about the probable existence of a temperature lag effect, and its potential to reconcile the apparent contradiction between previous epidemiological findings and experimental studies with chilled volunteers. No journal seemed particularly interested in my findings, nor did they seem to see much value in my encouraging others to look for similar lag effects or to be alert for any previously unsuspected physical mechanisms that might explain them.

Medical scientists, like scientists everywhere, have known for years that the most important sources of advancement in science are invariably unpredicted and very often serendipitous. This is the single most important reason why support for "basic" research is always said to be so vitally important. But the history of science also reveals a less obvious truth: that the profound significance of most of the major ideas put forward in the past, and many of the key discoveries made in science, have gone quite unrecognized during the first few years after the publication of those ideas and discoveries. Scientific "merit" and scientific utility are not given out big and bold for all to read at first glance. It should not surprise us then that by 1990 it was also becoming clear that in medicine, as in psychology and many other scientific disciplines, the degree of agreement between independent reviewers of grant submissions and of journal submissions turns out to be distressingly low.[6] We should always remember, if the future is *terra incognita*, the road into it simply cannot be mapped.

The "Common Cold" of Medical Intelligence Work

Given all this, one might suppose that a recognition of the *futility* of trying to forecast the merit of proposed new projects or theories, of trying to forecast the eventual importance of new discoveries or new hypotheses, would be an article of faith among scientific peer reviewers. Instead, however, illusions of possessing a hard-won clinical sagacity and deep scientific insight affect medical intelligence personnel (and their patrons) no less than they do those who work in almost every other branch of science. Such illusions are human. They are ubiquitous. Only the rare Socrates among us can overcome them, nor do I count myself as one of these admirable few.

Illusions of insight lead on to a conviction that one's own scientific understanding will most likely prove to be the correct understanding, and that some other view will probably not prove to be the correct view. While knowledge of the power and prevalence of these illusions is a necessary first step to overcoming them (just as it is with common perceptual illusions that we all experience), still, by itself, this knowledge does not keep one from continuing to experience the illusions of possessing gifted discrimination and special access to the truth. Thus, illusory insight constitutes the common cold of medical intelligence work. It is ubiquitous, contagious, and draining. It delays the advance of knowledge. And like the common cold, there is no vaccine in sight that might save us from its ills.

Now it happens that during the dozen years that I have spent working on this book, I have caught six or seven colds. Similarly, over that same time period, I have experienced half a dozen instances of the temporary conviction that at last I really knew exactly who was right and who wrong about how I may have caught most of those colds. This continues to be true. And so, at one level I know it may yet prove to be the case that no temperature lag effects really exist; that those data from Salisbury and Toronto convincing me otherwise might possibly reflect nothing more than a mirage cast up either by the workings of perfidious chance or by the existence of unsuspected contaminating variables present in the research samples with which I worked. It is likely that my current bias against a theory of aerosol transmission for most wild cold viruses (or even the aerosol transmission of some infective factor that triggers commensal colds) may yet prove to be embarrassingly nearsighted. Moreover, the serious problems faced by any theory of frequent commensal colds probably ought to prove much more sobering to me than they do. These non-rational prejudices, these egocentric illusions, these wonderful hunches, all come with the scientific territory. Regular treatment with vitamin C does not seem to cure them. Nor, alas, will reading (or even writing) this book.

You probably recognized similar responses and biases in yourself as you studied this intelligence report. No doubt you have your own pet data, your own pet theories, and your own prime suspects in this little drama of petty illness. Perhaps for a time, like me, you may take to your bed to read, with the hope that soon your head will clear and the truth will emerge triumphant. To you, then, as to all of us, I say: *get well soon.*

Notes

INTRODUCTION

1   From Sitt's fourth edition, p. 435, as quoted on p. 451 in George B. Foster, Jr., "The etiology of common colds," *Journal of Infectious Diseases,* 1917, vol. 21, pp. 451–75.
2   From Osler's 7th edition of *The Principles and Practice of Medicine,* New York: D. Appleton & Co., 1911, p. 593, as cited in the *Journal of the American Medical Association,* 1967, vol. 202, no. 6, p. 164.

CHAPTER 1

1   All this information is contained in records at the Rockefeller Archive Center detailing the work of Dr. Smillie's groups. In particular, see: Rockefeller Foundation Archives, RF 1.1, series 100M, box 54, folders 530 and 531; and, RF 1HD, record group 5, series 3, box 5. Information on Dr. Paul's early life appears in *Who Was Who in America,* 1974–76, vol. 6, p. 318. Dr. Paul died in 1971 after a life of considerable foreign travel. His later work was primarily as an epidemiologist with special concern for yellow fever and malaria. He married in 1936, and had one daughter.
2   J. H. Paul and H. L. Freese published their findings in the *American Journal of*

Hygiene, 1933, vol. 17, no. 3 (May), pp. 517–35. Their report was received for publication August 20, 1932. Its title was "An epidemiological and bacteriological study of the 'common cold' in an isolated arctic community (Spitzbergen)." The quotation here is from p. 518.

3 See for instance pp. 734–35 in the D. F. Milam and W. G. Smillie report entitled "A bacteriological study of 'colds' on an isolated tropical island," *Journal of Experimental Medicine,* 1931, vol. 53.

4 From Paul and Freese, pp. 520–21.

5 Ibid., pp. 532–34.

6 See J. Harlan Paul, *The Last Cruise of the Carnegie,* 1932, Baltimore: Williams and Wilkins Co., especially pp. 116–17 and 281–82.

CHAPTER 2

1 From A. Hilding, *Archives of Otolaryngology,* 1930, vol. 12, (2).

2 The report, entitled "Epidemiological study of the minor respiratory diseases by the Public Health Service," appeared in the *United States Weekly Public Health Reports,* 1924, vol. 39, no. 43, pp. 2669–80. In 1927, a more detailed description of the study and its findings was published by J. G. Townsend and Edgar Sydenstricker under the title "Epidemiological study of minor respiratory diseases." It appeared in the *United States Weekly Public Health Reports,* vol. 42, no. 2, pp. 99–121. Some of my descriptions of this project are taken from information given in the later publication and so may not match information to be found only in the 1924 preliminary report. The USPHS studies reported by Townsend and his colleagues owed a great deal to Wade Hampton Frost, who earlier initiated this large-scale look at colds across America.

3 Some northern Californians may be distressed to learn that, from the perspective of Townsend in Washington, D.C., all of the University of California at Berkeley was located in San Francisco, not simply the UC medical school.

4 From Townsend, 1924, p. 2674.

5 From Townsend and Sydenstricker, 1927, pp. 103–4. Italics in the original.

CHAPTER 3

1 From p. 53 of J. J. van Loghem, M.D., "An epidemiological contribution to the knowledge of the respiratory diseases," *The Journal of Hygiene* (Cambridge), 1928, vol. 28, pp. 33–54.

2 Ibid.

3 Ibid., p. 33.

4 Ibid., p. 35.

5 There were four publications in this series. First was a brief preliminary report,

"An experimental study of a possible mechanism for the excitation of infection of the pharynx and tonsils," in the *American Journal of Physiology*, 1919, vol. 49, pp. 144–45. The next article appeared in the *Journal of Medical Research*, 1919, vol. 40, pp. 53–101. Then "A further experimental study on excitation of infections of the throat" appeared in *The Journal of Experimental Medicine*, 1920, vol. 32, pp. 87–112. And lastly, "The etiology of acute inflammation of the nose, pharynx, and tonsils," *Annals of Otology, Rhinology and Laryngology*, 1921, vol. 30, pp. 1–73.

6   From van Loghem, 1928, p. 35.

7   Ibid., p. 37.

8   Ibid., p. 37.

9   Ibid., p. 40.

10   This "distance" or strength of association is suggested by the square of a raw correlation coefficient. Squaring 0.83 gives 0.69.

11   From van Loghem, 1928, p. 41.

CHAPTER 4

1   From p. 259 of the article entitled "Common colds on Tristan da Cunha," by M. Shibli, S. Gooch, H. E. Lewis, and D. A. J. Tyrrell, *Journal of Hygiene* (Cambridge), 1971, vol. 69, pp. 255–62.

2   Much of the history of the islanders of Tristan da Cunha, medical and social, can be found in two adjacent articles appearing in the *British Medical Journal* (ii) for 1963. The first, by Norman Samuels, bears the title "Experiences of a medical officer on Tristan da Cunha, June–October, 1961." This article is on pp. 1013–17. The second article, on pp. 1018–24, is by J. A. Black, C. K. M. Thacker, H. E. Lewis, and A. K. Thould. It is entitled "Tristan da Cunha: general medical investigations."

3   This was first called to scientific attention in a symposium on medical problems at Tristan da Cunha, the discussion from which was published by E. J. S. Woolley, *Transactions of the Royal Society for Tropical Medicine and Hygiene*, 1963, vol. 54, p. 24. See also "Common colds on Tristan da Cunha," by M. Shibli et al. per note 1 above.

4   From Black et al., 1963, cited in note 2 above, p. 1018.

5   Thus began the project that led eventually to the 1971 publication by M. Shibli et al. noted in 1 above.

CHAPTER 5

1   From H. M. S. Watkins et al., "Epidemiologic investigations in Polaris submarines," in the book by I. H. Silver (ed.), *Aerobiology: Proceedings of the*

third international symposium held at the University of Sussex, England, 1969,
1970, Academic Press, p. 9.

2   From p. 219 of the 1958 American edition of Thor Heyerdahl's *Aku-aku: The Secret of Easter Island,* Chicago: Rand McNally & Co.

3   See H. M. S. Watkins et al., pp. 9–10.

4   Ibid., pp. 17–18.

5   Derived from Figure 10 provided by Watkins on p. 52.

6   While Watkins did not choose to report patrol data for just common colds, his figures show that 86 percent of the visits in the combined categories of respiratory disease and gastrointestinal disease were for respiratory complaints.

7   Derived from Table 16 provided by Watkins on p. 42. A single extreme datum of "119" was rescored as "50" for this analysis.

8   This study, by D. G. Boyden, entitled "The bacterial flora in fleet ballistic missile submarines during prolonged submergence," appeared in 1962 as report no. 386 in the series *U.S. Naval Medical Research Laboratory Reports.* It was in vol. 21, no. 17.

9   See "Seroepidemiological studies of Polaris submarine crews: I. Acute respiratory infections," by R. L. Sphar, Jr. and A. S. Evans, *Military Medicine,* January 1976, vol. 141, no. 1, pp. 25–28.

CHAPTER 6

1   A. S. Cameron and B. W. Moore, "The epidemiology of respiratory infection in an isolated Antarctic community," *Journal of Hygiene* (Cambridge), 1968, vol. 66, pp. 427–37.

2   See *The Heart of the Antarctic* by E. H. Shackleton, C.V.O. (two volumes), published in 1909 by J. B. Lippincott Co.

3   From Appendix 6, written by Dr. Eric Marshall, in Shackleton, 1909, p. 427.

4   For instance, compare this quotation from E. E. Hedblom, "The medical problems encountered in Antarctica," *Military Medicine,* 1961, vol. 126, p. 821: "Occasionally virulent organisms in fur clothing, etc., have indisputably caused flurries of upper respiratory infection in isolated camps . . ." See also T. R. Allen, "Common colds in Antarctica," *Journal of Hygiene* (Cambridge), 1973, vol. 71, p. 653. The error appears earlier with Sir Leonard Hill and Mark Clement, on p. 19 of their 1929 book *Common Colds.* It was even reinforced by Sir Christopher Andrewes in his Dunham lecture at Harvard: see the *New England Journal of Medicine,* 1950, vol. 242, p. 240.

5   Said to be from p. 546 of *Parry's Second Voyage,* by Captain William Edward Parry, London, 1824; as quoted by Peter Heinbecker and Edith I. M. Irving-Jones in their article "Susceptibility of Eskimos to the common cold and a study of their natural immunity to diphtheria, scarlet fever, and bacterial filtrates," *Journal of Immunology,* 1928, vol. 15, pp. 397–98. No such account appears to

be in Parry's book, however, and the source appears to have been elsewhere.

6   From pp. 395–96, Heinbecker and Irving-Jones, per note 5, above.

7   See "Biological and medical research based on USS *Staten Island*, Antarctica, 1958–59," *The Polar Record*, 1960, vol. 10, pp. 146–48, by W. J. L. Sladen and R. Goldsmith.

8   According to Cameron and Moore, 1968, p. 428, and according to M. J. Holmes and T. R. Allen in "Viral respiratory diseases in isolated communities: a review," *British Antarctic Survey Bulletin*, June 1973, no. 35, p. 23.

9   From Paul A. Siple, "Living on the Polar ice cap," in S. M. Horvath (ed.), *Cold Injury: Transactions of the Sixth Conference, July 1958*. Josiah Macy Jr. Foundation, 1960, pp. 89–115, with particular reference to pp. 95–101.

10 Initial speculation that this may have been the case occurred in Cameron and Moore, 1968, p. 432; but no firm confirmation was provided. Later, in Holmes and Allen, 1973, p. 23, it was asserted definitely that the virus was influenza A2, without citation or explanation.

11 Published in "The medical problems encountered in Antarctica," *Military Medicine*, 1961, vol. 126, pp. 818–24, by Captain E. E. Hedblom, U.S. Navy medical consultant.

12 Ibid., p. 821.

13 Ibid.

14 Cameron and Moore, 1968, pp. 427–37.

15 Ibid., pp. 430–31. The presence of muscle aches mentioned in this passage may signal that the illnesses being described were not caused by one of the common cold viruses. But the symptoms were clearly thought by those suffering them to reflect common colds.

16 Ibid., pp. 432–33.

17 Ove Wilson, "Human adaptation to life in Antarctica," *Monographiæ Biologicæ*, 1965, vol. 15, pp. 690–752. This information comes from p. 707.

18 See p. 433 of Cameron and Moore, 1968.

19 Reported in M. J. Holmes, T. R. Allen, A. F. Bradburne, and E. J. Stott, "Studies of respiratory viruses in personnel at an Antarctic base," *Journal of Hygiene* (Cambridge), 1971, vol. 69, pp. 187–99.

20 See E. C. Dick, R. S. Jerde, D. M. Warshauer, A. D. Mandel, L. W. Fusch, D. L. Tullius, and H. G. Muchmore, "Lack of increased susceptibility to colds in the McMurdo winter parties of 1975 and 1976," *Antarctic Journal of the U.S.*, October 1977, vol. 12, no. 4, pp. 3–5. And see E. C. Dick, F. Polyak, K. S. Kapitan, D. M. Warshauer, A. D. Mandel, B. S. Thomas, and J. Rankin, "Respiratory virus transmission at McMurdo Station and Scott Base (New Zealand) during the winter-fly-in period, 1977," *Antarctic Journal of the U.S.*, October 1978, vol. 13, no. 4, pp. 170–72.

21 From Table 1, Dick et al., 1977, p. 4, per note 20 above.

22 See Dick et al., 1978, cited in note 20 above.

23 Reported in T. R. Allen, "Common colds in Antarctica," *Journal of Hygiene*

(Cambridge), 1973, vol. 71, pp. 649–56. (See note 4 above.)

24   See T. R. Allen, A. F. Bradburne, E. J. Stott, C. S. Goodwin, and D. A. J. Tyrrell, "An outbreak of common colds at an Antarctic base after seventeen weeks of complete isolation," *Journal of Hygiene* (Cambridge), 1973, vol. 71, pp. 657–67.

25   No attempt was made by Allen et al. to assay rhinovirus antibody because so many different varieties of this type of cold virus exist. Thus a rhinovirus might easily have been responsible for the outbreak and would be consistent with the other negative findings reported in the search for a cause.

26   See note 24, pp. 661–63.

27   See note 24, pp. 665–66.

28   See T. R. Allen, "Common colds in Antarctica," *Journal of Hygiene* (Cambridge), 1973, vol. 71, p. 653.

29   This work by G. Meldorf is summarized by Holmes and Allen in "Viral respiratory diseases in isolated communities: a review," *British Antarctic Survey Bulletin*, no. 35, June 1973, p. 24. The original references are (1) "Epidemiske sygdomme i Grønland; influenza og epidemske katarrhalske affektioner af luftvejs-slimhinderne," *Meddr. Grønland*, 1907, vol. 33, no. 7, pp. 129–304; and (2) "Epidemske sygdomme i Grønland; influenza og akute affektioner af luftvejs-slimhinderne ikke medregmede," *Meddr. Grønland*, 1912, vol. 50, no. 6, pp. 187–347.

30   See Arne Høygaard's article, "Acute epidemic diseases among the Eskimos in Angmagssalik," in *The Lancet*, January 28, 1939, vol. 236, pp. 245–46.

31   See O. Abs, "Über Epidemien von unspezifischen Katarrhen der Luftwege auf Svalbard," *Skrifter om Svalbard og Ishavet*, 1930, no. 32, Oslo, pp. 1–27. Discussions of this paper appear on p. 245 of Høygaard's article, and on pp. 24–25 of Holmes and Allen.

CHAPTER 7

1   Quoted with some slight changes in punctuation and paragraphing from Boswell's *The Life of Dr. Johnson*; J. M. Dent & Sons, the Everyman's Library Edition of 1976; pp. 344–45 (A.D. 1786).

2   Quoted in the "Report on the Pandemic of Influenza," 1918–1919, being *Report #4* of the *Reports on Public Health and Medical Subjects* by the British Ministry of Health, 1920, p. 151.

3   Ibid., pp. 151–53.

4   Schade published three papers in German in 1919 and 1920. These were: (1) "Beiträge zur Umgrenzung und Klärung einer Lehre von der Erkältung," *Zeitschrift für der ges. exper. Medizinische*, 1919, vol. 7, pp. 225–374; (2) "Untersuchungen in der Erkältungsfrage [Part I]," *Muenchener Medizinische Wochenschrift*, September 1919, vol. 66, pp. 1021–26; and (3) "Untersuchungen

in der Erkältungsfrage [Part II]," *Muenchener Medizinische Wochenschrift*, April 1920, vol. 67, pp. 449–54. A summary of this work appeared in at least two English articles in 1921, and in a German article in 1922. The first article in English was by Stuart Mudd, Samuel B. Grant, and Alfred Goldman: "The etiology of acute inflammations of the nose, pharynx and tonsils," *Annals of Otology, Rhinology and Laryngology*, 1921, vol. 30, pp. 1–73. On p. 14, this article rather misrepresents the correct timing of certain illnesses studied by Schade, implying incorrectly that greater illness was seen in the trenches themselves, rather than a few days after having been in the trenches once back in the barracks. A brief summary of Schade's work also appeared in Arthur Bloomfield's article, "Variations in the bacterial flora of the upper air passages during the course of common colds," *Johns Hopkins Hospital Bulletin*, 1921, vol. 32, pp. 121–30. On p. 123, Bloomfield seems to confound a fourfold increase in colds seen in a three-day study of exposure in the trenches with what was actually just a doubling of the illness rate seen in a comparison of two winters of different severity. Finally, an extensive German summary of Schade's work appeared in Max Gähwyler's article, "Der heutige Stand der Erkältungsfrage," *Schweizerische Medizinische Wochenschrift*, 1922, vol. 52, pp. 648–54. Gähwyler was incorrectly given the credit for Schade's work by Anderson Hilding in his summary of the same studies appearing on p. 136 in his article "The common cold," *Archives of Otolaryngology*, 1930, vol. 12, pp. 133–50.

5   See Figure 3 and p. 1022 from the September 1919 article in *Muenchener Medizinische Wochenschrift*. (See note 4 above.)

6   See for instance Table 8, p. 422, in E. O. Jordan, J. F. Norton, and W. B. Sharp, "The common cold," *Journal of Infectious Diseases*, 1923, vol. 33, pp. 416–33. "Heart function strains" include chilling, exposure to cold, draughts, wet shoes, etc.

7   See p. 423 of Jordan et al., 1923. The campuses were the University of Chicago, the California Institute of Technology in Pasadena, and the University of Texas Medical School in Galveston.

8   Per Table 10 in Jordan et al., 1923, p. 424.

9   A prototypic example of such studies would be that reported in D. F. Smiley's article "Seasonal factors in the incidence of the acute respiratory infections," *American Journal of Hygiene,* 1926, vol. 6, pp. 621–26. It examined twelve years of records on four thousand male students at Cornell University.

10   See for instance *Common Colds: Causes and Preventive Measures*, by Sir Leonard E. Hill and Mark Clement, London: William Heinemann, 1929.

11   See for instance D. F. Smiley, 1926, p. 626, as per note 9, above.

12   The association actually examined was between cold incidences and mean weekly temperatures after each had been expressed as a percentage of their yearly average weekly values. See the *Statistical Bulletin of the Metropolitan Life Insurance Co.*, vol. IV, November 1923, no. 11, pp. 1–3, for the article entitled "One year of common colds and associated infections."

13   From p. 3 of the report cited in note 12.

14   See the figure on p. 2 of the report cited in note 12.

15   R. E. Hope Simpson, "Symposium on the Epidemiology of non-infectious diseases: (a) common upper respiratory diseases," *Journal of the Royal Society of Health*, 1958, vol. 78, p. 595.

16   Ibid., p. 595, and Figure 2 on p. 596. In this published report Hope Simpson describes his figure as reporting percentage deviations from the median. In fact, the "median" he reports is the mid-range for yearly values, and the "deviation" is the percentage deviation within the semi-range, not a percentage of the mid-range value itself. Thus +100% represents the highest value for the year, and –100% the lowest. This confusion was cleared up for me in a letter from Hope Simpson dated March 8, 1990.

17   Ibid., p. 595.

18   Ibid., p. 598.

19   Ibid., p. 599. Hope Simpson also published two other notes in 1958 about his five-year study of colds in Cirencester. One appeared in the *British Medical Journal* for January 25, 1958, on p. 214. The other appeared in *The Practitioner*, vol. 180, pp. 356–57.

CHAPTER 8

1   This is the opening sentence in the article by Lidwell et al. (see note 4 below), p. 427.

2   This study appeared in the August 21, 1961, issue of *The Lancet*, pp. 338–41, under the title "Influence of the weather on respiratory and heart disease." The authors were W. W. Holland, C. C. Spicer, and J. M. G. Wilson. Because all the data were blocked by months, consisting of monthly averages, and because common colds were only included in these counts of respiratory disease when the colds were rather severe, the data do not necessarily tell us about the effects of weather variables on individual colds.

3   Ibid., p. 338.

4   This article bears the title "The epidemiology of the common cold. IV. The effect of weather." It was published in the *Journal of Hygiene* (Cambridge), 1965, vol. 63, pp. 427–39. The subtitle indicates that it is the fourth article published in a series, all deriving from the same large longitudinal study. The other articles, which describe the populations from which the data on colds were obtained, and different analyses, were also published in the same journal and with the same supertitle. Part I appeared without subtitle in vol. 59, 1961, pp. 309–19. Part II, subtitled "Cross-infection and immunity" appeared in vol. 59, 1961, pp. 321–34. And part III, subtitled "The effect of ventilation, air disinfection, and room size" appeared in vol. 60, 1962, pp. 341–52.

5   The technique for determining normal averages for the time of year involved

averaging in a special way all the data for any one cold season studied. Each year or season was slightly different, and a year with more colds (or more humidity, or more cold weather) was allowed to have a higher normal average for colds (or humidity, or cold weather) on any given date than would be true for the same date in a year with fewer colds or less humidity, etc. In calculating this normal expected value for any particular date, Lidwell and his colleagues assumed that as the year went on the true normal averages, when plotted on a graph for each passing day, varied gently and continuously in a rising and falling curve that could be "fitted" to the less regular, yet similar, values given by plotting running averages on each variable in question. Those running averages were based on data from the ten days nearest to each date being plotted. The assumption was that the underlying true curves each had one peak (in winter) and one trough (in summer), or vice versa, and that the observed running averages were just random deflections from this true curve which, in consequence, could be supposed to pass through the center of all the plot points representing the observed data. Reasoning thus, Lidwell et al. fit a smooth sine curve to their data, passing as close as possible to all the plotted ten-day averages. And it was the values along this ideal curve that defined the normal average values to be expected on each day during each different year of the study.

There was one variable for which this technique had to be modified, however. The incidence of common colds did not seem to follow a nice neat sine wave, gliding up and down once each year the way average temperature, humidity, and other variables did. The problem came with the data from September and October of each year. There was seen a "substantial peak" of colds, rising well above any curve that fit the data from the rest of the year. The solution adopted by Lidwell et al. was to fit the sine curve to the data from November through May and then to fit a second curve, a bell-shaped "normal" curve, to the mountain of colds seen in each autumn period. The overall compound curve was then used to determine the average expected number of colds on any particular day of the year, and it provided the basis for looking at days where the frequency of colds was either above or below what might otherwise have been expected at the time.

The September peak in colds was proportionally much higher in London than in Newcastle, requiring separate curves generated for each city. This becomes significant soon when we reconsider data on colds in rural settings (such as Hope Simpson's) where no peak at all is reported in September, and where a sine wave alone appears to describe those cold data when they are blocked by months.

6   See note 5 above for more about this marked September epidemic.

7   Reported in O. M. Lidwell and T. Sommerville, "Observations on the incidence and distribution of the common cold in a rural community during 1948 and 1949," *Journal of Hygiene* (Cambridge), 1951, vol. 49, 365 ff.

8   From p. 437 of Lidwell et al., 1965.

CHAPTER 9

1   From pp. 733 and 734 of Milam and Smillie's article entitled "A bacteriological
     study of 'colds' on an isolated tropical island," *Journal of Experimental
     Medicine*, 1931, vol. 53, pp. 733–52.

2   In the course of a year, the average daily maximum at Cruz Bay was about 84
     degrees and the average daily minimum was about 72 degrees (29 and 22
     degrees Celsius, respectively). The lowest average maximum seen during the
     year of the study (averaged over a full week) was 80 degrees, and the lowest
     minimum temperature seen was 67 degrees (27 and 19 degrees Celsius, respec-
     tively). The highest average daily maximum seen during any week of the study
     was 90 degrees and the highest minimum seen was 77 degrees (32 and 25
     degrees Celsius, respectively).

3   Milam and Smillie, 1931, pp. 737–38.

4   Ibid., p. 750. The references here to the work in Alabama are references to data
     partially reported in two articles appearing in the *Journal of Experimental
     Medicine*, 1929, vol. 50. The first article had the title "A study of pneumonia in
     rural areas in southern Alabama," and it appeared on pp. 233–44. The second
     article had the title "Nasopharyngeal flora in health and during respiratory dis-
     ease in isolated communities in Alabama and Labrador." It appeared on pp.
     643–63.

5   Though, compare the more severe colds reported for Tristan da Cunha, for
     Easter Island, and in the unchanging mild interior spaces of nuclear sub-
     marines on patrol.

6   See R. N. P. Sutton, "Minor illness in Trinidad: a longitudinal study," *Transactions
     of the Royal Society of Tropical Medicine and Hygiene*, 1965, vol. 59, pp. 212–20.
     Despite the title of this article, the study covered a period of just eighteen
     months in 1961 and 1962.

7   See A. S. Monto and K. M. Johnson, "A community study of respiratory infec-
     tions in the tropics. I. Description of the community and observations on the
     activity of certain respiratory agents," *American Journal of Epidemiology*, 1967,
     vol. 86, pp. 78–92. Most of the information reported in the text is found in
     this first article. Two others followed in the same series, however, printed in the
     same journal. The second bore the subtitle "II. The spread of six rhinovirus
     isolates within the community," 1968, vol. 88, pp. 55–68. The third, by
     Monto only, was subtitled "III. Introduction and transmission of infections
     within families," 1968, vol. 88, pp. 69–79.

8   I base this estimate not on any actual incidences reported in the text of these
     articles but on the data shown in Figure 1 of the first article, p. 82. It would
     take a continuous incidence of eighty-three cases per month per thousand to
     equal one cold per person per year. Figure 1 shows only two brief occasions in
     four years when the incidence of respiratory disease exceeded eighty per month.
     Allowance must be made for the fact that respiratory illness was only recorded

in this study if brought to the attention of the nurse at the local free clinic, or if revealed by the somewhat chancy method of detecting a rise in antibody levels to some of the known cold viruses, in blood sera collected periodically from the volunteers.

9   See A. S. Evans, D. J. D'Alessio, L. Espiritu–Campos, and E. C. Dick, "Acute respiratory disease in University of the Philippines and University of Wisconsin students," *Bulletin of the World Health Organization*, 1967, vol. 36, pp. 397–407.

10   However, primary atypical (viral) pneumonia and infectious mononucleosis were each, for whatever reason, much less common in Quezon City than in Madison, Wisconsin.

11   See Evans et al., 1967, p. 406.

12   See for instance C. S. Wilder, "Acute respiratory illnesses reported to the U.S. National Health Survey during 1957 to 1962," *American Review of Respiratory Diseases*, 1963, (Supp.) vol. 88, pp. 14–21.

13   The data from this study were reported in an invited address, the 1984 Jeremiah Metzger Lecture, given by Gwaltney to the American Climatological and Clinical Association. The address was published in the *Transactions* of the Association for 1984, vol. 96, pp. 159–75. Most of the data I will discuss from this article were summarized in its Table 2, p. 171.

14   This was true in the first three years of the study, and presumably changed little over the next thirteen years. These data come from the article "Rhinovirus infections in an industrial population: I. The occurrence of illness," by J. M. Gwaltney, Jr., J. O. Hendley, G. Simon, and W. S. Jordan, Jr., *New England Journal of Medicine*, 1966, vol. 275, pp. 1261–68.

15   During three of the years of study the city and the local county schools did not open in the same week, but usually they did.

16   From the 1984 Metzger lecture, p. 173. The conclusion expressed here was first suggested in 1969 in an article entitled "Rhinovirus infections in an industrial population. IV. Infections within families of employees during two fall peaks of respiratory illness," by J. O. Hendley, J. M. Gwaltney Jr., and W. S. Jordan, Jr., in the *American Journal of Epidemiology*, vol. 89, pp. 184–96.

CHAPTER 10

1   From "Limitations of the germ theory," *The Lancet*, 1968, vol. 1, p. 1077.

2   This was before the time Dr. George B. Foster, Jr. began looking for a viral cause of the common cold. See his article "The etiology of common colds," *Journal of the American Medical Association*, April 15, 1916, vol. 66, pp. 1180–83. *M. catarrhalis* was first described by Pfeiffer and *B. rhinitis* was first described by Tunnicliff. Recall that a *catarrh* is a profuse discharge of mucous from the sinuses, originally supposed to issue from the brain. *Rhinitis* refers literally to an infection in the nose, but it is commonly used medically as a synonym for "runny nose."

3   See "The etiology of common colds," *Journal of Infectious Diseases*, 1917, vol. 21, p. 451.

4   See Kruse's brief note, "Die Erreger von Husten und Schnupfen," in the *Muenchener Medizinische Wochenschrift*, July 14, 1914, vol. 61, p. 1547.

5   For a historical summary of early investigations see P. H. Long, J. A. Doull, J. M. Bourn, and E. McComb, "The etiology of acute upper respiratory infection (common cold)," in the *Journal of Experimental Medicine*, 1931, vol. 53, pp. 447–70.

6   The reference to H. Dold's work is *Münch. med. Woch.*, 1917, vol. 64, p. 143.

7   See Foster's "The etiology of common colds," in the *Journal of the American Medical Association*, 1916, vol. 66, pp. 1180–83, and his second article with the same title in the *Journal of Infectious Diseases*, 1917, vol. 21, pp. 451–75.

8   Foster, 1916, p. 1182.

9   See particularly K. C. Mills, G. S. Shibley, and A. R. Dochez, *Journal of Experimental Medicine*, 1928, vol. 47, p. 193; and G. S. Shibley, K. C. Mills, and A. R. Dochez, *Proceedings of the Society for Experimental Biology and Medicine*, 1929, vol. 27, p. 59. See also P. K. Olitsky and J. E. McCartney, "Studies on the nasopharyngeal secretions from patients with common colds," *Journal of Experimental Medicine*, 1923, vol. 38, pp. 427–40; "Studies of the etiology of the common cold," by G. S. Shibley, K. C. Mills, and A. R. Dochez, *Journal of the American Medical Association*, 1930, vol. 95, pp. 1553–56; and P. H. Long et al., 1931, as per note 5 above.

10 See for instance P. Schmidt, in *Deutsch. med. Wehnschr.*, 1920, vol. 46, p. 1181; A. W. Williams, M. Nevens, and C. R. Gurley, *Journal of Immunology*, 1921, vol. 6, p. 5; S. E. Branham and I. C. Hall, *Journal of Infectious Diseases*, 1921, vol. 28, p. 148; and R. C. Robertson and R. L. Groves, "Experimental human inoculations with filtered nasal secretions from acute coryza," *Journal of Infectious Diseases*, 1924, vol. 34, pp. 400–406.

11 A. R. Dochez, G. S. Shibley, and K. C. Mills, "Studies in the common cold: IV. Experimental transmission of the common cold to anthropoid apes and human beings by means of a filtrable agent," *Journal of Experimental Medicine*, 1930, vol. 52, pp. 701–16.

12 Ibid., pp. 711–12.

13 As a psychologist, of course, I find the causal roles (if any) played by "stress," moods, expectations, etc., in causing colds to be particularly interesting. As I mentioned in the introduction to this book, there is enough to say about the evidence for and against the hypothesis that these are important determinants of colds that this topic deserves its own separate consideration elsewhere.

14 For both a layman's description and photographs of the eight types of cold virus, see W. B. Murphy, *Coping with the Common Cold*, 1981, Time–Life Books, pp. 20–21. For a technical discussion of these viruses see A. S. Evans, *Viral Infections of Humans: Epidemiology and Control*, 1976, Plenum.

15 See C. H. Andrewes, "The Common Cold," in *Scientific American*, February

1951, vol. 184, pp. 39–44. This quotation comes from p. 42.

16 This work was summarized in a paper entitled "Susceptibility and immunity to common upper respiratory viral infections—the common cold," by George G. Jackson, Harry F. Dowling, Truman O. Anderson, Louise Riff, Jack Saporta, and Marvin Turck. It appeared in *Annals of Internal Medicine*, 1960, vol. 53, pp. 719–38.

17 This work was reported in an article entitled "Exposure to cold environment and rhinovirus common cold: Failure to demonstrate effect," by R. G. Douglas, Jr., K. M. Lindgren, and R. B. Couch. The article appeared in the *New England Journal of Medicine*, 1968, vol. 279, pp. 742–47. How or why a prisoner in Texas comes to "volunteer" in a study of this sort is not explained in the article, but keep in mind that in England there was often little problem in getting civilian volunteers to come and risk a cold for science.

18 Ibid., p. 746.

Chapter 11

1 See Walter F. Winholt and Edwin O. Jordan, "Epidemiology of colds in infants," *Journal of the American Medical Association*, 1923, vol. 81, pp. 280–82.

2 Previous suggestions that contagion from humans to humans is anything but automatic, even when infectious nasal fluids are taken from a human donor and dropped into the nose of human volunteers, was seen in the work of others before and after 1934. For a list of some of the more important studies see note 10 for chapter 10.

3 This work was reported in two different journals under almost the same title: "Transmissibility of the common cold: exposure of susceptible individuals under controlled conditions." It was first published in the *Proceedings of the Society for Experimental Biology and Medicine*, 1934, vol. 31, pp. 713–15, and then in more complete form in *Transactions of the Association of American Physicians*, 1934, vol. 49, pp. 245–51.

4 From p. 248 in *Transactions of the AAP*, 1934. See note 3 above.

5 See the work of M. W. Jennison in the *Scientific Monthly of New York*, 1941, vol. 52, p. 24.

6 This study, by R. B. Bourdillon and O. M. Lidwell, was entitled "Sneezing and the spread of infection." It appeared in *The Lancet*, 1941, vol. 241, pp. 365–67.

7 Ibid., p. 366.

8 This lecture, the third of the Edward K. Dunham Lectures for the promotion of the medical sciences, was delivered at the Harvard Medical School and published soon thereafter in the *New England Journal of Medicine*, February 16, 1950, vol. 242, pp. 235–40.

9 Ibid., p. 236.

10 A brief summary of this research was communicated in the introduction to the

report of another experiment carried out on a small Scottish island, in the article "An experiment on the transmission of colds," by C. H. Andrewes, J. E. Lovelock, and T. Sommerville, *The Lancet*, 1951, vol. 260, p. 25.

[11] This work was reported in "Observations on the incidence and distribution of the common cold in a rural community during 1948 and 1949," by O. M. Lidwell and T. Sommerville, *Journal of Hygiene* (Cambridge), 1951, vol. 49, pp. 365–81.

[12] Ibid., p. 372.

[13] Ibid.

[14] These experiments were first reported in an article entitled "Further studies on the natural transmission of the common cold," appearing in *The Lancet*, 1952, vol. 263, pp. 657–60. The authors were J. E. Lovelock, J. S. Porterfield, A. T. Roden, T. Sommerville, and C. H. Andrewes.

[15] Briefly summarized on p. 660 of Lovelock et al., 1952.

[16] Ibid.

Chapter 12

[1] From p. 21 of the initial report of the Cleveland family study cited in note 2 below.

[2] The first full description of the plan and methods of this study appeared in an article entitled "A study of illness in a group of Cleveland families: I. Plan of study," *American Journal of Hygiene*, 1953, vol. 58, pp. 16–30. The authors were John H. Dingle, George F. Badger, A. E. Feller, Richard G. Hodges, William S. Jordan, Jr., and Charles H. Rammelkamp, Jr.

[3] See p. 32 in the second article in this series: "A study of illness in a group of Cleveland families: II. Incidence of the common respiratory diseases," *American Journal of Hygiene*, 1953, vol. 58, pp. 31–40. The senior author of this article was George F. Badger.

[4] See Table 1, p. 33, in Badger et al., 1953.

[5] See Figure 1, p. 34, Badger et al., 1953.

[6] See Figure 2, p. 35, Badger et al., 1953.

[7] These data appear in Table 2, p. 36, Badger et al., 1953.

[8] See Figure 3 and Table 4, on pp. 37 and 38, Badger et al., 1953.

[9] See the third article in this series: "A study of illness in a group of Cleveland families: III. Introduction of respiratory infections into families," *American Journal of Hygiene*, 1953, vol. 58, pp. 41–46. The senior author of this article was George F. Badger.

[10] If I say "arguably" in this passage it is because I hold a different view from that of some other common cold researchers who say that the frequency of silent infections is "known." The studies that have led to these "known" frequency estimates are not large in number, and few if any of them have been repeated in different settings by different investigators. These studies have been carried out

on only a small proportion of cold viruses, primarily on some rhinoviruses, of which more than a hundred varieties are now known. I question how stable and enduring the findings of these studies would be in different cities and at different times. I also question their generalizability to other varieties of cold virus.

11 These data appeared in the fourth article in the series, under the title "A study of illness in a group of Cleveland families: IV. The spread of respiratory infections within the home," *American Journal of Hygiene*, 1953, vol. 58, pp. 174–78. The senior author of this article was George F. Badger.

12 See Table 4, p. 176, of Badger et al. per note 11 above.

13 This conclusion was argued in the fifth article in the series, entitled "A study of illness in a group of Cleveland families: V. Introductions and secondary attack rates as indices of exposure to common respiratory diseases in the community," *American Journal of Hygiene*, 1953, vol. 58, pp. 179–82. The senior author of this article was also George F. Badger.

14 See O. M. Lidwell and T. Sommerville, *Journal of Hygiene* (Cambridge), 1951, vol. 49, p. 372.

15 Published under the title "Further studies on stability of resistance to the common cold: the importance of constitution," by Frederick Sargent, Olive Lombard, and Virginia Sargent, *American Journal of Hygiene*, 1947, vol. 45, pp. 29–32.

16 See Table 2 on p. 31 in Sargent et al., 1947.

17 This study was reported in an article by The Commission on Acute Respiratory Diseases, under the title "Experimental transmission of minor respiratory illness to human volunteers by filter-passing agents: II. Immunity on reinoculation with agents from the two types of minor respiratory illness and from primary atypical pneumonia," *Journal of Clinical Investigation*, 1947, vol. 26, pp. 974–82. The members of the Commission included John H. Dingle, Director, George F. Badger, and eight other members of the Army Medical Corps. The two distinct cold viruses were not typed, and were identified only as a long-incubation-period disease characterized by sore throat ("filtrate ARD") and a coryza-like illness of short incubation time ("filtrate S-CC").

18 The study was entitled "Acute upper respiratory infections in families," *American Journal of Hygiene*, 1956, vol. 63, pp. 1–12. The author was Carol Buck. This article is only rarely cited and one wonders why. It is characterized by some insightful analyses and comments, but the sample size was small enough that not everything reported reaches the preferred level of statistical significance. Still, much that is suggestive, useful, and in agreement with later findings is to be found in this article.

19 From p. 10 of Buck, 1956.

20 Reported in the December 19, 1953, issue of *The Lancet*, vol. 265, pp. 1303–6, in an article entitled "Colds among office workers," by D. D. Reid, R. E. O. Williams, and Ann Hirch.

21 This study was reported in 1957 in the *Journal of Laboratory and Clinical*

Medicine, vol. 50, pp. 516–25 under the title "Transmission of the experimental common cold in volunteers," by Harry F. Dowling, George G. Jackson, and Tohru Inouye.

22 This is the study described at the end of chapter 10, by George G. Jackson et al., entitled "Susceptibility and immunity to common upper respiratory viral infections — the common cold," *Annals of Internal Medicine*, 1960, vol. 53, pp. 719–38.

CHAPTER 13

1   From p. 290 of J. M. Gwaltney, Jr., J. O. Hendley, G. Simon, and W. S. Jordon, "Rhinovirus infections in an industrial population: 2. Characteristics of illness and antibody response," *Journal of the American Medical Association*, 1967, vol. 202, pp. 494–500.

2   This work was described in *Pediatrics*, 1960, vol. 25, pp. 829–39. The authors were Heinz F. Eichenwald and Olga Kotsevalov, from the department of pediatrics at New York Hospital–Cornell Medical Center.

3   This article appeared in *The Medical Clinics of North America*, 1963, vol. 47, no. 5, pp. 1171–84. The authors were Lewis B. Lefkowitz, Jr., George G. Jackson, and Harry F. Dowling, at the University of Illinois College of Medicine in Chicago, Ill.

4   See Figure 3, p. 1177, in Lefkowitz, et al., 1963. These data originally came from G. G. Jackson and H. F. Dowling, "Transmission of the common cold to volunteers under controlled conditions: IV. Specific immunity to the common cold," *Journal of Clinical Investigation*, 1959, vol. 38, pp. 762–69.

5   See p. 1178 in Lefkowitz et al., 1963. This report derived from an earlier study reported by T. O. Anderson, L. Riff, and G. G. Jackson, entitled "Immuno-electrophoresis of nasal secretions collected during a common cold: Observations which suggest a mechanism of seroimmunity in viral respiratory infections," *Journal of Immunology*, 1962, vol. 89, pp. 691–97.

6   For the antibody data, see T. R. Cate, R. D. Rossen, R. G. Douglas, Jr., W. T. Butler, and R. B. Couch, "The role of nasal secretion and serum antibody in the rhinovirus common cold," *American Journal of Epidemiology*, 1966, vol. 84, pp. 352–63. For the associated infection and illness data, see R. G. Douglas, Jr., T. R. Cate, P. J. Gerone, and R. B. Couch, "Quantitative rhinovirus shedding patterns in volunteers," *American Review of Respiratory Disease*, 1966, vol. 94, pp. 159–67.

7   This was true at the time of writing in 1995, but happily it is becoming better understood as this book goes to press.

8   See p. 165 in Douglas et al., 1966. See also R. D. Rossen, W. T. Butler, T. R. Cate, C. F. Szwed, and R. B. Couch, "The protein composition of nasal secretion during respiratory virus infection," *Proceedings of the Society of Experimental Biology and Medicine*, 1965, vol. 119, p. 1169.

9   Described by W. E. Pierce, W. T. Stille, and L. F. Miller in "A preliminary report on effects of routine military inoculations on respiratory illness," *Proceedings of the Society for Experimental Biology and Medicine*, 1963, vol. 114, pp. 369–72.

10 In 1963, at the Great Lakes Naval Training Center, these included: polio, influenza, smallpox, tetanus, diphtheria, and typhoid.

11 See J. H. Dingle and A. D. Langmuir, "Epidemiology of acute respiratory disease in military recruits," *American Review of Respiratory Diseases*, 1968, vol. 97, (no. 6, part 2) pp. 1–33.

12 Per Table 1, p. 11 of Dingle and Langmuir, 1968.

13 See J. M. Gwaltney, Jr., J. O. Hendley, G. Simon, and W. S. Jordan, Jr., "Rhinovirus infections in an industrial population: I. The occurrence of illness," *New England Journal of Medicine*, 1966, vol. 275, pp. 1261–68, particularly p. 1266. Then, see also Gwaltney et al., 1967, as per note 1 above, particularly Tables 1 and 2, p. 499.

14 See Figure 6, p. 498, Gwaltney et al., 1967.

15 See for instance L. B. Lefkowitz, Jr. and G. G. Jackson, "Dual respiratory infection with parainfluenza and rhinovirus, the pathogenesis of transmitted infection in volunteers," *American Review of Respiratory Diseases*, 1966, vol. 93, pp. 519–28. See also their references 15 and 16 on p. 528.

16 See T. R. Cate, R. G. Douglas, Jr., and R. B. Couch, "Interferon and resistance to upper respiratory virus illness," *Proceedings of the Society for Experimental Biology and Medicine*, 1969, vol. 131, pp. 631–36.

17 See J. O. Hendley, W. P. Edmondson, Jr., and J. M. Gwaltney, Jr., "Relation between naturally acquired immunity and infectivity of two rhinoviruses in volunteers," *Journal of Infectious Diseases*, 1972, vol. 125, pp. 243–48.

18 For this earlier study see J. O. Hendley, J. M. Gwaltney, Jr., and W. S. Jordan, Jr., "Rhinovirus infections in an industrial population: IV. Infections within families of employees during two fall peaks of respiratory illness," *American Journal of Epidemiology*, 1969, vol. 89, pp. 184–96.

CHAPTER 14

1   See H. F. Eichenwald, Olga Kotsevalov, and L. A. Fasso, "The 'cloud baby': an example of bacterial-viral interaction," *American Journal of Diseases of Children*, 1960, vol. 100, pp. 161–73. The epigraph to this chapter is drawn from an editorial introduction to this article, appearing on p. 160.

2   See the last few pages of chapter 11 in this book, and notes 14–15 for that chapter.

3   This work was reported by F. E. Buckland, M. L. Bynoe, and D. A. J. Tyrrell in "Experiments on the spread of colds: II. Studies in volunteers with coxsackievirus 21," *Journal of Hygiene* (Cambridge), 1965, vol. 63, pp. 327–43.

4   See T. R. Cate, R. B. Couch, W. F. Fleet, W. R. Griffith, P. J. Gerone, and V. Knight, "Production of tracheobronchitis in volunteers with rhinovirus in

small-particle aerosol," *American Journal of Epidemiology*, 1965, vol. 81, pp. 95–105. The virus employed in this study was known at the time as NIH 1734, and the aerosol droplets were between 0.2 and 3 microns across.

5   See R. B. Couch, T. R. Cate, W. F. Fleet, P. J. Gerone, and V. Knight, "Aerosol-induced adenoviral illness resembling the naturally occurring illness in military recruits," *American Review of Respiratory Diseases*, 1966, vol. 93, pp. 529–35. The virus used was adenovirus type 4.

6   Reported with other data in R. B. Couch, T. R. Cate, R. G. Douglas, Jr., P. J. Gerone, and V. Knight, "Effect of route of inoculation on experimental respiratory viral disease in volunteers and evidence for airborne transmission," *Bacteriological Reviews*, 1966, vol. 30, pp. 517–29. Three viruses were used in the studies reported in this article. Only the data from coxsackievirus A type 21 are being discussed here.

7   The "volunteers" were informed prisoners who agreed to a change in their daily routine that produced a certain amount of (different) restriction and discomfort.

8   A "preliminary report" of this study was included in the 1966 article published in *Bacteriological Reviews*, cited above. A much more complete description of this study and its somewhat complex results appeared four years later in R. B. Couch, R. G. Douglas, Jr., K. M. Lindgren, P. J. Gerone, and V. Knight, "Airborne transmission of respiratory infection with coxsackievirus A type 21," *American Journal of Epidemiology*, 1970, vol. 91, pp. 78–86.

9   See J. O. Hendley, R. P. Wenzel, and J. M. Gwaltney, Jr., "Transmission of rhinovirus colds by self-inoculation," *New England Journal of Medicine*, 1973, vol. 288, pp. 1361–64.

10   The article does not say to what extent (if any) the ten subjects were alerted in advance to the fact that their fingers would soon be rinsed in the search for virus, nor whether they were or were not enjoined from wiping their noses prior to having their fingers tested. The four subjects who were tested with cough and sneeze samples were not, apparently, the same four subjects from whom virus was recovered on the fingers. The amount of virus recovered from the nose, saliva, and cough samples from four subjects was reported in the article, but the amount of virus recovered from the fingers of the four subjects was not reported.

11   Reported in C. Andrewes, *The Common Cold*. London: Weidenfeld & Nicholson Co., 1965.

12   The abstracts exist as: D. J. D'Alessio, C. R. Dick, and E. C. Dick, "Transmission of rhinovirus type 55 in human volunteers," *International Virology, vol. 2: Proceedings of the Second International Congress for Virology*, J. L. Melnick (ed.), Basel: S. Karger, 1972, p. 115. Also as: J. A. Peterson, D. J. D'Alessio, and E. C. Dick, "Studies on the failure of direct oral contact to transmit rhinovirus infection between human volunteers," *Abstracts of the Annual Meeting of the American Society for Microbiology*, 1973, p. 213.

13   J. M. Gwaltney, Jr. wrote a long and careful review of all that was known about the rhinoviruses as of 1975. In this review he expressed some of his reservations

about the importance of aerosol transmission. The review appeared in print twice, both times under the simple title "Rhinoviruses." It appeared first in *The Yale Journal of Biology and Medicine*, 1975, vol. 48, pp. 17–45. Subsequently it appeared as a chapter in A. S. Evans (ed.) *Viral infections of humans: epidemiology and control*, 1976, New York: Plenum, pp. 383–408, and later (revised) in the 2nd edition of this book, 1982, New York: Plenum Medical Book Co., pp. 491–517.

14 See p. 31 in Gwaltney's 1975 *Yale Journal* article.

15 As the source for this information Gwaltney cites R. G. Douglas, Jr., "Pathogenesis of rhinovirus common colds in human volunteers," *Annals of Otolaryngology Rhinology Laryngology*, 1970, vol. 79, pp. 563–71. On p. 569 in that article Douglas says simply, ". . . a study of ours (unpublished) failed to demonstrate airborne transmission." It is Gwaltney who describes the barracks and wire mesh barrier.

16 The reference here is to the 1972 D'Alessio, Dick, and Dick abstract, per note 12 above. Later, another brief description of this unpublished study would be given in D. J. D'Alessio, J. A. Peterson, C. R. Dick, and E. C. Dick, "Transmission of experimental rhinovirus colds in volunteer married couples," *Journal of Infectious Diseases*, 1976, vol. 133, pp. 28–36. (See the first two pages.)

17 Also from p. 569 of the 1970 Douglas article cited in note 15 above.

18 See Sylvia E. Reed, "An investigation of the possible transmission of rhinovirus colds through indirect contact," *Journal of Hygiene* (Cambridge), 1975, vol. 75, pp. 249–58.

19 Both quotations are from p. 257 of Dr. Reed's article.

20 From p. 258 of Dr. Reed's article.

CHAPTER 15

1 The final report on the Cleveland study of approximately sixty families during each year between 1948 and 1957 was published as a book in 1964 under the title *Illness in the Home: A study of 25,000 illnesses in a group of Cleveland families*, by John H. Dingle, George F. Badger, and William S. Jordan, Jr. (Cleveland: The Press of Western Reserve University). The New York virus watch looked at a group of approximately fifty families living in a high-rise apartment complex in downtown Manhattan in the period from 1961 to 1965, with some comparative data gathered from families living in a rural setting on Shelter Island east of Long Island between 1961 and 1963. A number of articles were generated by this virus watch. The first, describing its methods, was J. P. Fox, L. R. Elveback et al., "The Virus Watch program: a continuing surveillance of viral infections in metropolitan New York families: I. Overall plan, methods of collecting and handling information, and a summary report of specimens collected and illnesses observed," *American Journal of Epidemiology*,

1966, vol. 83, pp. 389–412. One of the last articles from the N.Y. virus watch, of particular relevance to this chapter, was A. Ketler, C. E. Hall, J. P. Fox, L. Elveback, and M. K. Cooney, "The Virus Watch program: a continuing surveillance of viral infections in metropolitan New York families: VIII. Rhinovirus infections: observations of virus excretion, intrafamilial spread and clinical response," *American Journal of Epidemiology*, 1969, vol. 90, pp. 244–54. The Seattle virus watch programme was also initiated by Dr. John Fox after he moved from New York to Seattle. In Seattle, data were collected from approximately sixty families per year (all including at least one infant) from July 1967 to July 1969, with fewer families in the two years prior. This study was described in J. P. Fox, C. E. Hall, M. K. Cooney, R. E. Luce, and R. A. Kronmal, "The Seattle Virus Watch: II. Objectives, study population and its observation, data processing and summary of illnesses," *American Journal of Epidemiology*, 1972, vol. 96, pp. 270–85. One of the last articles from the Seattle virus watch, of particular relevance to this chapter, was J. P. Fox, M. K. Cooney, and C. E. Hall, "Epidemiologic observations of rhinovirus infections, 1965–1969, in families with young children," *American Journal of Epidemiology*, 1975, vol. 101, pp. 122–43. Members of the Department of Epidemiology and the virus laboratory in the School of Public Health at the University of Michigan (Ann Arbor) carried out a general survey of respiratory diseases in the small community of Tecumseh, Michigan, between 1965 and 1969. The sample being monitored averaged about nine hundred family members per week. This study was introduced in A. S. Monto, J. A. Napier, and H. L. Metzner, "The Tecumseh study of respiratory illness: I. Plan of study and observations on syndromes of acute respiratory disease," *American Journal of Epidemiology*, 1971, vol. 94, pp. 269–79. A later article of particular relevance to this chapter was A. S. Monto, and J. J. Cavallaro, "The Tecumseh study of respiratory illness: IV. Prevalence of rhinovirus serotypes 1966–1969," *American Journal of Epidemiology*, 1972, vol. 96, pp. 352–60. In Chicago, approximately 110 medical student volunteers were followed each year from 1960 to 1964. This study was introduced in D. Hamre, and J. J. Procknow, "Virologic studies on common colds among young adult medical students," *American Review of Respiratory Diseases*, 1963, vol. 88, pp. 277–81. A later article of particular relevance to this chapter was D. Hamre, A. P. Connelly, Jr., and J. J. Procknow, "Virologic studies of acute respiratory disease in young adults: IV. Virus isolations during four years of surveillance," *American Journal of Epidemiology*, 1966, vol. 83, pp. 238–49. The Charlottesville study was carried out on approximately four hundred employees of a large insurance company between 1963 and 1966. It was first reported in J. M Gwaltney, Jr., J. O. Hendley, G. Simon, and W. S. Jordan, Jr., "Rhinovirus infections in an industrial population: I. The occurrence of illness," *The New England Journal of Medicine*, 1966, vol. 275, pp. 1261–68. (We have already discussed the data relating to fall epidemics of colds that emerged from this surveillance study, at the end of chapter 9.) Of relevance again is the later publication in the series: J. O. Hendley, J. M. Gwaltney, Jr., and W. S. Jordan, Jr., "Rhinovirus infections in an industrial population: IV. Infections within families of employees during two fall peaks of respiratory illness," *American Journal of Epidemiology*, 1969, vol. 89, pp. 184–96.

2   See p. 133 and Table 11 in Fox et al., 1975, as per note 1 above.

3   Ibid., p. 140.

4   Reported in D. J. D'Alessio, J. A. Peterson, C. R. Dick, and E. C. Dick, "Transmission of experimental rhinovirus colds in volunteer married couples," *Journal of Infectious Diseases*, 1976, vol. 133, pp. 28–36.

5   These words appear in a footnote to Table 5 on p. 34 of the D'Alessio et al. study. There is no further explanation as to how to interpret the so-called "direct contact" scores, which range from a low of five hours during the week to a high of thirty-nine hours during the week. The median "direct contact" score given was thirteen hours over seven days, which implies that these young married couples were embracing and kissing for an average of about two hours each day. In two of eleven couples, the time spent in this form of "direct contact" was said to average four or more hours each day for the full week. To which I find myself thinking: "Oh."

6   See Table 5, p. 34, from D'Alessio et al., 1976.

7   See J. M. Gwaltney, Jr., P. B. Moskalski, and J. O. Hendley, "Hand-to-hand transmission of rhinovirus colds," *Annals of Internal Medicine*, 1978, vol. 88, pp. 463–67.

8   The rhinovirus used was not yet assigned a type number, and was known at the time simply as strain HH.

9   See p. 465 in Gwaltney, Moskalski, and Hendley, 1978.

10   By J. M. Gwaltney, Jr. and J. O. Hendley, in the *American Journal of Epidemiology*, 1978, vol. 107, pp. 357–61. This paper was given earlier as a talk at the American Clinical and Climatological Association meetings held in Colorado Springs, Colorado, October 23–26, 1977, and it was later published in the *Transactions* of that association. It is interesting that this article barely mentioned the potential role of weather and climate, but focused instead on suggesting studies for interrupting the transmission of cold virus. I should add that probably the title is "wonderful" only if you happen to be a reader of a certain age and education, such that at school you were made to learn "The Midnight Ride of Paul Revere."

11   This work was never published so far as I am aware. It was summarized in a renewal grant application to the U.S. National Science Foundation (NSF Grant DPP76–83918), filed in 1980 and written by Dr. Elliot C. Dick, a copy of which was kindly sent to me on request to Dr. Dick. The grant renewal application was entitled "A study of respiratory virus transmission among the personnel at McMurdo Station, Antarctica, during the 'WINFLY' isolation period."

12   Quoted from the first paragraph of p. 3 of the 1980 grant renewal application. (See note 11 above.) Italics in the original. It is of some significance that important

clues for interpreting the medical intelligence provided by experimental studies of the common cold, clues such as this very interesting failure to replicate Dr. Dick's previously published experimental findings, can be very difficult to publish given an editorial culture that considers such findings to be "negative" and "unexplained" and therefore unreliable or uninformative. I hold that such information could be very informative to the prepared mind, and that it is not possible to predict in advance which published studies, or notes about studies, will lead to advances in science. All should be published.

13 Quoted from p. 2, Section II of the 1980 grant renewal application.

14 See E. C. Dick, L. C. Jennings, C. K. Meschievitz, D. MacMillan, and J. Goodrum, "Possible modification of the normal winter fly-in respiratory disease outbreak at McMurdo Station," *Antarctic Journal of the U.S.*, 1980, vol. 15, no. 3, pp. 173–74.

CHAPTER 16

1 D. J. D'Alessio, C. K. Meschievitz, J. A. Peterson, C. R. Dick, and E. C. Dick, "Short-duration exposure and the transmission of rhinoviral colds," *Journal of Infectious Diseases*, 1984, vol. 150, p. 189.

2 See V. Knight, "Viruses as agents of airborne contagion," *Annals of the New York Academy of Sciences*, 1980, vol. 353, pp. 147–56. These numbers were drawn from the information on p. 147.

3 See Figure 1, p. 148, of Knight's article.

4 See D'Alessio et al., 1984. The quotation is from the abstract of the article, p. 189.

5 The virus tested here was RV55. The inoculum used was reported to be the same as that used in the married couple experiment carried out in the late 1970s. Thus these data appear to have been gathered before the 1980 grant application was written.

6 The rhinovirus used was again RV55. The cold developed on the fifth day after the initial exposure to the donors. See p. 191 of D'Alessio et al., 1984.

7 From p. 191 of D'Alessio et al. Again RV55 was used.

8 See C. K. Meschievitz, S. B. Schultz, and E. C. Dick, "A model for obtaining predictable natural transmission of rhinoviruses in human volunteers," *Journal of Infectious Diseases*, 1984, vol. 150, pp. 195–201. This article and the previous one were published together in the same journal, some of the authors being different and with the emphases and conclusions being different as well, although I would argue that this second article was in fact on the same topic as, and a proper continuation of, the first.

9 Plotting the six pairs of trial scores on a graph, and in particular plotting the *logarithm* of each DHE score (which has the effect of bringing larger and larger numbers closer and closer together, this being one appropriate way for recognizing that the additional impact of each additional exposure hour will probably

become less and less important as the total exposure time accumulates) resulted in a graph on which all six of the data points (each representing the pair of scores from one trial) fell almost exactly on a straight line. Figure 16.1 shows this graph (adapted from the original) with its striking straight line fitting the transformed data from the six experimental trials (i.e., "experiments" A through F).

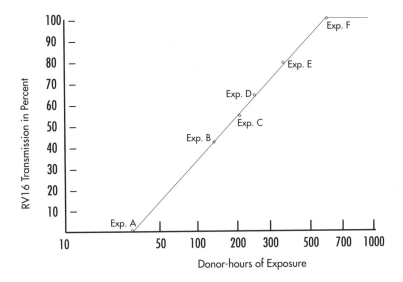

Figure 16.1

The percentage of susceptible recipients in each of the six experimental trials who became infected following exposures for varying lengths of time to multiple symptomatic donors experimentally infected with RV16. Donor-hours of exposure have been plotted logarithmically to reflect the diminishing importance of each additional hour of exposure. Adapted from Meschievitz, Schultz, and Dick, Journal of Infectious Diseases, 1984, vol. 150, p. 200 (Figure 3 in the original).

Exact relationships like this are actually rather common in a science investigating chemical behavior; they are much rarer in a science of cell behavior; and they are practically unheard of in a science involving matters of health. Across all six experimental trials in this study there were a total of just thirty-nine recipients studied, twenty-three of whom caught a donor's cold and sixteen of whom did not. The transmission percentages for individual experimental trials were generally based upon the data from just five recipients. If even *one* of any five recipients had behaved differently, the resulting transmission percentage for the corresponding trial would have changed (up or down) by a full 20 percent, completely distorting the straight-line effect shown in the graph. And if just two of the thirty-nine participants in this study were to have shown a different health status at the end of their trial, these results would look very different indeed.

Furthermore, the two trials on which zero percent and 100 percent of the recipients were infected ("Exp. A" and "Exp. F," respectively) also happened to fall exactly on the straight line of the reported graph, although presumably any trial with fewer than 45 DHE would also have been plotted at zero percent, while any trial with more than the 585 DHE would also have been plotted at 100 percent. Each of those kinds of trials would thus fall well to the left or well to the right of whatever straight line fit the data from the intermediate four trials, the four that really might fall on a straight line if the association really were nearly perfect. Thus, it seems a rather improbable coincidence that the shortest trial just happened to be exactly and only long enough to avoid the first successful transmission, while the longest trial just happened to be exactly and only long enough to first achieve a 100 percent transmission rate. One cannot explain this latter DHE score by supposing that the longest trial was stopped as soon as the last infection was detected. That detection only came later, and the stopping time had presumably been planned from the outset. (The stopping time for that trial was at the same hour of the day as most of the other trials.)

In short, the authors of the 1984 Wisconsin study were using data from six trials to fit a line that more properly should have depended on only four of those trials, four trials that were based upon quite small numbers of participants with their attendant highly unreliable estimates of any "true" transmission percentages. Nonetheless, as we shall see, these remarkably "linear" data, linking increasing exposure times to regularly increasing risks of transmission, would later become a key exhibit in the case claiming that aerosols are indeed the most important sources of natural transmission of rhinoviruses.

10   The authors of the study do not report this estimate but it can be inferred from the data in Table 3, p. 199, and from their Figure 3 on p. 200.

11   Reported in E. C. Dick, S. U. Hossain, K. A. Mink, C. K. Meschievitz, S. B. Schultz, W. J. Raynor, and S. L. Inhorn, "Interruption of transmission of rhinovirus colds among human volunteers using virucidal paper handkerchiefs," *Journal of Infectious Diseases*, 1986, vol. 153, pp. 352–56.

12   See J. D. Holtz, S. U. Hossain, K. R. Smith, S. B. Shultz, E. C. Dick, and T. W. Schafer, " 'Avert' virucidal facial tissue: in vitro efficacy," in *Programs and Abstracts of the Inter-American Society for Chemotherapy. St. Petersburg, Florida, 1984,* Inter-American Society for Chemotherapy.

13   From p. 353 of the 1986 Dick et al. paper.

14   While the 1986 paper by Dick et al. was being written, a study at the University of Virginia was in press showing that regular paper tissues would indeed reduce finger contamination, by a considerable degree. This study and a follow-up field trial using the control materials suggested here are discussed in chapter 17. See G. F. Hayden et al., 1985 and B. M. Farr et al., 1988, and notes 10 and 14 for that chapter.

15 See p. 355 of the 1986 Dick et al. paper. In August of 1994 I wrote to Dr. Dick asking about the fate of these follow-up experiments "in progress," but in this instance I received no reply.

16 See E. C. Dick, L. C. Jennings, K. A. Mink, C. D. Wartgow, and S. L. Inhorn, "Aerosol transmission of rhinovirus colds," *Journal of Infectious Diseases*, 1987, vol. 156, pp. 442–48.

17 This quotation is from the discussion section, p. 447 of the published article.

18 The amounts of virus found are reported in two sentences appearing on pp. 445 and 447. They are reported for samples (approximately 7 ml) larger in volume than are generally used to assay virus.

19 For the nature of this "other evidence" see Table 1 in the published report, p. 446. In particular, donor sneezes, donor symptoms, and donors' touching of their own faces were considerably higher during the first two trials.

20 The statistical rule of thumb for *estimating* how much change might occur in repeated samplings of the difference between two proportions (here the proportion of infections seen in restrained versus control recipients) given this case with twelve recipients of each type, suggests that about half the time the change up or down from 41 percent can be expected to exceed 12.5 percent. On one occasion in twenty, such change up or down can be expected to exceed 36 percent.

CHAPTER 17

1 From p. 162 of Gwaltney's Metzger lecture entitled "Climatology and the Common Cold," *Transactions of the American Climatological and Clinical Association*, 1984, vol. 96, pp. 159–75.

2 See J. M. Gwaltney, Jr., "Epidemiology of the common cold," *Annals of the New York Academy of Sciences*, 1980, vol. 353, pp. 54–60.

3 The negative results with rhinovirus by Dr. Couch and his colleagues were well known, even if unpublished. Gwaltney had the details from Couch himself. The positive results with coxsackievirus A type 21 obtained in the same room were first published in 1966 and then more fully in 1970. (See notes to chapter 14.) Gwaltney cites these data on p. 55 of his 1980 article. Further details are given in J. O. Hendley and J. M. Gwaltney, Jr., "Mechanisms of transmission of rhinovirus infections," *Epidemiologic Reviews*, 1988, vol. 10, on p. 247, in Table 1. There we learn that twenty participants were exposed for twenty-six days to the rhinovirus donors on the other side of the double wire barrier, all to no effect.

4 See J. M. Gwaltney Jr., J. O. Hendley, G. Simon, and W. S. Jordan, Jr., "Rhinovirus infections in an industrial population: II. Characteristics of illness and antibody response," *Journal of the American Medical Association*, 1967, vol. 202, pp. 494–500.

5 See Gwaltney's Table 1, p. 57, in the 1980 review.

6   Gwaltney was here referring to the same studies by R. B. Couch et al., the published reports of which appeared in 1966 and 1970 (see again the notes in chapter 14). But some of the unpublished data came via personal communications between Couch and Gwaltney.

7   See pp. 56–57 in Gwaltney's 1980 review.

8   See F. Pancic, D. C. Carpentier, and P. E. Came, "Role of infectious secretions in the transmission of rhinovirus," *Journal of Clinical Microbiology,* 1980, vol. 12, pp. 567–71.

9   See J. M. Gwaltney, Jr. and J. O. Hendley, "Transmission of experimental rhinovirus infection by contaminated surfaces," *American Journal of Epidemiology,* 1982, vol. 116, pp. 828–33. The rhinovirus employed in this study was never typed (numbered) and is identified only as "strain HH." This was the same virus supplied to Pancic, Carpentier, and Came for use in their study.

10   See G. F. Hayden, J. O. Hendley, and J. M. Gwaltney, Jr., "The effect of placebo and virucidal paper handkerchiefs on viral contamination of the hand and transmission of experimental rhinovirus infection," *Journal of Infectious Diseases,* 1985, vol. 152, pp. 403–7. In this study too, one rhinovirus used was "strain HH" and the other was RV39.

11   Although masculine pronouns are used in the text's description, donors and recipients in this study were of both sexes, with the ratio of women to men unspecified.

12   From p. 406 in Hayden et al., 1985.

13   It was Kimberley–Clark, the well-known Wisconsin paper company, that provided the CMS tissues and placebo look-alikes for the studies carried out at the Universities of Wisconsin and Virginia.

14   See B. M. Farr, J. O. Hendley, D. L. Kaiser, and J. M. Gwaltney, Jr., "Two randomized controlled trials of virucidal nasal tissues in the prevention of natural upper respiratory infections," *American Journal of Epidemiology,* 1988, vol. 128, pp. 1162–72.

15   See J. O. Hendley and J. M. Gwaltney, Jr., "Mechanisms of transmission of rhinovirus infections," *Epidemiologic Reviews,* 1988, vol. 10, pp. 242–58.

16   This information was kindly provided to me by Drs. Gwaltney and Hendley in a letter dated August 30, 1994. In response to my questions of them they wrote in part: "After this study was completed, we spent several years and considerable effort trying to develop a virucidal hand lotion that would be effective and also well-tolerated and cosmetically acceptable. Had we been able to develop such a thing, we planned on repeating the hand treatment intervention study. Our efforts to develop a practical hand lotion treatment have so far been unsuccessful, so we decided to publish what we had using the iodine treatment."

17   Most of the families during each year were new.

18   This sentence in the text, while moderately disfluent, is being deliberately careful. Usually, statistical tests of significance are reported as if they gave the probability that chance factors alone caused the effects seen in some scientific study.

But the low probability sought in a statistical analysis is, unfortunately, not the probability that chance is responsible for the findings being analyzed; rather it is something quite different, yet something that can sound like it is the same. What statistical analysis really tells us (unless it is Bayesian, in which case certain prior assumptions must be reported) is the probability of seeing data that are this suggestive in a world where the treatment given always does nothing, i.e., where chance alone determines all outcomes. What we are really given at the end of a statistical test procedure is the probability of *seeing* such suggestive results *whenever and if* chance alone has caused them, and *not* the probability that chance alone has caused them.

19   The immune status of the mothers was only determined for rhinovirus colds here. Mothers in this study were immune to 44 percent of the rhinovirus colds introduced into their families, and I have used this figure as an estimate of the corresponding probability of immunity to all other colds as well. (See p. 253 of the published report.)

20   Hendley and Gwaltney did not report the beliefs of the twenty-seven susceptible mothers exposed to natural rhinovirus, nor the relationship of beliefs about treatment to illness history while under study. It should be possible to begin to see to what extent this concern about unblinding was justified by analyzing separately the data of those who did and did not believe they were in the virucidal condition.

CHAPTER 18

1   From Mims's book *The Pathogenesis of Infectious Diseases*, New York: Grave & Stratton, p. 129. As quoted by R. B. Couch in the *Journal of Infectious Diseases*, 1984, vol. 150, p. 172.

2   I wish to express my enduring thanks to each one of these generous volunteers. In addition there were more than forty student assistants who volunteered their time to make these trials succeed, providing liaison with the participants and helping to score and enter the voluminous data generated in this study. These assistants, and the generous amounts of time they donated, truly made this study possible. There were also more than a dozen staff in the offices of the Registrars at the four participating colleges on campus who included our mailing describing the study in documents sent to incoming students and who then sorted the returned forms so generated by potential volunteers. There were also university personnel who facilitated ethical review and data entry and computer operations and printing of research forms and so many other activities. (You people know who you are, and I do too, and I thank you here again.) Because of these many volunteers, the funds required to carry out this research were modest, and were kindly provided by small grants from my department (of psychology) at the University of Toronto. Outside research funds were sought, but

were denied because the granting agencies approached were apparently persuaded that students would not volunteer to participate in the study, or, if they did, they would not provide sufficiently complete data to be analyzed.

3   All data provided by the participants were anonymous and confidential. They were sealed upon collection and identified only through a special four-digit code number appearing on each data sheet. It was repeatedly stressed to each participant that frankness and accuracy were necessary if their contributions were to be of real value, and that they should feel free to leave blank any question for which their memory might be unreliable or which they would prefer not to answer. The anonymity provided by the research forms, and the stress laid upon ensuring the accuracy of the daily responses at the expense of the possible completeness of each daily form, led to frank and typically full reporting by a large majority of respondents. Answers to some of the more personal questions about daily moods and feelings were omitted by a few respondents on a few occasions. Most of the volunteers who felt at all uncomfortable taking time to give full and frank daily self-reports took advantage of a special opportunity to drop out of the study that was provided each year at the end of the second week on campus. It was stressed, however, that each participant was free to drop out of the study at any time before the end of each trial. A small proportion of the participants dropped out later, during the progress of each trial.

4   The voluminous personal data from the volunteers, detailing their daily moods and stress levels as they may be related to subsequent illness, were only partly analyzed at the time of this writing. They amplify a topic that may be more appropriate in a separate book dealing with research studies on psychological factors and the common cold. (A number of such studies exist, not examined in this book, and the picture they paint is as interesting and complex as the one painted here.) The data that I have analyzed from my Toronto study suggest that experiences of anger, anxiety, depression, and guilt, and the levels of one's general mood each day, all have similar and undifferentiated effects on the risk of catching colds. Those effects are not often strong, and they were not always seen, but they appear to be reliable. Of greatest interest is the suggestion that a negative and temporary *change* in mood or stress level sometimes results in an increased risk of infection (just like temperature changes) only *after* a delay of between twenty-four and forty-eight hours, and not at the time of changing stress itself.

5   In fact, such change scores wax and wane in size over the year so that at certain times (i.e., in the fall) a drop of four degrees Celsius might be relatively common (and so considered "small"), while at other times (i.e., in the spring) the same drop might be relatively unusual (and considered "large"). Consequently, the actual analysis of these change scores was carried out on so-called "standardized change scores" having a mean of zero and a standard deviation of 1.00. These standard scores were produced by subtracting the running thirty-day mean from each daily change score, then dividing by the running standard

deviation of the daily change scores over the previous thirty days.

6   The first four trials, respectively, produced 28, 22, 44, and 44 colds, in 26, 21, 39, and 39 different students (because a very few students contributed two colds each) starting on 19, 21, 34, and 34 different dates, in a contributing sample of 76, 72, 71, and 71 students over a period of 60, 90, 60, and 60 days respectively. The mean standardized temperature change scores (see the previous note) for the ten days leading up to and ending on the first day of symptoms, in each of the four trials, were, respectively:

Trial 1: −.15   −.29   +.28   +.27   **+.37**   **−.35**   −.15   +.03   −.28 and −.17
Trial 2: +.02   +.14   +.12   −.06   **−.33**   +.19   −.06   −.21   +.03 and +.04
Trial 3: +.01   −.02   +.03   +.15   +.07   **+.21**   −.08   **−.23**   −.13 and −.16
Trial 4: +.10   +.14   +.03   −.06   **−.31**   +.15   +.07   −.05   −.12 and −.21

With the limited numbers of uncomplicated colds to work with in each trial, the $p < .05$ (two-tailed) statistical significance level for a single average score value (if specified in advance) from each of the four trials was, respectively, plus and minus .37, .43, .30, and .30. Values in bold were the trial maxima.

7   The magnitude of these average temperature changes was in each case about one-third of the (running) standard deviation, approximately 1.5 degrees Celsius.

8   The two significant trials, during the spring and the fall of 1986, produced, respectively, 24 and 61 colds, in 21 and 55 different students, starting on 21 and 36 different dates, in contributing samples of 84 and 121 students over periods of 72 and 50 days. The mean standardized temperature change scores for the ten days leading up to and ending on the first day of symptoms, in each of the four trials, were, respectively:

Trial 7: +.36   +.37   −.12   −.19   −.18   +.21   +.15   **−.45**   +.05 and **+.42**
Trial 8: +.10   −.14   +.04   −.20   −.09   −.05   **+.26**   −.05   +.09 and −.08

The $p < .05$ (two-tailed) statistical significance level for a single average score value (if specified in advance) from each of the two trials was, respectively, plus and minus .41 and .25. Values in bold were the trial maxima.

9   The applicable statistical test of this clustering, contrasting just days 2 through 5 with days 6 through 9, and using what is called Fisher's Exact Test, produces a significance value of $p < .003$. Translated, this means that if chance alone were always dealing out the maximum and notable daily average scores, at random, then clustering of this order would happen less than three times in every one thousand such studies. It seems unlikely, then, that chance explains this study's results.

10 Dr. David A. J. Tyrrell and his staff at the unit were most hospitable and helpful in offering space, time, and access to the trial records. Dr. Tyrrell also helped arrange for access to the meteorological records at nearby Boscombe

Down air base, with the cooperation of Peter Wakefield, the chief met officer there. I am grateful to all of them for their aid in carrying out this study.

11 "Control" volunteers challenged with placebo were ignored in each trial. Nine separate correlation coeffiecients were generated for each virus type, so that there were nine numbers, each indexing the degree of association observed between (1) the various temperature change scores on the same trial day in each trial (e.g., "the day before the challenge") and (2) the varying percentages of colds that later developed among the challenged volunteers on each trial with that virus.

The relative *strength* of any association between (1) temperature changes occurring at a given point in time relative to the time of challenge and (2) the associated incidence of colds seen on trials of a particular virus, can best be estimated and described by squaring each of the nine correlation coefficients so generated. Thus, I report these smaller, squared values to indicate the relative (percentage) strength of association. However, I retain positive correlational signs (indicating warming) and negative correlational signs (indicating cooling) to show which direction of temperature change was linked to greater numbers of colds for each virus.

12 I called any squared correlation coefficient "notable" if (1) it represented a strength of association of at least 15 percent (i.e., with r>.38) and (2) if it was at least one-half larger than the next largest squared correlation seen for that virus, or (3) if the underlying correlation coefficient exceeded the so-called "p=.05 level of statistical significance" for a single correlation coefficient based on the same number of paired scores. On average, squared indices of association for the RV2 trials (with a low of fourteen trials of data) could be expected to change by approximately plus or minus 18 percent in any replication study while the correlations for RV9 trials (with a high of twenty-five trials of data) would only be expected to change by about plus or minus nine percent in any replication study. (These two percentage figures represent, respectively, the two squared values of the estimated standard error for the difference between two correlations.) The actual (unsquared) correlation coefficients for trials with each of the four different virus types, for, respectively, the five days preceding challenge, and then for the day of challenge itself, and then for the following three days of "incubation" were as follows:

					DOC			
229E:	+.13	−.02	+.08	**−.44**	+.12	+.33	−.09	+.33	−.01
RV2:	−.27	−.09	+.25	**−.42**	+.20	+.06	+.14	+.14	+.16
RV9:	−.04	**+.69**	−.05	−.10	**−.39**	+.27	−.35	−.04	+.04
RV14:	+.20	−.41	+.13	**+.50**	−.47	−.16	+.38	+.15	+.16

"Notable" correlations above appear in boldface. DOC indicates the day of challenge.

13 For coronavirus 229E, and for RV2, RV9, and RV14, respectively, these four

indices of association were 10.9, 0.4, 7.3, and –2.6 percent. For the three rhinoviruses the magnitude of these indices was in every case less than half of that seen on one or both of the two previous days.

14 See again O. M. Lidwell, R. W. Morgan, and R. E. O. Williams, "The epidemiology of the common cold: IV. The effect of weather," *Journal of Hygiene* (Cambridge), 1965, vol. 63, pp. 427–39. This work was discussed in detail in the second half of chapter 8.

15 See the middle of chapter 6 for the details. These observations were reported in T. R. Allen, A. F. Bradburne, E. J. Stott et al., "An outbreak of common colds at an Antarctic base after seventeen weeks of complete isolation," *Journal of Hygiene* (Cambridge), 1973, vol. 71, pp. 657–67.

16 The Cruz Bay study referred to here was discussed early in chapter 9. It was published in 1931. See note 1 of chapter 9 for the full reference.

17 The Quezon City study referred to here was discussed in the middle of chapter 9. It was published in 1967. See note 9 of chapter 9 for the full reference.

18 Reported by H. W. Gruchow, "Catecholamine activity and infectious disease episodes," *Journal of Human Stress*, 1979, vol. 5, pp. 11–17.

19 Reported by J. W. Mason, E. L. Buescher, M. L. Belfer et al., "A prospective study of corticosteroid and catecholamine levels in relation to viral respiratory illness," *Journal of Human Stress*, 1979, vol. 5, pp. 18–28.

20 See note 4 above, referring to evidence of such an observed lag effect in our Toronto Survey data, prior to 1987. See also, A. A. Stone, B. R. Reed, and J. M. Neale, "Changes in daily event frequency precede episodes of physical symptoms," *Journal of Human Stress*, 1987, vol. 13, pp. 70–74, and P. D. Evans, M. K. Pitts, and K. Smith, "Minor infection, minor life events and the four day desirability dip," *Journal of Psychosomatic Research*, 1988, vol. 32, pp. 533–39, and P. D. Evans and N. Edgerton, "Life-events and mood as predictors of the common cold," *British Journal of Medical Psychology*, 1991, vol. 64, pp. 35–44. And finally, for a prescient early hypothesis concerning why a time lag would be observed between exposure to cold weather and the onset of illness, see Louis S. Goldstein, "Cold weather as a factor in the epidemiology of grippe and the common cold," *Archives of Pediatrics*, 1951, vol. 68, pp. 577–84, with special attention to the discussions on p. 580 and p. 582.

CHAPTER 19

1 D. A. J. Tyrrell, "Some recent work at the Common Cold Unit, Salisbury," *Infection*, 1988, vol. 16, p. 262.

2 There are countless folk remedies for curing and/or preventing colds. It has not been the place of this book to look closely at claims for the efficacy of any of the various and popular prophylactics that are in use around the world. The extensive medical detective work on ascorbic acid and common colds is very interesting,

and all by itself it would be worthy of a companion volume to this one. Other such putative prophylactic substances (and various hygienic practices) have come under the scrutiny of medical intelligence over the years too. Perhaps I (or someone else) will choose one day to write that companion volume, dealing with this other fascinating body of research and more particularly with any roles that our minds may play in the coming and going of cold symptoms. As for the hope of a vaccine against colds: the sheer number of distinct cold viruses currently makes that an unworkable idea. Still, among the many as yet undiscovered mechanics of human biology there may be dozens of surprising opportunities for interventions that might prevent colds, even if vaccines prove to play no part in such opportunities.

3   From Lewis Thomas's chapter "A long line of cells," in William Zinsser (ed.), *Inventing the Truth*, 1987, Houghton Mifflin Co., Boston, pp. 127–48. The quotation here is taken from p. 148.

4   Of course we have seen in earlier chapters that colds do not always die out in every isolated population, at least not always quickly, and not so often when the population is larger than, say, three hundred.

5   I regret to report that even writing a book about colds does not seem to prevent their occurrence. Perhaps this is the place, too, to let my more dedicated readers know that for a time at least, following the publication of this book, email can be sent to me at ccold@netidea.com.

6   Readers interested in this literature could hardly do better than to begin with the 1991 article by D. V. Cicchetti dealing with typical reliabilities and validities for scientific reviews. This article became the focus of most subsequent discussions of what needed to be done (if anything) to change the traditional scientific peer-review process for the better. Cicchetti's article, together with thirty-four commentaries upon it (one of them my own) and Cicchetti's response to his critics, all appeared in *Behavioral and Brain Sciences*, vol. 14, pp. 119–86.

Acknowledgements

What does one do with gratitude? When thanked, many of the people who went far out of their way to help make this book a reality have said, in effect: "I was only doing my job" or "It was what I wanted to do." With such people there may be little one can do but to repay them with one's own random acts of kindness to *other* people. It is my hope that this book may prove to be one such act for some readers. Moreover, without readers, books don't get published; so I also acknowledge my thanks to you, my persevering reader.

I have tried in the chapter notes to acknowledge many of the people who helped directly in generating some of the information contained in this book. But in addition to those already mentioned, there were some wonderfully skillful, patient, and anonymous librarians who helped me find what I needed while I was steeping myself in the literature on the common cold. In this connection, I would particularly like to thank the staff at the Public Health Library on the Berkeley campus of the University of California, where I spent many hours prowling the stacks during two sabbatical seasons in the 1980s. And, I thank the splendid staff in the medical library at the University of Toronto who were always able to steer me to the desired range on the correct subfloor.

A special thanks is due to Dr. D. A. J. Tyrrell and his staff at the Salisbury Common Cold Research Unit for making me very welcome on three different occasions when I was able to visit England. Geir Nielsen, at the University of Bergen in Norway, made a special effort to help me get some of the nordic material for this book. R. Edgar Hope Simpson (whom I was never able to meet) gave me considerable encouragement along the way, including copies of some of his correspondence with J. J. van Loghem in Holland during the years 1954 through 1966. Both Elliot Dick and Jack M. Gwaltney, Jr. (whom also I have yet to meet) provided me with helpful information when it was needed. Gwaltney in particular, at a very busy time, carefully reviewed the penultimate draft of this book, thus providing me with an expert's mirror that I might remove some (but not quite all) of the traces of "egg" that otherwise would have remained on the face of this work. I salute him.

And then there is the editor, without whom it seems likely that this book might never have been published. Marnie Kramarich of Stoddart Publishing saw the merits of this book after many other editors and publishers had not. She then went on to edit the manuscript, noting countless ways to improve both the prose and the telling of the historical tale. This book now says much more what I had always wanted it to say, thanks to her skills and her efforts.

Finally, of course, there are all you research assistants and volunteers. How is it possible to acknowledge you? Well, please, take my gratitude.

Barney Gilmore
Kaslo, British Columbia
June, 1998

Index